적중 100

영어 기출 문제집

중**2**

천재 | 정사열

Best Collection

구성과 특징

교과서의 주요 학습 내용을 중심으로 학습 영역별 특성에 맞춰 단계별로 다양한 학습 기회를 제공하여
단원별 학습능력 평가는 물론 중간 및 기말고사 시험 등에 완벽하게 대비할 수 있도록 내용을 구성

Words & Expressions

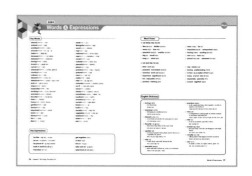

Step1	Key Words 단원별 핵심 단어 설명 및 풀이
	Key Expression 단원별 핵심 숙어 및 관용어 설명
	Word Power 반대 또는 비슷한 뜻 단어 배우기
	English Dictionary 영어로 배우는 영어 단어
Step2	실력평가 단원별 수시평가 대비 주관식, 객관식 문제풀이
Step3	서술형 대비 학업성취도 및 수행능력평가 대비 서술형 문제풀이

Conversation

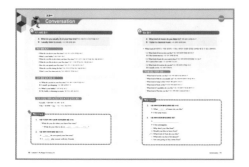

Step1	핵심 의사소통 소통에 필요한 주요 표현 방법 요약
	핵심 Check 기본적인 표현 방법 및 활용능력 확인
Step2	대화문 익히기 교과서 대화문 심층 분석 및 확인
Step3	교과서 확인학습 빈칸 채우기를 통한 문장 완성 능력 확인
Step4	기본평가 시험대비 기초 학습 능력 평가
Step5	실력평가 단원별 수시평가 대비 주관식, 객관식 문제풀이
Step6	서술형 대비 학업성취도 및 수행능력평가 대비 서술형 문제풀이

Grammar

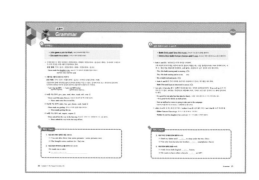

Step1	주요 문법 단원별 주요 문법 사항과 예문을 알기 쉽게 설명
	핵심 Check 기본 문법사항에 대한 이해 여부 확인
Step2	기본평가 시험대비 기초 학습 능력 평가
Step3	실력평가 단원별 수시평가 대비 주관식, 객관식 문제풀이
Step4	서술형 대비 학업성취도 및 수행능력평가 대비 서술형 문제풀이

Reading

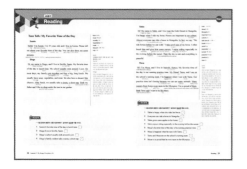

Step1	구문 분석 단원별로 제시된 문장에 대한 구문별 분석과 내용 설명
	확인문제 문장에 대한 기본적인 이해와 인지능력 확인
Step2	확인학습A 빈칸 채우기를 통한 문장 완성 능력 확인
Step3	확인학습B 제시된 우리말을 영어로 완성하여 작문 능력 키우기
Step4	실력평가 단원별 수시평가 대비 주관식, 객관식 문제풀이
Step5	서술형 대비 학업성취도 및 수행능력평가 대비 서술형 문제풀이
	교과서 구석구석 교과서에 나오는 기타 문장까지 완벽 학습

Composition

|영역별 핵심문제|

단어 및 어휘, 대화문, 문법, 독해 등 각 영역별 기출문제의 출제 유형을 분석하여 실전에 대비하고 연습할 수 있도록 문제를 배열

|단원별 예상문제|

기출문제를 분석한 후 새로운 시험 출제 경향을 더하여 새롭게 출제될 수 있는 문제를 포함하여 시험에 완벽하게 대비할 수 있도록 준비

|서술형 실전 및 창의사고력 문제|

학교 시험에서 점차 늘어나는 서술형 시험에 집중 대비하고 고득점을 취득하는데 만전을 기하기 위한 학습 코너

|단원별 모의고사|

영역별, 단계별 학습을 모두 마친 후 실전 연습을 위한 모의고사

교과서 파헤치기

- **단어Test1~3** 영어 단어 우리말 쓰기, 우리말을 영어 단어로 쓰기, 영영풀이에 해당하는 단어와 우리말 쓰기
- **대화문Test1~2** 대화문 빈칸 완성 및 전체 대화문 쓰기
- **본문Test1~5** 빈칸 완성, 우리말 쓰기, 문장 배열연습, 영어 작문하기 복습 등 단계별 반복 학습을 통해 교과서 지문에 대한 완벽한 습득
- **구석구석지문Test1~2** 지문 빈칸 완성 및 전문 영어로 쓰기

Contents

Lesson 1

Time to Start Again

의사소통 기능

- 의견 묻기
  What do you think of this diary?

- 희망 · 기대 표현하기
  I can't wait for his birthday party!

언어 형식

- to부정사의 형용사적 용법
  Do you have something **to say**?

- 접속사 that
  I think **(that)** I lost it.

교과서
Words & Expressions

Key Words

□ **activity**[æktívəti] 명 활동
□ **always**[ɔ́:lweiz] 부 항상
□ **anyway**[éniwèi] 부 어쨌든
□ **bell**[bel] 명 종
□ **boring**[bɔ́:riŋ] 형 지루한 (↔ interesting)
□ **busy**[bízi] 형 바쁜
□ **cafeteria**[kæfətíəriə] 명 카페테리아, 구내식당
□ **class**[klæs] 명 수업
□ **continue**[kəntínju:] 동 계속하다 (↔ stop)
□ **cool**[ku:l] 형 멋진, 시원한
□ **corner**[kɔ́:rnər] 명 구석
□ **cover**[kʌvər] 명 표지
□ **delicious**[dilíʃəs] 형 맛있는 (= tasty, yummy)
□ **diary**[dáiəri] 명 수첩, 일기
□ **dish**[diʃ] 명 접시, 요리
□ **excited**[iksáitid] 형 흥분한, 신이 난
□ **exciting**[iksáitiŋ] 형 신나는, 흥미진진한
□ **fan**[fæn] 명 팬, 부채
□ **final**[fáinl] 명 결승전
□ **floor**[flɔ:r] 명 바닥 (↔ ceiling)
□ **fresh**[freʃ] 형 신선한
□ **grow**[grou] 동 기르다, 재배하다
□ **hard**[ha:rd] 부 열심히, 어려운
□ **health**[helθ] 명 건강
□ **homeroom teacher** 담임선생님
□ **hurry**[hɔ́:ri] 동 서둘러 가다, 서두르다
□ **interesting**[íntərəstiŋ] 형 재미있는 (↔ boring 지루한)
□ **join**[dʒɔin] 동 가입하다

□ **judge**[dʒʌdʒ] 동 판단하다
□ **kind**[kaind] 형 친절한 (= friendly)
□ **magic**[mǽdʒik] 명 마법, 마술
□ **math**[mæθ] 명 수학
□ **mean**[mi:n] 동 의미하다
□ **note**[nout] 명 메모
□ **pleased**[pli:zd] 형 기쁜 (= glad)
□ **post**[poust] 동 게시[공고]하다
□ **practice**[prǽktis] 동 연습하다
□ **present**[préznt] 명 선물 (= gift)
□ **problem**[prábləm] 명 문제
□ **realize**[rí:əlàiz] 동 깨닫다
□ **really**[rí:əli] 부 정말
□ **remember**[rimémbər] 동 기억하다 (↔ forget 잊다)
□ **reply**[riplái] 동 대답하다
□ **right**[rait] 형 맞는 (↔ wrong), 알맞은
□ **saying**[séiiŋ] 명 속담 (= proverb)
□ **serious**[síəriəs] 형 진지한
□ **serve**[sə:rv] 동 제공하다
□ **shout**[ʃaut] 동 외치다
□ **solve**[salv] 동 풀다, 해결하다
□ **strict**[strikt] 형 엄격한
□ **take**[teik] 동 데리고 가다, 가져가다
□ **ticket**[tíkit] 명 표, 입장권
□ **together**[təɡéðər] 부 함께
□ **trick**[trik] 명 마술, 속임수
□ **trust**[trʌst] 동 믿다
□ **word**[wə:rd] 명 말, 단어

Key Expressions

□ **after school** 방과 후에
□ **be good for** ~에 좋다
□ **bump into** ~에 부딪히다
□ **can't wait for** ~이 몹시 기다려지다
□ **come over** 오다
□ **cut in on** (말·대화에) 끼어들다
□ **find out** ~을 알게 되다
□ **happen to+동사원형** 우연히 ~하게 되다
□ **look for** ~을 찾다

□ **lots of** 많은
□ **on one's way to** ~으로 가는 길에[도중에]
□ **pay someone back** ~에게 신세를 갚다
□ **play the ukulele** 우쿨렐레를 연주하다
□ **right now** 당장
□ **think of** ~에 대해 생각하다
□ **think to oneself** 마음속으로 생각하다
□ **this way** 이런 식으로
□ **this year** 올해

Word Power

※ 현재분사(-ing)와 과거분사(-ed)형 형용사

□ **amazing** (놀라운, 굉장한) – **amazed** (대단히 놀란)

□ **boring** (지루한) – **bored** (지루해하는)

□ **disappointing** (실망시키는) – **disappointed** (실망한)

□ **exciting** (흥미진진한) – **excited** (들뜬, 흥분한)

□ **interesting** (흥미로운) – **interested** (흥미 있어 하는)

□ **satisfying** (만족하게 하는) – **satisfied** (만족하는)

□ **surprising** (놀라운) – **surprised** (놀란)

□ **tiring** (피곤하게 만드는) – **tired** (피곤한, 지친)

English Dictionary

□ **cafeteria** 구내식당
→ a restaurant where you choose and pay for your meal at a counter and carry it to a table
카운터에서 선택하고 식사비를 지불하고 그것을 테이블로 가지고 가는 식당

□ **cover** 표지
→ the outer part of a book or magazine
책이나 잡지의 바깥 부분

□ **dish** 접시
→ a shallow container that you cook or serve food in
요리하거나 음식을 제공하는 데 쓰는 얕은 그릇

□ **fan** 팬
→ a person who admires someone or something or enjoys watching or listening to someone or something very much
누군가 또는 무언가를 동경하거나 누군가 또는 무언가를 보거나 듣는 것을 즐기는 사람

□ **final** 결승전
→ the last and most important game or race in a competition
시합에서 마지막이자 가장 중요한 경기 또는 경주

□ **grow** 재배하다
→ to make plants grow
식물을 자라게 하다

□ **hurry** 서두르다, 서둘러 가다
→ to move, act, or go quickly
급히 움직이거나 행동하거나 가다

□ **judge** 판단하다
→ to form an opinion about something or someone after careful thought
주의 깊이 생각한 후에 무언가 또는 누군가에 대한 견해를 형성하다

□ **magic** 마술
→ the art of doing tricks that seem impossible in order to entertain people
사람들을 즐겁게 하기 위해 불가능해 보이는 재주를 부리는 기술

□ **post** 게시[공고]하다
→ to put up a sign, notice, etc. so that it can be seen by many people
많은 사람이 볼 수 있도록 표지판, 게시문 등을 붙이다

□ **realize** 깨닫다
→ to understand or become aware of something
어떤 것을 이해하거나 알게 되다

□ **reply** 대답하다
→ to say or write something as an answer to someone or something
누군가 또는 무언가에 대한 대답으로 무언가를 말하거나 쓰다

□ **saying** 속담
→ an old and well-known phrase that expresses an idea that most people believe is true
대부분의 사람이 옳다고 믿고 있는 생각을 표현하는 오래되고 유명한 어구

□ **serve** 제공하다
→ to give food or drink to someone at a meal, in a restaurant, etc.
음식점 따위에서 식사할 때 음식이나 음료수를 사람에게 주다

□ **strict** 엄격한
→ demanding that rules, especially rules about behavior, should be obeyed
규칙, 특히 행동에 대한 규칙을 따라야 한다고 요구하는

□ **trust** 믿다
→ to believe that someone is honest or will not do anything bad or wrong
누군가가 정직하거나 또는 나쁘거나 잘못된 일을 하지 않을 것이라고 믿다

01 다음 중 짝지어진 단어의 관계가 나머지 넷과 <u>다른</u> 것은?

① present : gift　　② right : wrong
③ kind : friendly　　④ pleased : glad
⑤ delicious : tasty

02 다음 우리말에 맞도록 빈칸에 알맞은 것은?

> 너는 10분 후에 알게 될 거야.
> ➡ You'll find _____ in 10 minutes.

① up　　　　　② out
③ with　　　　④ into
⑤ over

 중요
03 다음 영영풀이에 해당하는 단어로 알맞은 것은?

> to put up a sign, notice, etc. so that it can be seen by many people

① throw　　　② join
③ mean　　　④ post
⑤ carry

중요
04 다음 빈칸에 알맞은 말이 바르게 짝지어진 것은?

> • I can't wait _____ this weekend.
> • I saw him bump _____ the wall.

① on – to　　　② for – up
③ with – in　　④ on – over
⑤ for – into

서답형
05 다음 짝지어진 두 단어의 관계가 같도록 빈칸에 알맞은 말을 쓰시오.

> strong : weak = _____ : boring

06 다음 빈칸에 들어갈 말로 적절하지 <u>않은</u> 것은?

> • They _____ food to poor people.
> • What does this sentence _____?
> • I have math problems to _____ today.
> • I'm going to _____ Dami with me.

① take　　　　② mean
③ solve　　　④ serve
⑤ find

서답형
07 다음 영영풀이에 해당하는 단어를 쓰시오.

> to move, act, or go quickly

➡ _____

서답형
08 다음 우리말에 맞게 빈칸에 알맞은 말을 쓰시오.

> 그는 숲 속에서 단서들을 찾고 있다.
> ➡ He is _____ _____ clues in the woods.

01 다음 짝지어진 두 단어의 관계가 같도록 빈칸에 알맞은 말을 쓰시오.

(1) interesting : boring = _____ : stop

(2) easy : difficult = _____ : remember

(3) glad : sad = right : _____

(4) kind : friendly = proverb : _____

02 다음 우리말에 맞게 빈칸에 알맞은 말을 쓰시오.

(1) 여기에 빨리 좀 와!

➡ Please _____ _____ here quickly!

(2) 나는 방과 후에 축구하는 것을 즐긴다.

➡ I enjoy playing soccer _____
_____.

(3) 나는 올해 호주를 방문할 계획이다.

➡ I plan to visit Australia _____
_____.

03 다음 빈칸에 공통으로 들어갈 말을 〈보기〉에서 골라 쓰시오.

┌─ 보기 ─┐
right   dish   hard

(1) • This test was _____.

• I studied _____ yesterday because of my English test.

(2) • The _____ really tastes good.

• She got honey and put it into a _____.

(3) • He's the _____ man for the job.

• The woman is bending her _____ arm.

04 다음 빈칸에 들어갈 알맞은 말을 〈보기〉에서 골라 쓰시오.

┌─ 보기 ─┐
fresh   boring   strict

(1) He looks very _____ and serious.

(2) The film was _____, so I fell asleep.

(3) He eats _____ vegetables and fruit every day.

05 다음 빈칸에 알맞은 말을 〈보기〉에서 골라 쓰시오.

┌─ 보기 ─┐
bump into   be good for   cut in on

(1) He _____ our talk.

(2) This will also _____ my health.

(3) You can _____ other people while using your phone.

06 다음 영영풀이에 해당하는 단어를 주어진 철자로 시작하여 쓰시오.

(1) f_____ : the last and most important game or race in a competition

(2) c_____ : the outer part of a book or magazine

(3) r_____ : to understand or become aware of something

Conventions

교과서

Conversation

> **A** What do you think of this diary? 이 수첩에 대해 어떻게 생각하니?
> **B** Its cover is cool. I think it's good for Minjun. 표지가 멋져. 민준에게 좋을 것 같아.

■ 상대방에게 의견을 물어볼 때에는 What do you think of ~?를 이용하고, 그에 대한 응답으로 자신의 의견을 표현할 때에는 I think ~. 표현을 이용한다.

- A: What do you think of my new brush? 너는 내 새 붓에 어떻게 생각하니?
  B: I think it's cool. 멋지다고 생각해.

의견 묻기 표현

- What do you think of[about] James? James에 대해 어떻게 생각해?
- What's your opinion on this matter? 이 문제에 관한 너의 의견은 무엇이니?
  (= Can I have your opinion of this matter?)
- What's your view on school uniforms? 교복에 대해 어떻게 생각하니?
- How do you like my new coat? 내 새 코트 어때?

의견 말하기 표현

- I think it's interesting. 나는 재미있다고 생각해.
- In my opinion, it's too expensive. 내 생각에 그것은 너무 비싸.
- In my view, it is great. 내 생각에 그것은 좋아.
- I have no idea. 잘 모르겠어.

핵심 Check

1. 다음 우리말과 일치하도록 빈칸에 알맞은 말을 쓰시오.

   (1) **A:** _____ do you _____ _____ today's lunch? (오늘의 점심에 대해 어떻게 생각하니?)

   B: _____ _____ it's okay. (괜찮다고 생각해.)

   (2) **A:** _____ is your _____ _____ the novel? (그 소설에 대한 너의 의견은 무엇이니?)

   B: _____ my _____, it's very interesting. (내 의견으로는, 그것은 매우 재미있어.)

❷ 희망 · 기대 표현하기

> **A** What do you think of my new dress? 내 새 드레스에 대해 어떻게 생각하니?
> **B** I think it's cool. 멋진 것 같아.
> **A** I can't wait for the party. 파티가 너무 기다려져.

■ I can't wait for ～.는 '나는 ～이 매우 기다려져. / 나는 ～이 무척 기대돼.'라는 뜻으로 희망이나 기대를 나타내는 표현이다.

- A: What do you think of my new ukulele? 내 새 우쿨렐레 어때?
  B: I think it's cool. 멋진 것 같아.
  A: I can't wait for the concert. 콘서트가 너무 기다려져.

희망 · 기대를 나타내는 표현

- I can't wait for+명사(구) ～. 나는 ～이[하는 것이] 매우 기다려진다.
- I can't wait to+동사원형 ～. 나는 빨리 ～하고 싶어.
- I'm looking forward to+(동)명사 ～. 나는 ～을 고대하고 있다.
- I'm expecting + 명사(구) / to+동사원형 ～. 나는 ～을 기대하고 있다.
- I hope[want] to+동사원형 ～. 나는 ～하기를 바란다[원한다].
- I would like to+동사원형 ～. 나는 ～하고 싶다.

- I can't wait for the art contest. 나는 미술 대회가 매우 기다려져.
  = I'm looking forward to the art contest.

핵심 Check

2. 다음 우리말과 일치하도록 빈칸에 알맞은 말을 쓰시오.

(1) **A:** When are you going to leave? (언제 떠날 예정이니?)

　　B: Next Tuesday. I can't ＿＿＿＿＿ ＿＿＿＿＿ the trip. (다음 주 화요일. 여행이 무척 기다려져.)

(2) **A:** When is Chuseok ＿＿＿＿＿ ＿＿＿＿＿? (올해 추석이 언제니?)

　　B: It's on October 1. I'm ＿＿＿＿＿ ＿＿＿＿＿ to it. (10월 1일이야. 나는 그것을 아주 고대하고 있어.)

Conversation 교과서 대화문 익히기

A. Start Off - Listen & Talk B

B: Let's join the Green Garden club together. ❶What do you think of it?

G: Okay. I like growing vegetables.

B: ❷You know what? I like eating vegetables.

G: Let's join the club right now. We can have a party with fresh vegetables every month.

B: Great. ❸The first party is on April 30.

G: ❹I can't wait for the party.

B: 초록 정원 동아리에 함께 가입하자. 그것에 대해 어떻게 생각하니?

G: 좋아, 나는 채소를 기르는 것을 좋아해.

B: 그거 알아?(있잖아.) 나는 채소를 먹는 것을 좋아해.

B: 지금 당장 그 동아리에 가입하자. 매달 신선한 채소가 있는 파티를 열 수 있어.

B: 좋아. 첫 번째 파티는 4월 30일이야.

B: 나는 파티가 너무 기다려져.

❶ What do you think of ~?: ~에 대해 어떻게 생각하니?=What's your opinion about[of, on] ~? / How do you like ~? / How do you feel about ~?(의견을 묻는 표현)

❷ You know what?: 너 그거 알아?, 있잖아.

❸ on April 30: on + 날짜

❹ I can't wait for the party.: 나는 파티가 너무 기다려져. = I'm looking forward to the party.

Check(√) True or False

(1) The girl likes to grow vegetables.   T ☐ F ☐

(2) They can have a party with fresh vegetables every week.   T ☐ F ☐

B. Step Up - Real-life Scene

I Can't Wait for His Class

Seho: Miso, what do you think of Mr. Park?

Miso: The new math teacher? ❶He looks very strict and serious.

Seho: ❷Don't judge a book by its cover.

Miso: What do you mean, Seho?

Seho: My first class with Mr. Park was great. ❸He was very kind, and his class was so exciting.

Miso: Really?

Seho: Yes. ❹During the first class, we did interesting math activities with our cell phones.

Miso: Wow! I can't wait for his class tomorrow. ❺It's my first math class this year.

나는 그의 수업이 너무 기다려져.

세호: 미소야, 박 선생님에 대해 어떻게 생각하니?

미소: 새로 오신 수학 선생님? 그는 매우 엄격하고 진지해 보이셔.

세호: 겉모습만으로 판단하지 마.

미소: 무슨 뜻이야, 세호?

세호: 박 선생님과의 첫 수업은 훌륭했어. 그는 매우 친절하셨고, 그의 수업은 매우 흥미로웠어.

미소: 정말?

세호: 응. 첫 수업 동안, 우리는 휴대 전화로 흥미로운 수학 활동을 했어.

미소: 와! 내일 그 선생님의 수업이 너무 기다려진다. 올해 첫 번째 수학 수업이야.

❶ look+형용사: ~하게 보이다 / strict: 엄격한 / serious: 진지한

❷ Don't judge a book by its cover.: 겉모습만으로 판단하지 마라.

❸ 주어가 그 감정을 느끼게 하는 것이므로 현재분사형 형용사 exciting이 알맞다.

❹ During the first class: during + 특정한 기간: ~ 동안

❺ It=his class

Check(√) True or False

(3) Mr. Park is very strict and serious.   T ☐ F ☐

(4) Miso is looking forward to Mr. Park's class.   T ☐ F ☐

Get Ready -2

1. G: ❶Hey, what do you think of this notebook?
   B: ❷It looks great! Is it for science?
   G: Yes. This year I'm going to study science harder with this notebook.
2. B: ❸Look at the teachers. Who's going to be our new homeroom teacher?
   G: ❹We'll find out in 10 minutes.
   B: I'm very excited. ❺I can't wait!
3. M: Hello, everyone! My name is Yun Kihun. I'm your English teacher.
   G&B: Glad to meet you, Mr. Yun.
   M: What do you think of English?
   G: It's interesting. I like English a lot.

❶ think of: ～에 대해 생각하다
❷ look+형용사: ～하게 보이다
❸ look at: ～을 보다
❹ find out: 알게 되다
❺ I can't wait.: 너무 기대된다.

Start Off - Listen & Talk A

1. B: This club looks good for you. What do you think of it?
   G: The health club? ❶I think it's boring.
   B: ❷Then which club do you want to join?
   G: I'll join the soccer club. I like playing soccer.
2. G: What do you think of the magic club?
   B: ❸I think it's the right club for me. I want to learn many interesting tricks.
   G: ❹I'll join it, too. When is the first meeting?
   B: Next Wednesday. ❺I can't wait for the first meeting!

❶ I think ～: 나는 ～라고 생각해. / boring: 지루한
❷ which+명사: 어느 ～
❸ right: 맞는, 알맞은
❹ it = the magic club
❺ I can't wait for the first meeting!=I'm looking forward to the first meeting!

Start Off - Speak Up

A: Look! What do you think of this diary?
B: ❶Its cover is cool. ❷I think it's good for Minjun.
A: ❸Yes, he'll like it a lot.
B: ❹I can't wait for his birthday party!

❶ Its = This diary's
❷ be good for: ～에 좋다
❸ it = this diary / a lot: 매우
❹ I can't wait for his birthday party! = I'm looking forward to his birthday party!

Express Yourself A

1. B: What do you think of today's lunch?
   G: I think it's okay. What's on tomorrow's menu?
   B: Wow! We can eat spaghetti tomorrow.
   G: ❶I can't wait for lunchtime tomorrow.
2. G: Look! ❷Two dishes of vegetables! What do you think of today's menu?
   B: ❸It's not bad. I like vegetables.
   G: I don't eat vegetables.
   B: Try some. ❹They are good for our health.

❶ I can't wait for lunchtime. = I'm looking forward to lunchtime.
❷ dish: 접시
❸ It = today's menu
❹ be good for: ～에 좋다 / health: 건강

Check Yourself - Listen & Speak

B: Let's join the School Band club together. What do you think of it?
G: Okay. ❶I like playing the flute.
B: I like playing the ukulele.
G: ❷Let's join the club right now. They practice after school every Tuesday and Thursday.
B: ❸They're going to have the first concert on July 15.
G: Great. ❹I hope to play in the concert.
B: Me, too. I can't wait for the concert.

❶ play the flute: 플루트를 연주하다
❷ Let's + 동사원형 ～: ～하자 / right now: 당장
❸ be going to+동사원형: ～할 예정이다
❹ I hope to+동사원형 ～: 나는 ～하고 싶다

● 다음 우리말과 일치하도록 빈칸에 알맞은 말을 쓰시오.

Get Ready - 2

1. **G:** Hey, what do you _____ of this notebook?

   B: It _____ great! Is it _____ science?

   G: Yes. _____ _____ I'm _____ to study science harder _____ this notebook.

2. **B:** _____ _____ the teachers. Who's _____ _____ be our new homeroom teacher?

   G: We'll _____ _____ in 10 minutes.

   B: I'm very _____. I can't _____!

3. **M:** Hello, everyone! My name is Yun Kihun. I'm _____ English teacher.

   G&B: Glad _____ meet you, Mr. Yun.

   M: _____ do you _____ of English?

   G: It's interesting. I like English _____ _____.

Start Off - Listen & Talk A

1. **B:** This club looks _____ _____ you. _____ do you think of it?

   G: The health club? I _____ it's _____.

   B: Then _____ club do you want _____ _____?

   G: I'll join the soccer club. I like _____ soccer.

2. **G:** What do you _____ _____ the magic club?

   B: I think it's the _____ club for me. I want _____ _____ many interesting tricks.

   G: I'll join it, _____. When is the _____ meeting?

   B: Next Wednesday. I can't _____ _____ the first meeting!

Start Off - Listen & Talk B

B: _____ join the Green Garden club together. What do you think of it?

G: Okay. I like _____ vegetables.

B: You know _____? I like eating vegetables.

G: _____ join the club _____ _____. We can have a party _____ fresh vegetables every month.

B: Great. The first party is _____ April 30.

G: I can't wait _____ the party.

1. G: 이 봐, 이 공책 어떻게 생각하니?
   B: 멋져 보여! 과학용이니?
   G: 응. 올해에는 이 공책을 가지고 과학을 더 열심히 공부할 거야.

2. B: 선생님들을 좀 봐. 누가 우리 새 담임선생님이 될까?
   G: 우리는 10분 후에 알게 될 거야.
   B: 너무 흥분돼. 너무 기대돼!

3. M: 안녕하세요, 여러분! 제 이름은 윤기훈입니다. 저는 여러분의 영어 선생님입니다.
   G&B: 만나서 반갑습니다, 윤 선생님.
   M: 여러분은 영어에 대해 어떻게 생각하세요?
   G: 재미있어요. 저는 영어를 매우 좋아해요.

1. B: 이 동아리는 너에게 맞는 것 같아. 그것에 대해 어떻게 생각하니?
   G: 헬스 동아리? 지루하다고 생각해.
   B: 그럼 넌 어떤 동아리에 가입하고 싶니?
   G: 난 축구 동아리에 가입할 거야. 나는 축구를 좋아해.

2. G: 마술 동아리에 대해 어떻게 생각하니?
   B: 나한테 맞는 동아리인 것 같아. 나는 재미있는 마술을 많이 배우고 싶어.
   G: 나도 가입할게. 첫 모임은 언제니?
   B: 다음 주 수요일이야. 나는 첫 모임이 너무 기다려져!

B: 초록 정원 동아리에 함께 가입하자. 그것에 대해 어떻게 생각하니?
G: 좋아. 나는 채소를 기르는 것을 좋아해.
B: 그거 알아?(있잖아.) 나는 채소를 먹는 것을 좋아해.
B: 지금 당장 그 동아리에 가입하자. 매달 신선한 채소가 있는 파티를 열 수 있어.
B: 좋아. 첫 번째 파티는 4월 30일이야.
B: 나는 파티가 너무 기다려져.

Step Up - Real-life Scene

I Can't Wait for His Class

Seho: Miso, _____ do you _____ _____ Mr. Park?

Miso: The new math teacher? He _____ very _____ and serious.

Seho: _____ _____ a book _____ its cover.

Miso: What do you _____, Seho?

Seho: My first class _____ Mr. Park was great. He was very kind, and his class was so _____.

Miso: Really?

Seho: Yes. _____ the first _____, we did interesting math activities _____ our cell phones.

Miso: Wow! I _____ _____ _____ his class tomorrow. It's my first math class _____ _____.

Express Yourself A

1. **B:** _____ do you think of today's lunch?

   G: _____ _____ it's okay. What's _____ tomorrow's menu?

   B: Wow! We _____ _____ spaghetti tomorrow.

   G: I _____ _____ _____ lunchtime tomorrow.

2. **G:** Look! Two _____ of vegetables! What do you _____ _____ today's menu?

   B: It's not _____. I like vegetables.

   G: I _____ _____ vegetables.

   B: _____ some. They are _____ for our health.

Check Yourself - Listen & Speak

B: _____ _____ the School Band club together. _____ do you think _____ it?

G: Okay. I like _____ the flute.

B: I like _____ the ukulele.

G: Let's join the club _____ _____. They practice _____ _____ every Tuesday and Thursday.

B: They're _____ _____ have the first concert _____ July 15.

G: Great. I hope _____ _____ in the concert.

B: Me, _____. I can't _____ _____ the concert.

나는 그의 수업이 너무 기다려져.
세호: 미소야, 박 선생님에 대해 어떻게 생각하니?
미소: 새로 오신 수학 선생님? 그는 매우 엄격하고 진지해 보이셔.
세호: 겉모습만으로 판단하지 마.
미소: 무슨 뜻이야, 세호?
세호: 박 선생님과의 첫 수업은 훌륭했어. 그는 매우 친절하셨고, 그의 수업은 매우 흥미로웠어.
미소: 정말?
세호: 응. 첫 수업 동안, 우리는 휴대 전화로 흥미로운 수학 활동을 했어.
미소: 와! 내일 수업이 너무 기다려진다. 올해 첫 번째 수학 수업이야.

1. B: 오늘 점심에 대해 어떻게 생각하니?
   G: 괜찮은 것 같아. 내일 메뉴는 뭐니?
   B: 와! 내일 우리는 스파게티를 먹을 수 있어.
   G: 내일 점심시간이 몹시 기다려진다.
2. G: 봐! 야채 두 접시! 오늘 메뉴 어때?
   B: 나쁘지 않아. 나는 야채를 좋아해.
   G: 나는 야채를 안 먹어.
   B: 조금 먹어 봐. 그것들은 우리 건강에 좋아.

B: 우리 학교 밴드 동아리에 같이 가입하자. 그것에 대해서 어떻게 생각하니?
G: 좋아. 나는 플루트 연주하는 것을 좋아해.
B: 난 우쿨렐레 연주하는 걸 좋아해.
G: 지금 당장 그 동아리에 가입하자. 그들은 매주 화요일과 목요일 방과 후에 연습을 해.
B: 그들은 7월 15일에 첫 번째 음악회를 열 거야.
G: 좋아. 나는 음악회에서 연주를 하고 싶어.
B: 나도. 나는 음악회가 너무 기다려져.

01 다음 대화의 빈칸에 공통으로 알맞은 것은?

> A: What do you _____ of having a pet?
> B: I _____ it is exciting.

① take ② think
③ introduce ④ see
⑤ thought

02 다음 대화의 빈칸에 들어갈 말로 알맞은 것은?

> A: What do you think of my new trick?
> B: I think it's cool.
> A: I can't wait for the _____.

① game ② concert
③ art contest ④ party
⑤ magic show

03 다음 대화의 빈칸에 올 수 없는 것은?

> A: What do you think of Emily?
> B: _____

① She is nice. ② I like her, too.
③ I think she's pretty. ④ I think she is a liar.
⑤ In my opinion, she is the best student in our class.

04 다음 주어진 표현과 의미가 같은 것은?

> I can't wait for the trip.

① What a nice trip! ② How was the trip?
③ I don't like the trip. ④ I can't go on the trip.
⑤ I'm looking forward to the trip.

[01~04] 다음 대화를 읽고, 물음에 답하시오.

B: Let's join the Green Garden club together.
___ⓐ___ do you think of it?
G: ___ⓑ___ I like growing vegetables.
B: You know what? I like eating vegetables.
G: Let's join the club right now. We can have a party with fresh vegetables every month.
B: Great. The first party is ___ⓒ___ April 30.
G: ⓓ나는 파티가 너무 기다려져.

01 위 대화의 빈칸 ⓐ에 알맞은 것은?

① How
② What
③ Why
④ When
⑤ Which

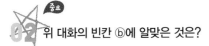

02 위 대화의 빈칸 ⓑ에 알맞은 것은?

① I don't think so.
② Don't mention it.
③ I think it's great.
④ I'm not so sure about it.
⑤ The Green Garden club isn't that good.

03 위 대화의 빈칸 ⓒ에 알맞은 것은?

① at
② in
③ on
④ of
⑤ by

04 위 대화의 밑줄 친 ⓓ의 우리말을 바르게 옮긴 것은?

① I'm waiting for the party.
② I must wait for the party.
③ I can't wait for the party.
④ I'm going to attend the party.
⑤ I'm thinking of attending the party.

[05~06] 다음 대화를 읽고, 물음에 답하시오.

G: Look! Two dishes of vegetables! ⓐWhat do you think of today's menu?
B: It's not bad. I like vegetables.
G: I don't eat vegetables.
B: Try some. They are good ___ⓑ___ our health.

05 위 대화의 밑줄 친 ⓐ와 바꿔 쓸 수 있는 것은?

① What is on today's menu?
② What's your opinion on today's menu?
③ What makes you think of today's menu?
④ Why don't you think of today's menu?
⑤ How about thinking of today's menu?

06 위 대화의 빈칸 ⓑ에 알맞은 것은?

① at
② of
③ for
④ with
⑤ from

[07~10] 다음 대화를 읽고, 물음에 답하시오.

I Can't Wait for His Class

Seho: Miso, ⓐ<u>what do you think of Mr. Park?</u>

Miso: The new math teacher? He looks very strict and serious.

Seho: Don't judge a book ___ⓑ___ its cover.

Miso: What do you mean, Seho?

Seho: My first class ___ⓒ___ Mr. Park was great. He was very kind, and his class was so exciting.

Miso: Really?

Seho: Yes. During the first class, we did interesting math activities ___ⓓ___ our cell phones.

Miso: Wow! I can't wait for his class tomorrow. It's my first math class this year.

07 위 대화의 밑줄 친 ⓐ의 의도로 알맞은 것은?

① 의견 묻기　　② 의견 동의하기

③ 능력 여부 묻기　　④ 선호에 대해 묻기

⑤ 제안이나 권유하기

08 위 대화의 빈칸 ⓑ에 알맞은 것은?

① of　　　　　② by

③ with　　　　④ from

⑤ about

서답형

09 위 대화의 빈칸 ⓒ와 ⓓ에 공통으로 알맞은 말을 쓰시오.

➡ _____

10 위 대화의 내용과 일치하지 <u>않는</u> 것은?

① Miso thinks Mr. Park looks very strict and serious.

② Seho liked his first class with Mr. Park.

③ Seho thinks that Mr. Park's class was boring.

④ Seho and his classmates did interesting math activities during the first class.

⑤ Miso is looking forward to Mr. Park's class tomorrow.

[11~13] 다음 대화를 읽고, 물음에 답하시오.

A: Look! What do you think ___ⓐ___ this diary?

B: Its ___ⓑ___ is cool. I think it's good for Minjun.

A: Yes, he'll like it a lot.

B: ⓒ나는 그의 생일 파티가 너무 기다려져.

11 위 대화의 빈칸 ⓐ에 알맞은 것을 <u>모두</u> 고르면?

① of　　　　　② for

③ about　　　④ on

⑤ over

서답형

12 위 대화의 빈칸 ⓑ에 다음 영영풀이에 해당하는 단어를 쓰시오.

the outer part of a book or magazine

➡ _____

서답형

13 위 대화의 밑줄 친 ⓒ의 우리말에 맞게 주어진 단어를 이용하여 영작하시오.

(wait)

➡ _____

[01~03] 다음 대화를 읽고, 물음에 답하시오.

> B: This club looks (A)[good / well] for you.
> ⓐ너는 그것에 대해 어떻게 생각하니?
> G: The health club? I think it's (B)[bored / boring].
> B: Then which club do you want to join?
> G: I'll join the soccer club. I like playing soccer.

01 위 대화의 괄호 (A)와 (B)에서 어법상 알맞은 것을 골라 쓰시오.

(A) _____ (B) _____

02 위 대화의 밑줄 친 ⓐ의 우리말을 주어진 단어를 이용하여 영어로 옮기시오.

(what / think)

➡ _____

03 What does the girl think of the health club? Answer in English.

➡ _____

04 다음 대화의 순서를 바르게 배열하시오.

> (A) I can't wait for his birthday party!
> (B) Look! What do you think of this diary?
> (C) Yes, he'll like it a lot.
> (D) Its cover is cool. I think it's good for Minjun.

➡ _____

[05~08] 다음 대화를 읽고, 물음에 답하시오.

> B: Let's join the Green Garden club together.
> _____ⓐ_____ do you think of it?
> G: Okay. I like growing vegetables.
> B: You know ____ⓑ____ ? I like eating vegetables.
> G: Let's join the club right now. We can have a party with fresh vegetables every month.
> B: Great. The first party is on April 30.
> G: ⓒ(can't / I / the party / for / wait)

05 위 대화의 빈칸 ⓐ와 ⓑ에 공통으로 알맞은 말을 쓰시오. (대·소문자 무시)

➡ _____

06 When can they have a party with fresh vegetables? Answer in English.

➡ _____
_____

07 When is the first party? Answer in English.

➡ _____

08 위 대화의 괄호 ⓒ 안의 단어를 바르게 배열하시오.

➡ _____

Grammar

1 to부정사의 형용사적 용법

- Do you have something **to say**? 너는 할 말이 있니?
- I have no time **to play**. 나는 놀 시간이 없다.
- A: Are you busy? 너 바쁘니?
  B: Yes. I have lots of homework **to do**. 응. 나는 해야 할 숙제가 많아.

■ to부정사가 명사나 부정대명사를 뒤에서 꾸며주는 형용사의 역할을 할 때는 '~할', '~해야 할'로 해석한다.

- Dami needs some water **to drink**. 다미는 마실 물이 좀 필요하다.
- He had no friends **to help** him. 그는 자기를 도와줄 친구가 하나도 없었다.
- You feel that you have nothing **to wear**. 너는 입을 것이 아무것도 없다고 느낀다.

■ 명사+to부정사+전치사: 수식받는 명사가 전치사의 목적어인 경우는 to부정사 뒤에 반드시 전치사를 쓴다.

- I need a pen **to write with**. 나는 쓸 펜이 한 자루 없다.
- She's looking for a chair **to sit on**. 그녀는 앉을 의자를 찾고 있다.
- We have no house **to live in**. 우리는 살 집이 필요하다.
- He needs a friend **to talk to**. 그는 말할 친구가 필요하다.
- She bought some paper **to write on**. 그녀는 쓸 종이를 좀 샀다.

cf. -thing+형용사+to부정사: -thing으로 끝나는 부정대명사는 형용사가 뒤에서 수식하며, 이를 다시 to부정사가 뒤에서 수식한다.

- I want something cold **to drink**. 나는 차가운 마실 것을 원한다.

핵심 Check

1. 다음 괄호 안에서 알맞은 것을 고르시오.
   (1) It's time (go / to go) to school.
   (2) Give me a pen (to write / to write with).
   (3) Seho has a lot of friends (helping / to help).
   (4) Would you like something (to drink cold / cold to drink)?

2. 다음 주어진 단어를 빈칸에 알맞은 형태로 바꾸어 쓰시오.
   (1) Is there nobody _____ _____ to my story? (listen)
   (2) I have something important _____ _____ you. (tell)
   (3) There are so many places _____ _____ in my town. (visit)

② 접속사 that

- I think **(that)** I lost it. 나는 그것을 잃어버린 것 같아.
- A: Look! There's a schoolbag. 봐! 책가방이 있어.
  B: I think **that** it's a boy's bag. 내 생각에는 소년의 가방인 것 같아.

■ 접속사는 절과 절을 연결하는 역할을 하므로 접속사 that은 「주어+동사+that+주어+동사 ~」의 형태로 쓰인다.

- I think **that** he is a genius. 나는 그가 천재라고 생각해.
- I believe **that** she will come to the party. 나는 그녀가 파티에 올 것이라고 믿는다.

■ 접속사 that이 이끄는 절은 문장 안에서 주어, 목적어, 보어의 역할을 하므로 이때의 that을 명사절 접속사라 한다. 목적어 역할을 하는 명사절을 이끄는 that은 생략 가능하다.

- **That** he plays soccer well is true. [주어 역할] 그가 축구를 잘한다는 것은 사실이다.
- I think **(that)** he is American. [목적어 역할] 나는 그가 미국인이라고 생각한다
- The truth is **that** she is a liar. [보어 역할] 사실은 그녀가 거짓말쟁이라는 것이다.

cf. that은 '저것'을 뜻하는 지시대명사나 지시형용사로 사용될 수도 있으므로, 문장 안에서 명사 역할을 하는 접속사 용법과 구분하도록 한다.

- I need **that** pen. 나는 저 펜이 필요해.
- I want **that** blue shirt. 나는 저 파란색 셔츠를 원해.

핵심 Check

3. 다음 괄호 안에서 알맞은 것을 고르시오.

(1) I think (what / that) he is honest.

(2) I know (that / when) she was a teacher.

4. 다음 문장에서 that이 들어갈 수 있는 곳에 V표를 하시오.

(1) I hope you get better.

(2) Miss. Susan says the Han River is beautiful.

(3) He thinks his dog went away.

01 다음 우리말과 일치하도록 빈칸에 알맞은 말을 쓰시오.

perform 공연하다

(1) 그녀는 내가 숙제를 했다고 믿는다.

➡ She _____ _____ I did my homework.

(2) 그는 내가 공연을 잘했다고 생각한다.

➡ He _____ _____ I performed well.

02 다음 괄호 안에 주어진 단어를 바르게 배열하시오.

only 유일한
person 사람

(1) He is the only person _____ _____ _____. (help / to / us)

(2) There are _____ _____ _____ _____. (do / things / to / many)

03 다음 우리말과 같도록 괄호 안의 단어를 바르게 배열하여 문장을 완성하시오.

(1) 나는 Jenny가 집에 있다고 생각한다.

(at / is / home / Jenny / that / think)

➡ I _____.

(2) 나는 우리 부모님이 건강하길 바란다.

(that / hope / are / healthy / my parents)

➡ I _____.

(3) 그녀는 그가 돌아올 거라고 믿었다.

(he / back / believed / come / that / would)

➡ She _____.

04 다음 우리말과 일치하도록 빈칸에 알맞은 말을 쓰시오.

busy 바쁜
a lot of 많은
work 일

(1) 여기는 덥다. 나는 마실 것을 원한다.

➡ It's hot in here! I want something _____ _____.

(2) Vicky는 이번 주말에 읽을 흥미로운 책이 필요하다.

➡ Vicky needs an interesting book _____ _____ this weekend.

(1) 나는 매우 바쁘다. 나는 오늘 해야 할 일이 많다.

➡ I'm so busy. I have a lot of work _____ _____ today.

01 다음 우리말과 같도록 빈칸에 알맞은 것은?

> 나는 학교 다닐 때 탈 자전거를 사고 싶다.
> ➡ I want to buy a bike _____ to school.

① ride ② rides ③ to ride
④ riding ⑤ to riding

02 다음 중 접속사 that이 들어갈 알맞은 곳은?

> I (①) hope (②) I have (③) a lot of
> (④) money (⑤).

① ② ③ ④ ⑤

03 다음 중 밑줄 친 부분의 쓰임이 나머지 넷과 다른 것은?

① We have no time to waste.
② I need a friend to talk to.
③ I have a lot of books to read.
④ They decided to leave home.
⑤ We cannot find a place to park our car.

04 다음 문장의 빈칸에 알맞지 않은 것은?

> I _____ that he is sick today.

① know ② believe
③ heard ④ think
⑤ made

05 다음 우리말을 참고하여 빈칸에 알맞은 말을 쓰시오.

> 나는 내 숙제를 도와 줄 누군가가 필요하다.
> ➡ I need somebody _____ _____
> me with my homework.

06 다음 중 밑줄 친 that의 쓰임이 나머지 넷과 다른 하나는?

① I think that honesty is the most important thing.
② I think that Jinny has a dog.
③ Ann believes that man is my husband.
④ Susan thinks that he is very smart.
⑤ Runa believes that her hometown is New York.

07 다음 빈칸에 공통으로 알맞은 것은?

> • Would you like something _____ drink?
> • Jenny has some money _____ spend on everyday things.

① on ② to ③ as
④ for ⑤ with

08 다음 문장에서 어법상 틀린 부분을 찾아 바르게 고쳐 쓰시오.

> She thinks what the English teacher is handsome.

_____ ➡ _____

서답형

09 다음 문장에서 어법상 어색한 부분을 찾아 고쳐 쓰시오.

> I need some medicine taking right away.

_____ ➡ _____

중요

10 다음 밑줄 친 that 중 생략할 수 없는 것은?

① I think that you are so beautiful.
② I hope that I will get good grades.
③ I believe that Jenny is a kind girl.
④ I believe that he will be an engineer.
⑤ I know that man is Ann's math teacher.

11 다음 중 밑줄 친 부분의 쓰임이 나머지 넷과 다른 하나는?

① I have something to eat.
② My brothers have books to read.
③ Sarah let her son go to the park.
④ Joe has a lot of homework to do.
⑤ Ken has many friends to help him.

서답형

12 다음 두 문장의 빈칸에 공통으로 알맞은 말을 쓰시오.

> • I believe _____ I can fly in the air.
> • We don't hope _____ you will like it.

서답형

13 다음 문장에서 어법상 어색한 부분을 찾아 고쳐 쓰시오.

> They found a nice house to live.

_____ ➡ _____

14 다음 밑줄 친 부분 중 어법상 어색한 것은?

① Jane has a lot of things to do.
② There's nothing to worry about.
③ Check prices for clothes to buy.
④ I had a lot of work to complete.
⑤ Let me get you a chair to sit.

서답형

15 다음 우리말과 같도록 주어진 어휘를 바르게 배열하시오.

> 나는 진우가 훌륭한 리더가 될 것이라고 생각한다.
> (Jinwoo / great / be / will / that / think / I / a / leader).

➡ _____

중요

16 다음 문장의 빈칸에 공통으로 알맞은 것은?

> • I don't have any friends to play _____.
> • Kelly is looking for a pencil to write _____.

① of ② to
③ for ④ with
⑤ 필요 없음

17 다음 중 〈보기〉의 밑줄 친 that과 쓰임이 같은 것은?

> ─── 보기 ───
>
> He thinks that science is a useful subject.

① Look at that old temple.

② Where did you find that pencil?

③ He walked this way and that way.

④ I know that man sings very well.

⑤ I believe that everything will be fine.

18 다음 밑줄 친 부분 중 용법이 다른 하나는?

① I went to the cafeteria to have lunch.

② I'm glad to meet you.

③ I need some medicine to take.

④ She grew up to become a doctor.

⑤ He must be rich to buy that car.

서답형

19 다음 문장에서 어법상 어색한 부분을 찾아 고쳐 쓰시오.

> I don't know that he will come to the meeting.

_____ ➡ _____

20 다음 중 어법상 어색한 것은?

① He has no friends to talk to.

② I bought some books to read.

③ She's looking for something reading.

④ I got up early to see her.

⑤ I have a lot of homework to do.

21 다음 중 밑줄 친 부분의 쓰임이 나머지 넷과 다른 것은?

① I need some money to buy a bicycle.

② I don't have anything to drink.

③ You have to study hard to get good grades.

④ He is buying a bike to ride in the race.

⑤ She wants a pair of shoes to wear during the tour.

22 다음 괄호 안에 주어진 단어를 이용하여 우리말에 맞도록 문장을 완성하시오.

> 그녀는 앉을 의자가 필요하다. (sit)
>
> ➡ She needs _____ .

23 다음 중 문장의 빈칸에 들어갈 말이 다른 하나는? (대·소문자 무시)

① Do you know _____ man?

② I think _____ she is pretty.

③ Do you know _____ he is sick?

④ _____ you finish it, let me know.

⑤ _____ he never came back is true.

중요

24 다음 중 밑줄 친 부분의 쓰임이 같은 것끼리 묶인 것은?

> ⓐ I need something to drink.
> ⓑ She wants to become a teacher.
> ⓒ The girl had nothing to wear.
> ⓓ She went out to meet her boyfriend.

① ⓐ, ⓑ   ② ⓑ, ⓓ

③ ⓑ, ⓒ   ④ ⓐ, ⓒ

⑤ ⓒ, ⓓ

01 다음 빈칸에 공통으로 알맞은 말을 쓰시오.

• Mike had no time _____ do his homework.
• We are going to buy a house _____ live in.

02 다음 두 문장을 한 문장으로 만드시오.

(1) They believe. + There is an alien here.

➡ _____

(2) I know. + You came back home late.

➡ _____

03 중요 다음 〈보기〉에서 알맞은 단어를 골라 문장을 완성하시오.

┌─── 보기 ───┐
sit buy eat drink talk wear

(1) I'm hungry. I need some food _____ _____.

(2) I'm very thirsty. I need something _____ _____.

(3) There's no chair here. I need a chair to _____ _____.

(4) Tony feels lonely. He needs friends to _____ _____.

04 다음 빈칸에 공통으로 알맞은 말을 쓰시오.

• I believe _____ the story is true.
• Does your mother know _____ boy in the room?

05 중요 다음 우리말과 같도록 주어진 단어를 바르게 배열하시오.

그녀는 입을 뭔가가 필요하다.
(put / something / on / she / needs / to)

➡ _____

06 다음 괄호 안에 주어진 단어와 that을 이용하여 바르게 배열하시오.

(1) (Chinese / I / is / think / he)

➡ _____ that _____.

(2) (is / wife / know / I / a / wise / she)

➡ _____ that _____.

07 다음 두 문장을 to부정사를 이용하여 한 문장으로 고쳐 쓰시오.

(1) I want some snacks. I will eat them in the afternoon.

➡ _____

(2) They need four chairs. They'll sit on the chair.

➡ _____

08 중요 다음 주어진 문장에서 어법상 어색한 부분을 바르게 고쳐 다시 쓰시오.

Do you have warm something to wear?

➡ _____

중요

09 다음 문장에서 어법상 <u>어색한</u> 부분을 찾아 바르게 고쳐 쓰시오.

(1) He needs a chair to sit.

_____ ➡ _____

(2) There are many places visiting in Paris.

_____ ➡ _____

10 다음 주어진 우리말을 영작하시오.

나는 나의 영어 선생님이 예쁘다고 생각한다.

➡ _____

중요

11 다음 우리말과 일치하도록 주어진 어구를 이용하여 영작하시오.

(1) 그녀는 자신을 도울 힘센 누군가가 필요하다.
(someone / help)

➡ _____

(2) 그는 같이 놀 친구들이 없다. (no / play)

➡ _____

중요

12 다음 우리말과 같도록 괄호 안의 단어를 바르게 배열하시오.

(1) 나는 네가 모든 것을 할 수 있다고 생각한다.
(everything / do / you / can / that)

➡ I think _____.

(2) 너는 그녀가 예쁘다고 생각하니?
(is / think / she / pretty / that / you)

➡ Do _____?

13 다음 〈보기〉와 같이 두 문장을 한 문장으로 바꿔 쓰시오.

┌─ 보기 ─────────────────────┐
│ Brian has a lot of books. + He will │
│ read a lot of books. │
│ ➡ Brian has a lot of books to read. │
└───────────────────────────┘

(1) We cannot find a place. + We will park our car.

➡ _____

(2) Dave wants to buy a bike. + He will ride a bike to school.

➡ _____

(3) Kate has a lot of homework. + She will do a lot of homework.

➡ _____

중요

14 다음 우리말에 맞게 빈칸에 알맞은 말을 쓰시오.

그녀는 쓸 펜이 필요하다.
➡ She needs _____ _____ _____
_____ _____.

15 다음 괄호 안에 주어진 단어를 이용하여 우리말을 영어로 옮기시오.

(1) 그는 그녀가 부자라는 것을 안다.
(know / that)

➡ _____

(2) 나는 그가 미국인이라고 생각하지 않는다.
(think / that)

➡ _____

고난이도

16 다음 주어진 어구를 바르게 배열하시오.

(1) (anything / don't have / they / about / to talk).

➡ _____

(2) (we / in Paris / are looking for / stay at / to / a hotel)

➡ _____

Reading

The Tickets

Seho and Jihun were talking in the hallway when Dami came over.
과거진행형: be동사의 과거형+-ing(~하고 있었다) 접 ~할 때 come over: 오다

"Happy birthday!" she said to Seho. "Here. They're from my dad."
= two KBL tickets

"Wow, two KBL tickets! Thanks!"

"Who are you going to take with you?" Dami asked.
be going to: ~할 것이다

"Minjun. He took me to a soccer game before. So, it's time to pay him
take A to B: A를 B로 데려가다   pay someone back: ~에게 신세를 갚다

back."

"You know what?" Jihun cut in. "Minjun isn't a fan of basketball. But
(말·대화에) 끼어들다

I am!"

"Well, I'll ask him first anyway," replied Seho.
= Minjun

"He won't go with you. Trust me," said Jihun.
will not의 줄임말

"Who is this guy?" Dami thought to herself, "He wants Minjun's
think to oneself: 마음속으로 생각하다

ticket."

"Oh! There's the bell. See you later," said Dami. She hurried to class.
종이 울린다.

"Come on, Jihun," said Seho, and he started to run.
start to+동사원형: ~하기 시작하다

Vocabulary (sidebar):

hallway 복도
ticket 표, 입장권
take 데려가다
before 전에
fan 팬
anyway 어쨌든
reply 대답하다
trust 믿다
later 나중에
class 수업

확인문제

● 다음 문장이 본문의 내용과 일치하면 T, 일치하지 <u>않으면</u> F를 쓰시오.

1 Dami said to Seho, "Happy birthday!" ☐

2 Dami gave Jihun two KBL tickets. ☐

3 Minjun took Jihun to a soccer game before. ☐

4 Jihun said Minjun is not a fan of basketball. ☐

5 Dami thought to herself, "Jihun wants Minjun's ticket." ☐

6 Dami hurried to class when the bell rang. ☐

At the corner, Seho bumped into someone. "Sorry!" he said and
bump into: ~에 부딪히다
continued to run. Just then, Jihun saw something on the floor.
continue+to부정사: 계속해서 ~하다   바로 그때

"Wait, Seho!" he said, but Seho was not there.

After class, Seho went to Dami and said, "I can't find one of my
수업이 끝난 후에   one of: ~ 중 하나
tickets. Did you happen to see it?"
            우연히 ~하다   = a ticket

"No," she answered. "Isn't it in your bag?"

"No, it's not there. I think I lost it," said Seho.

On her way home, Dami saw Jihun. He had the ticket in his hand.
집으로 오는 도중에
Dami got angry and said, "Hey! Why do you ...?"
    get+형용사 = become+형용사

Just then, Jihun saw Seho and shouted, "Seho! I found a ticket in the

hallway. I think it's yours."
            =your ticket
"Thanks! I was looking for that!" said Seho.
            look for: ~을 찾다
"He's not so bad," Dami thought.

"So, what were you saying? Do you have something to say, Dami?"
                                            to부정사의 형용사적 용법
asked Jihun.

"Um, how about going to the school basketball game with me this
    How about -ing ~?: ~하는 게 어때?   ~와 함께
Friday? It's the finals."
= the school basketball game
Jihun looked really pleased. "I'd love to!"
    look+형용사: ~하게 보이다   = I would

floor 바닥
find 발견하다
answer 대답하다
sad 슬픈
shout 외치다
hallway 복도
final 결승전
pleased 기쁜

📎 **확인문제**

● 다음 문장이 본문의 내용과 일치하면 T, 일치하지 않으면 F를 쓰시오.

1 Seho bumped into someone at the corner. ☐

2 Jihun saw something on the ground. ☐

3 After school, when Dami saw one of Seho's tickets in Jihun's hand, she got angry. ☐

4 Dami and Jihun are going to the school basketball game together this Friday. ☐

● 우리말을 참고하여 빈칸에 알맞은 말을 쓰시오.

1 Seho and Jihun _____ _____ in the hallway _____ Dami came _____.

2 "Happy birthday!" she _____ _____ Seho.

3 "Here. They're _____ my dad."

4 "Wow, two KBL _____! Thanks!"

5 "Who are you _____ to take _____ you?" Dami asked.

6 "Minjun. He _____ me _____ a soccer game before.

7 So, it's time to _____ him _____."

8 "You know _____?" Jihun cut _____.

9 "Minjun _____ a _____ of basketball. _____ I am!"

10 "Well, I'll ask him first _____," _____ Seho.

11 "He _____ go with you. _____ me," said Jihun.

12 "Who is this guy?" Dami _____ _____ _____, "He wants Minjun's ticket."

13 "Oh! _____ the bell. See you _____," said Dami.

14 She _____ to class.

15 "Come _____, Jihun," said Seho, and he started _____ _____.

16 _____ the corner, Seho _____ _____ someone.

17 "Sorry!" he said and _____ _____ run.

18 _____ then, Jihun saw something _____ the floor.

1 세호와 지훈이는 다미가 왔을 때 복도에서 이야기를 나누고 있었다.

2 "생일 축하해!" 다미가 세호에게 말했다.

3 "이거 받아. 우리 아빠가 주신 거야."

4 "와, KBL 입장권 두 장! 고마워!"

5 "넌 누구를 데려 갈 거니?" 다미가 물었다.

6 "민준이. 그가 전에 나를 축구 경기에 데려갔어.

7 그래서 그에게 신세를 갚아야 할 때야."

8 "그거 알아?" 지훈이가 끼어들었다.

9 "민준이는 농구 팬이 아니야. 하지만 난 농구 팬이야!"

10 "음, 어쨌든 먼저 민준이에게 물어볼 거야." 세호가 대답했다.

11 "그는 너와 함께 가지 않을 거야. 날 믿어." 지훈이가 말했다.

12 "이 녀석은 누구지?" 다미는 "그는 민준이의 입장권을 원하는구나." 라고 마음속으로 생각했다.

13 "아, 종이 울린다. 나중에 보자," 다미가 말했다.

14 그녀는 서둘러 수업에 들어갔다.

15 "어서, 지훈아," 세호는 말하고 달리기 시작했다.

16 모퉁이에서, 세호는 누군가와 부딪혔다.

17 그는 "미안해!"라고 말하고는 계속 달렸다.

18 바로 그때, 지훈이가 바닥에 있는 무언가를 보았다.

19 "Wait, Seho!" he said, _____ Seho _____ _____ there.

20 _____ class, Seho went _____ Dami and said, "I can't find _____ _____ my tickets.

21 Did you _____ _____ see it?"

22 "No," she _____ .

23 "_____ it _____ your bag?"

24 "No, it's _____ there. I think I _____ it," said Seho.

25 _____ her way home, Dami _____ Jihun.

26 He _____ the ticket _____ his hand.

27 Dami got _____ and said, "Hey! _____ do you ...?"

28 _____ _____ , Jihun saw Seho and _____ , "Seho! I found a ticket _____ the hallway.

29 I think it's _____ ."

30 "Thanks! I was _____ _____ that!" said Seho.

31 "He's _____ so bad," Dami _____ .

32 "So, what _____ you _____ ?

33 Do you have something _____ _____ , Dami?" _____ Jihun.

34 "Um, how _____ going _____ the school basketball game _____ me this Friday?

35 It's the _____ ."

36 Jihun _____ really _____ . "I'd _____ _____ !"

19 "기다려, 세호야!"라고 그가 말했지만 세호는 거기에 없었다.

20 수업이 끝난 후, 세호는 다미에게 가서 말했다. "내 입장권 한 장을 찾을 수 없어.

21 너 혹시 입장권을 봤니?"

22 "아니," 그녀가 대답했다.

23 "네 가방 안에 있지 않니?"

24 "아니, 거기에 없어. 내 생각에 그것을 잃어버린 것 같아," 세호가 말했다.

25 집으로 돌아오는 길에 다미는 지훈을 보았다.

26 그는 손에 입장권을 가지고 있었다.

27 다미는 화가 나서 "이봐! 너가 왜 ...?"라고 말했다.

28 바로 그때, 지훈이는 세호를 보고 소리쳤다. "세호야! 내가 복도에서 입장권을 찾았어.

29 네 것 같아."

30 "고마워! 나는 그것을 찾고 있었어!" 세호가 말했다.

31 "그는 그렇게 나쁘진 않아."라고 다미는 생각했다.

32 "그래서, 무슨 말을 하고 있었던 거야?

33 너 할 말이 있니, 다미야?" 지훈이가 물었다.

34 "음, 이번 금요일에 나랑 학교 농구 경기에 같이 가는 게 어때?

35 그것은 결승전이야."

36 지훈은 정말 기뻐 보였다. "가고 싶어!"

● 우리말을 참고하여 본문을 영작하시오.

1 ▶ 세호와 지훈이는 다미가 왔을 때 복도에서 이야기를 나누고 있었다.
➡ _____

2 ▶ "생일 축하해!" 다미가 세호에게 말했다.
➡ _____

3 ▶ "이거 받아. 우리 아빠가 주신 거야."
➡ _____

4 ▶ "와, KBL 입장권 두 장! 고마워!"
➡ _____

5 ▶ "넌 누구를 데려 갈 거니?" 다미가 물었다.
➡ _____

6 ▶ "민준이. 그가 전에 나를 축구 경기에 데려갔어.
➡ _____

7 ▶ 그래서 그에게 신세를 갚아야 할 때야."
➡ _____

8 ▶ "그거 알아?" 지훈이가 끼어들었다.
➡ _____

9 ▶ "민준이는 농구 팬이 아니야. 하지만 난 농구 팬이야!"
➡ _____

10 ▶ "음, 어쨌든 먼저 민준이에게 물어볼 거야." 세호가 대답했다.
➡ _____

11 ▶ "그는 너와 함께 가지 않을 거야. 날 믿어." 지훈이가 말했다.
➡ _____

12 ▶ "이 녀석은 누구지?" 다미는 "그는 민준이의 입장권을 원하는구나."라고 마음속으로 생각했다.
➡ _____

13 ▶ "아, 종이 울린다. 나중에 보자."라고 다미가 말했다.
➡ _____

14 ▶ 그녀는 서둘러 수업에 들어갔다.
➡ _____

15 ▶ "어서, 지훈아." 세호는 말하고 달리기 시작했다.
➡ _____

16 ▶ 모퉁이에서, 세호는 누군가와 부딪혔다.
➡ _____

17 ▶ 그는 "미안해!"라고 말하고는 계속 달렸다.
➡ _____

18 ▶ 바로 그때, 지훈이가 바닥에 있는 무언가를 보았다.
➡ _____

19 "기다려, 세호야!" 그가 말했지만 세호는 거기에 없었다.

➡ _____

20 수업이 끝난 후, 세호는 다미에게 가서 말했다, "내 입장권 한 장을 찾을 수 없어.

➡ _____

21 너 혹시 입장권을 봤니?"

➡ _____

22 "아니," 그녀가 대답했다.

➡ _____

23 "네 가방 안에 있지 않니?"

➡ _____

24 "아니, 거기에 없어. 내 생각에 그것을 잃어버린 것 같아." 세호가 말했다.

➡ _____

25 집으로 돌아오는 길에 다미는 지훈을 보았다.

➡ _____

26 그는 손에 입장권을 가지고 있었다.

➡ _____

27 다미는 화가 나서 "이봐! 너가 왜 ...?"라고 말했다.

➡ _____

28 바로 그때, 지훈이는 세호를 보고 소리쳤다. "세호야! 내가 복도에서 입장권을 찾았어.

➡ _____

29 네 것 같아."

➡ _____

30 "고마워! 나는 그것을 찾고 있었어!" 세호가 말했다.

➡ _____

31 "그는 그렇게 나쁘진 않아." 다미는 생각했다.

➡ _____

32 "그래서, 무슨 말을 하고 있었던 거야?

➡ _____

33 너 할 말이 있니, 다미야?" 지훈이가 물었다.

➡ _____

34 "음, 이번 금요일에 나랑 학교 농구 경기에 같이 가는 게 어때?

➡ _____

35 그것은 결승전이야."

➡ _____

36 지훈은 정말 기뻐 보였다. "가고 싶어!"

➡ _____

[01~05] 다음 글을 읽고, 물음에 답하시오.

At the corner, Seho bumped ⓐ someone. "Sorry!" he said and continued to run. Just then, Jihun saw something on the floor.

"Wait, Seho!" he said, ⓑ Seho was not there.

After class, Seho went to Dami and said, "I can't find one of my tickets. Did you happen to see ⓒit?"

"No," she answered.

"Isn't it in your bag?"

"No, it's not there. I think I lost it," said Seho.

01 위 글의 빈칸 ⓐ에 알맞은 것은?

① up   ② to
③ at   ④ into
⑤ over

02 위 글의 빈칸 ⓑ에 알맞은 것은?

① so   ② but
③ for   ④ or
⑤ and

서답형

03 위 글의 밑줄 친 ⓒ가 가리키는 것을 영어로 쓰시오.

➡ _____

서답형

04 위 글에서 다음 영영풀이에 해당하는 단어를 찾아 쓰시오.

the flat surface that you stand on inside a building

➡ _____

서답형

05 위 글을 읽고, 다음 질문에 완전한 문장으로 답하시오.

Q: What did Seho drop on the floor?

A: _____

[06~10] 다음 글을 읽고, 물음에 답하시오.

Seho and Jihun were talking in the hallway when Dami came ⓐ .

"Happy birthday!" she said to Seho. "Here. ⓑThey're from my dad."

"Wow, two KBL tickets! Thanks!"

"Who are you going to take with you?" Dami asked.

"Minjun. He took me ⓒ a soccer game before. ⓓ , it's time to pay him back."

06 위 글의 빈칸 ⓐ에 알맞은 것은?

① off   ② out
③ at   ④ over
⑤ across

서답형

07 위 글의 밑줄 친 ⓑ가 의미하는 것을 영어로 쓰시오.

➡ _____

서답형

08 위 글의 빈칸 ⓒ에 알맞은 전치사를 쓰시오.

➡ _____

09 위 글의 빈칸 ⓓ에 알맞은 것은?

① But　　　　② Also

③ Then　　　④ However

⑤ So

10 위 글의 내용과 일치하지 <u>않는</u> 것은?

① 세호와 지훈이는 복도에서 이야기하고 있었다.

② 농구 입장권은 다미의 아빠가 다미에게 주신 것이다.

③ 다미가 농구 입장권 두 장을 세호에게 주었다.

④ 세호는 민준이와 함께 농구를 보러 갈 거라고 말했다.

⑤ 세호는 민준이에게 돈을 빌린 적이 있다.

[11~15] 다음 글을 읽고, 물음에 답하시오.

　　　ⓐ_____ her way home, Dami saw Jihun. He had the ticket in his hand. Dami got angry and said, "Hey! Why do ①you ...?"

　Just then, Jihun saw Seho and shouted, "Seho! ②I found a ticket in the hallway. I think it's yours."

　"Thanks! I was looking for that!" said Seho.

　"③He's not so bad," Dami thought.

　"So, what were you saying? Do you have something ⓑto say, Dami?" asked Jihun.

　"Um, how about going to the school basketball game with ④me this Friday? ⓒIt's the finals."

　Jihun looked really pleased. "⑤I'd love to!"

11 위 글의 빈칸 ⓐ에 알맞은 것은?

① At　　　　② In

③ On　　　　④ To

⑤ Over

12 위 글의 밑줄 친 ①~⑤ 중 지칭하는 대상이 다른 하나는?

①　　　②　　　③　　　④　　　⑤

13 위 글의 밑줄 친 ⓑ와 쓰임이 같은 것은?

① I got up early <u>to see</u> her.

② He has many friends <u>to help</u> him.

③ He did his best <u>to solve</u> the problem.

④ <u>To play</u> the guitar is not easy.

⑤ He studies hard <u>to pass</u> the exam.

14 위 글의 밑줄 친 ⓒIt이 가리키는 것을 찾아 쓰시오.

➡ _____

15 위 글을 읽고, 답할 수 <u>없는</u> 질문은?

① When did Dami see Jihun?

② Why did Dami get angry?

③ Where did Jihun find a ticket?

④ What time is the school basketball game?

⑤ Who will Dami go to see the school basketball game with?

[16~20] 다음 글을 읽고, 물음에 답하시오.

"You know what?" Jihun cut _____ⓐ_____.
"Minjun isn't a fan of basketball. But ①I am!"

"Well, I'll ask him first anyway," replied Seho.

"②He won't go with you. _____ⓑ_____ me," said Jihun.

"Who is ③this guy?" Dami thought _____ⓒ_____ herself, "④He wants Minjun's ticket."

"Oh! There's the bell. See you later," said Dami. She hurried to class.

"Come on, ⑤Jihun," said Seho, and he started to run.

16 위 글의 빈칸 ⓐ에 알맞은 것은?

① in
② off
③ out
④ on
⑤ down

17 위 글의 밑줄 친 ①~⑤ 중 지칭하는 대상이 다른 하나는?

① ② ③ ④ ⑤

서답형

18 위 글의 빈칸 ⓑ에 다음 영영풀이에 해당하는 단어를 주어진 철자로 시작하여 쓰시오.

to believe that someone is honest or will not do anything bad or wrong

➡ T_____

서답형

19 위 글의 빈칸 ⓒ에 알맞은 전치사를 쓰시오.

➡ _____

서답형

20 위 글을 읽고, 다음 질문에 대한 답을 완성하시오.

Q: Why did Dami hurry to class?
A: Because _____.

[21~26] 다음 글을 읽고, 물음에 답하시오.

①On her way to home, Dami saw Jihun. He had the ticket in his hand. Dami got angry and said, "Hey! _____ⓐ_____ do you ...?"

Just then, Jihun saw Seho and shouted, "Seho! I found a ticket in the _____ⓑ_____. ⓒI think it's yours."

"Thanks! I ②was looking for that!" said Seho.

"He's not so bad," Dami thought.

"So, what were you ③saying? Do you have something ④to say, Dami?" asked Jihun.

"Um, ⓓhow about going to the school basketball game with me this Friday? It's the finals."

Jihun looked really ⑤pleased. "I'd love to!"

21 위 글의 밑줄 친 ①~⑤ 중 어법상 틀린 것은?

① ② ③ ④ ⑤

22 위 글의 빈칸 ⓐ에 알맞은 것은?

① What
② How
③ Why
④ Where
⑤ When

서답형

23 위 글의 빈칸 ⓑ에 다음 영영풀이에 해당하는 단어를 주어진 철자로 시작하여 쓰시오.

> a passage in a building or house that leads to many of the rooms

➡ h_____

서답형

24 위 글의 밑줄 친 ⓒ에서 생략된 말을 추가하여 문장을 다시 쓰시오.

➡ _____

서답형

25 위 글의 밑줄 친 ⓓ를 다음과 같이 바꿔 쓸 때 빈칸에 알맞은 말을 쓰시오.

> _____ _____ _____ go to the school basketball game with me this Friday?

26 위 글의 내용과 일치하지 <u>않는</u> 것은?

① 다미는 집에 가는 도중에 지훈이를 만났다.

② 다미는 지훈이가 입장권을 가지고 있는 것을 보고 화가 났다.

③ 지훈이는 복도에서 입장권을 발견했다.

④ 다미는 지훈이가 나쁜 소년이라는 생각이 바뀌지 않았다.

⑤ 다미와 지훈이는 이번 주 금요일에 학교 농구 경기에 갈 것이다.

[27~29] 다음 글을 읽고, 물음에 답하시오.

> At the corner, Seho bumped into someone. (①) "Sorry!" ⓐhe said and continued to run. Just then, Jihun saw something ___(A)___ the floor. (②)
>
> "Wait, Seho!" ⓑhe said, but Seho was not there. (③)
>
> After class, Seho went to Dami and said, "ⓒI can't find one ___(B)___ my tickets. (④)"
>
> "No," she answered.
>
> "Isn't it in "ⓓyour bag?"
>
> "No, it's not there. (⑤) I think ⓔI lost it," said Seho.

27 위 글의 빈칸 (A)와 (B)에 알맞은 말이 바르게 짝지어진 것은?

① in – from   ② at – for

③ from – in   ④ over – about

⑤ on – of

28 위 글의 ①~⑤ 중 주어진 문장이 들어갈 알맞은 곳은?

> Did you happen to see it?

①   ②   ③   ④   ⑤

29 위 글의 밑줄 친 ⓐ~ⓔ 중 지칭하는 대상이 <u>다른</u> 하나는?

① ⓐ   ② ⓑ   ③ ⓒ   ④ ⓓ   ⑤ ⓔ

[01~04] 다음 글을 읽고, 물음에 답하시오.

Seho and Jihun were talking in the hallway when Dami came (A)[out / over].

"Happy birthday!" she said to Seho. "Here. They're from my dad."

"Wow, two KBL tickets! Thanks!"

"Who are you going to take with you?" Dami asked.

"Minjun. He took me to a soccer game before. So, ⓐ그에게 신세를 갚아야 할 때야."

"You know what?" Jihun cut (B)[in / out]. "Minjun isn't a fan of basketball. But I am!"

"Well, I'll ask him first anyway," replied Seho.

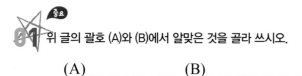

01 위 글의 괄호 (A)와 (B)에서 알맞은 것을 골라 쓰시오.

(A) _____ (B) _____

02 Who did Dami give two basketball tickets to? Answer in English.

➡ _____

03 Who does Seho want to go to a basketball game with? Answer in English.

➡ _____

04 위 글의 밑줄 친 ⓐ의 우리말에 맞도록 주어진 어구를 순서대로 배열하시오.

(him / back / to / it's / pay / time)

➡ _____

[05~08] 다음 글을 읽고, 물음에 답하시오.

At the corner, Seho bumped into someone. "Sorry!" he said and continued to run. Just then, Jihun saw something on the floor.

"Wait, Seho!" he said, but Seho was not there.

After class, Seho went to Dami and said, "I can't find one of my tickets. Did you happen to see it?"

"No," she answered.

"Isn't it in your bag?"

"No, it's not ⓐthere. ⓑ나는 그것을 잃어버린 것 같아," said Seho.

05 Where did Seho bump into someone? Answer in English.

➡ _____

06 What did Seho say to Dami when he went to her? Answer in Korean.

➡ _____

➡ _____

07 위 글의 밑줄 친 ⓐ가 의미하는 것을 영어로 쓰시오.

➡ _____

08 위 글의 밑줄 친 ⓑ의 우리말을 주어진 단어와 필요한 단어를 추가하여 영어로 옮기시오.

(think / it)

➡ _____

[09~12] 다음 글을 읽고, 물음에 답하시오.

"You know what?" ⓐ민준이가 끼어들었다. "Minjun isn't a fan of basketball. But ⓑI am!"

"Well, I'll ask him first anyway," replied Seho.

"He won't go with you. Trust me," said Jihun.

"Who is this guy?" ⓒ다미는 마음속으로 생각했다, "He wants Minjun's ticket."

"Oh! There's the bell. See you later," said Dami. She hurried to ⓓ .

"Come on, Jihun," said Seho, and he started to run.

09 위 글의 밑줄 친 ⓐ의 우리말에 맞게 빈칸에 알맞은 말을 쓰시오.

> Minjun cut _____ .

10 위 글의 밑줄 친 ⓑ 다음에 생략된 말을 보충하여 다시 쓰시오.

➡ _____

11 위 글의 밑줄 친 ⓒ의 우리말에 맞게 주어진 단어를 이용하여 영어로 옮기시오. (필요하면 어형을 바꿀 것)

> (think / her)

➡ _____

12 위 글의 빈칸 ⓓ에 다음 영영풀이에 해당하는 단어를 쓰시오.

> a series of meetings in which students are taught a particular subject or activity

➡ _____

[13~16] 다음 글을 읽고, 물음에 답하시오.

ⓐ집으로 오는 도중에, Dami saw Jihun. He had the ticket in his hand. Dami got angry and sad, "Hey! Why do you ...?"

Just then, Jihun saw Seho and shouted, "Seho! I found a ticket in the hallway. I think it's yours."

"Thanks! I was looking for that!" said Seho.

"He's not so bad," Dami thought.

"So, what were you saying? Do you have something to say, Dami?" asked Jihun.

"Um, how about going to the school basketball game with me this Friday? It's the _____ ⓑ ."

13 위 글의 밑줄 친 ⓐ의 우리말에 맞게 빈칸에 알맞은 말을 쓰시오.

> _____ _____ _____ home

14 Why did Dami get angry? Answer in English.

➡ _____

15 Where did Jihun find the ticket? Answer in English.

➡ _____

16 위 글의 빈칸 ⓑ에 다음 영영풀이에 해당하는 단어를 쓰시오. (복수형으로 쓸 것)

> the last and most important game in a competition

➡ _____

교과서

구석구석

Express Yourself - C

Do you have something <u>to say</u> about the school cafeteria? Then post your
  to부정사의 형용사적 용법(~할)

notes here!

• I think the line is too long. Are there any ways to solve this problem?
  명사절을 이끄는 접속사 that 생략

• I think the chairs are too high. Do you have any plans to change <u>them</u>?
                                                        = the chairs

• I think the chicken was really delicious. Do you have any plans to serve <u>it</u>
                                                        = the chicken

more often?

구문해설 • cafeteria: 구내식당 • post: 게시[공고]하다 • note: 메모 • problem: 문제
• delicious: 맛있는 • serve: 제공하다

Project - Link to the World

가는 말이 고와야 오는 말이 곱다.

This saying means "Nice words for nice words" <u>in English</u>. I will say nice
                                              영어로

words to others first. Then they will say nice words to me, too. I believe
                                        = a lot of, many
that I can make lots of good friends <u>this way</u>. This year, I will <u>always</u> try to
명사절을 이끄는 접속사 that(목적어 역할)   이런 식으로   빈도부사는 일반동사 앞이나 be동사, 조동사 뒤에 위치한다.

remember this saying and say nice words to others.

구문해설 • saying: 속담 • mean: 의미하다 • word: 말 • this way: 이런 식으로 • always: 항상
• remember: 기억하다(↔ forget 잊다)

Learning Diary - Read & Write

<u>Dami gave Seho two basketball tickets</u>. Jihun wanted to go to the basketball
  = Dami gave two basketball tickets to Seho.
game with Seho. Seho dropped <u>one</u> of the tickets <u>on his way to</u> class. Jihun
                              ~ 중 하나   ~로 가는 도중에
found Seho's ticket in the hallway. Dami saw Seho's ticket in Jihun's hand, and

she thought, "He's a bad boy." Jihun <u>gave</u> the ticket <u>back to</u> Seho, and Dami
                                    give A back to B: A를 B에게 돌려주다
<u>realized that</u> she was wrong. Dami wanted to go to the school basketball game
명사절을 이끄는 접속사 that(목적어 역할)
with Jihun. Jihun was really pleased.

구문해설 • drop: 떨어뜨리다 • class: 수업 • hallway: 복도 • realize: 깨닫다 • pleased: 기쁜

해석

학교 구내식당에 대해 할 말이 있니? 그럼 여기 네 메모를 게시해!
• 줄이 너무 긴 것 같아. 이 문제를 해결할 방법이 있을까?
• 의자가 너무 높다고 생각해. 의자를 바꿀 계획이 있는가?
• 닭고기가 정말 맛있었다고 생각해. 닭고기를 더 자주 제공할 계획이 있는가?

가는 말이 고와야 오는 말이 곱다
  이 속담은 영어로 '좋은 말에는 좋은 말로'를 뜻한다. 나는 먼저 다른 사람들에게 좋은 말을 할 것이다. 그러면 그들도 나에게 좋은 말을 할 것이다. 나는 이런 식으로 좋은 친구들을 많이 사귈 수 있다고 믿어. 올해, 나는 항상 이 속담을 기억하고 다른 사람들에게 좋은 말을 하려고 노력할 것이다.

다미가 세호에게 농구 입장권 두 장을 주었다. 지훈이는 세호와 농구 경기에 가고 싶어했다. 세호는 수업에 가는 길에 입장권 하나를 떨어뜨렸다. 지훈이는 복도에서 세호의 입장권을 발견했다. 다미는 지훈이의 손에 있는 세호의 입장권을 보았고 그녀는 "그는 나쁜 소년이야."라고 생각했다. 지훈이는 세호에게 입장권을 돌려주었고 다미는 그녀가 틀렸다는 것을 깨달았다. 다미는 지훈이와 함께 학교 농구 경기에 가고 싶었다. 지훈이는 정말 기뻐했다.

영역별 핵심문제

01 다음 영영풀이에 해당하는 단어로 알맞은 것은?

> to form an opinion about something or someone after careful thought

① reply   ② expect

③ promise   ④ realize

⑤ judge

02 다음 빈칸에 알맞은 것은?

> I met her _____ my way to school.

① on   ② at

③ from   ④ in

⑤ over

03 다음 중 짝지어진 두 단어의 관계가 <u>다른</u> 것은?

① right : wrong   ② floor : ceiling

③ tasty : delicious   ④ ask : answer

⑤ remember : forget

04 다음 우리말과 같도록 빈칸에 알맞은 말을 주어진 철자로 시작하여 쓰시오.

> 우리 선생님은 엄격하시고 진지하시다.
> ➡ My teacher is strict and s_____.

05 다음 빈칸에 공통으로 알맞은 말을 주어진 철자로 시작하여 쓰시오.

> • They _____ traditional French food.
> • Their job is to _____ and protect people.

➡ s_____

06 다음 빈칸에 우리말에 맞도록 알맞은 말을 쓰시오.

> 올해 우리는 화이트 크리스마스를 기대하고 있다.
> ➡ We are expecting a white Christmas _____ _____.

07 다음 대화의 빈칸에 알맞은 것은?

> A: What did you think of the musical, Kelly?
> B: _____
> A: I agree with you. I enjoyed it a lot.

① You're right.

② I thought so, too.

③ Sounds great. Let's go.

④ I think it was great.

⑤ I don't think you're right.

08 다음 대화의 빈칸에 들어갈 말로 적절하지 <u>않은</u> 것은?

> A: What are you going to do this Sunday?
> B: I'm going to watch a *Harry Potter* movie. _____

① I'm looking forward it.
② I'm expecting it.
③ I can't wait to watch it.
④ I'm worried about it.
⑤ It will be nice to watch it.

09 다음 대화의 순서를 바르게 배열하시오.

> (A) I can't wait for lunchtime tomorrow.
> (B) What do you think of today's lunch?
> (C) Wow! We can eat spaghetti tomorrow.
> (D) I think it's okay. What's on tomorrow's menu?

➡ _____

[10~14] 다음 대화를 읽고, 물음에 답하시오.

> B: Let's join the Green Garden club together. ⓐ너는 그것에 대해 어떻게 생각하니?
> G: Okay. I like growing vegetables.
> B: You know what? I like eating vegetables.
> G: Let's join the club right ___ⓑ___ . We can have a party with fresh vegetables every month.
> B: Great. The first party is ___ⓒ___ April 30.
> G: ⓓI can't wait for the party.

10 위 대화의 밑줄 친 ⓐ를 영어로 옮길 때 빈칸에 알맞은 말을 쓰시오.

> _____ do you _____ _____ it?

11 위 대화의 빈칸 ⓑ에 알맞은 것은?

① on   ② at
③ in   ④ from
⑤ now

12 위 대화의 빈칸 ⓒ에 알맞은 전치사를 쓰시오.

➡ _____

13 위 대화의 밑줄 친 ⓓ와 바꿔 쓸 수 있는 것은?

① I can't attend the party.
② I don't expect the party.
③ I don't want to have the party.
④ I'm not going to go to the party.
⑤ I'm looking forward to the party.

14 위 대화를 읽고, 답할 수 <u>없는</u> 질문은?

① Does the girl want to join the Green Garden club?
② Does the girl like growing vegetables?
③ Does the boy like eating vegetables?
④ How often do they have a party with fresh vegetables?
⑤ What day does the first party take place?

15 다음 우리말과 일치하도록 빈칸에 알맞은 말을 쓰시오.

나는 이 아이스크림이 맛있다고 생각한다.

➡ I _____ _____ this ice cream is
delicious.

16 다음 문장의 빈칸에 알맞은 것은?

The doctor has a lot of patients _____.

① taken care
② to take care
③ take care of
④ taking care of
⑤ to take care of

17 다음 밑줄 친 that 중 쓰임이 다른 하나는?

① I think <u>that</u> the movie was terrible.
② I know <u>that</u> Sally doesn't have a job.
③ I think <u>that</u> bag is yours.
④ I hope <u>that</u> he will be my boyfriend.
⑤ I know <u>that</u> she will go abroad to study.

18 다음 중 밑줄 친 부분의 쓰임이 나머지 넷과 다른 것은?

① I need a skirt <u>to wear</u> tomorrow.
② I decided <u>to write</u> a letter to her.
③ I have a lot of homework <u>to do</u>.
④ New York is a great city <u>to visit</u>.
⑤ I am looking for a chair <u>to sit</u> on.

19 다음 우리말과 일치하도록 주어진 단어를 바르게 배열하시오.

우리는 그녀가 파티에 올 것이라고 믿지 않는다.
(party / the / she / come / to / that / will /
don't / believe / we)

➡ _____

20 다음 문장에서 어법상 어색한 부분을 찾아 고치시오.

I have no friends to talk.

_____ ➡ _____

21 다음 중 어법상 어색한 문장은?

① That sounds good.
② That would be great.
③ I'm going to have a party.
④ I think that the girl pretty.
⑤ I hope that you enjoy your trip.

22 다음 중 밑줄 친 that의 쓰임이 〈보기〉와 같은 것은?

┌─ 보기 ─┐
I think <u>that</u> you already did your
homework.

① Look at <u>that</u>!
② I'm sorry to hear <u>that</u>.
③ <u>That</u> cat is drinking water.
④ <u>That</u> he has a cold is true.
⑤ I want to make movie like <u>that</u>.

23 다음 〈보기〉의 우리말을 영어로 바르게 옮긴 것은?

┤ 보기 ├
그는 살 좋은 집을 갖기를 원한다.

① He wants to have a good house live.
② He wants to have a good house live in.
③ He wants to have live in a good house.
④ He wants to have to live in a good house.
⑤ He wants to have a good house to live in.

24 다음 우리말과 같도록 주어진 단어를 바르게 배열하시오.

그녀는 그가 잘생겼다고 생각하지 않았다.
(he / handsome / think / that / was / didn't)
➡ She _____.

25 다음 중 어법상 어색한 문장은?

① I want something to drink.
② I need a house to live.
③ There is a bench to sit on.
④ He went to the store to buy a toy.
⑤ She grew up to be a pianist.

26 다음 주어진 단어를 이용하여 우리말을 영어로 옮기시오.

나는 읽을 책이 한 권 필요하다. (need / read)

➡ _____

[27~33] 다음 글을 읽고, 물음에 답하시오.

Seho and Jihun were talking in the hallway ____ⓐ____ Dami came over. "Happy birthday!" she said to Seho. "Here. They're from my dad."

"Wow, two KBL tickets! Thanks!"

"Who are you going to take ____ⓑ____ you?" Dami asked.

"Minjun. He took me to a soccer game before. ____ⓒ____, it's time ⓓto pay him back."

"You know ____ⓔ____?" Jihun cut in. "Minjun isn't a fan of basketball. ____ⓕ____ I am!"

"Well, I'll ask him first anyway," replied Seho.

"He won't go with you. Trust me," said Jihun.

"Who is this guy?" Dami thought ⓖ herself, "He wants Minjun's ticket."

"Oh! There's the bell. See you later," said Dami. She hurried to class.

27 위 글의 빈칸 ⓐ와 ⓔ에 알맞은 말이 바르게 짝지어진 것은?

① if – how   ② that – when
③ where – what   ④ when – what
⑤ because – how

28 위 글의 빈칸 ⓑ에 알맞은 전치사를 쓰시오.

➡ _____

29 위 글의 빈칸 ⓒ와 ⓕ에 알맞은 말이 바르게 짝지어진 것은?

① But – Or   ② So – But
③ Then – For   ④ Also – And
⑤ However – So

30 위 글의 밑줄 친 ⓓ와 쓰임이 같은 것은?

① His dream was to draw pictures.
② It's easy to memorize English words.
③ I have a lot of work to do today.
④ He wants to play tennis after school.
⑤ She studied very hard to pass the exam.

31 위 글의 빈칸 ⑨에 알맞은 것은?

① at
② on
③ to
④ in
⑤ of

32 위 글에서 다음 영영풀이에 해당하는 단어를 찾아 쓰시오.

at a time in the future

➡ _____

33 위 글을 읽고, 답할 수 없는 질문은?

① Where were Seho and Jihun talking?
② Who did Dami's dad get the basketball tickets from?
③ Who did Dami give two basketball tickets to?
④ Why does Seho want to go to the basketball game with Minjun?
⑤ Why did Dami hurry to class?

[34~37] 다음 글을 읽고, 물음에 답하시오.

(①) This saying means "Nice words for nice words" ___ⓐ___ English. (②) I will say nice words to others first. (③) I believe that I can make ⓑlots of good friends this way. (④) This year, I will always try to remember this saying and say nice words to others. (⑤)

34 위 글의 ①~⑤ 중 다음 문장이 들어갈 알맞은 곳은?

Then they will say nice words to me, too.

①   ②   ③   ④   ⑤

35 위 글의 빈칸 ⓐ에 알맞은 전치사를 쓰시오.

➡ _____

36 위 글의 밑줄 친 ⓑ를 한 단어로 바꿔 쓰시오.

➡ _____

37 위 글의 제목으로 알맞은 것은?

① 농담 속에 진실이 많다.
② 행하기보다는 말하기가 쉽다.
③ 쉽게 얻은 것은 쉽게 나간다.
④ 가는 말이 고와야 오는 말이 곱다.
⑤ 낮말은 새가 듣고 밤 말은 쥐가 듣는다.

01 출제율 90%

다음 짝지어진 두 단어의 관계가 같도록 빈칸에 알맞은 말을 쓰시오.

> dangerous : safe = remember : _____

02 출제율 95%

다음 빈칸에 공통으로 알맞은 것을 쓰시오.

> • Sam is looking _____ his teddy bear.
> • Vegetables are good _____ our health.

➡ _____

03 출제율 90%

다음 중 영영풀이가 잘못된 것은?

① grow: to make plants grow
② boring: dull and uninteresting
③ floor: the inside surface at the top of a room
④ join: to become a member of a group or organization
⑤ cover: the outer part of a book or magazine

04 출제율 100%

다음 우리말에 맞도록 빈칸에 알맞은 말을 쓰시오.

> 수지는 마음속으로 생각했다.
> ➡ Suji _____ _____ _____.

05 출제율 95%

다음 빈칸에 알맞은 말이 바르게 짝지어진 것은?

> • I bumped _____ a basketball post yesterday.
> • My dad promised to buy a cake _____ his way home.

① at – in
② in – for
③ with – at
④ into – on
⑤ from – on

06 출제율 85%

다음 빈칸에 공통으로 들어갈 알맞은 말을 주어진 철자로 시작하여 쓰시오.

> • The referee blew the _____ whistle.
> • At the _____ game, Korea beat Japan 3-0.

➡ f_____

07 출제율 90%

다음 대화의 빈칸에 알맞은 것은?

> A: _____
> B: I think he works hard.
> A: He always tries to do his best. That's why students like him.

① What does Mr. Kim do on weekends?
② Who does Mr. Kim live with?
③ Who does Mr. Kim work with?
④ Why does Mr. Kim work hard?
⑤ What do you think about Mr. Kim?

[08~11] 다음 대화를 읽고, 물음에 답하시오.

G: What do you think of the magic club?
B: ⓐ그것은 나에게 맞는 동아리인 것 같아. I want to learn many interesting ____ⓑ____.
G: I'll join ⓒit, too. When is the first meeting?
B: Next Wednesday. ⓓI can't wait for the first meeting!

08 위 대화의 밑줄 친 ⓐ의 우리말에 맞도록 주어진 단어를 이용하여 영어로 옮기시오. (8단어)

(right / for / think)

➡ _____

09 위 대화의 빈칸 ⓑ에 다음 영영풀이에 해당하는 단어를 주어진 철자로 시작하여 쓰시오. (복수형으로 쓸 것)

a clever and skillful action that someone performs to entertain or amuse people

➡ t_____

10 위 대화의 밑줄 친 ⓒ가 가리키는 것을 찾아 쓰시오.

➡ _____

11 위 대화의 밑줄 친 ⓓ의 의도로 알맞은 것은?

① 금지하기　　　② 이의 제기하기
③ 기대 표현하기　④ 놀람 표현하기
⑤ 상기시켜 주기

12 다음 빈칸에 들어갈 말로 알맞은 것은?

My father says _____ I should study more.

① when　　　② that
③ if　　　　④ while
⑤ before

13 다음 문장의 빈칸에 알맞은 것은?

We want to introduce _____ water.

① saving a way　　② to save a way
③ a way save　　　④ a way saving
⑤ a way to save

14 다음 괄호 안에 주어진 단어를 이용하여 우리말을 영어로 옮기시오.

(1) 그녀는 딸이 아프다고 생각한다.
(think / that / sick)
➡ _____

(2) 나는 Nick이 파티에 올 것이라고 믿지 않는다.
(believe / that)
➡ _____

15 다음 중 밑줄 친 부분의 용법이 나머지 넷과 다른 것은?

① She met Mike to play table tennis.
② I have no house to live in.
③ He saved money to buy a new bike.
④ I turned on the TV to watch the news.
⑤ Amy went to London to meet her friend.

16 출제율 85%

다음 두 문장을 한 문장으로 쓸 때 빈칸에 알맞은 말을 쓰시오.

> I need a friend. + I play with the friend.
> ➡ I need a friend _____.

17 출제율 95%

다음 중 밑줄 친 부분의 쓰임이 다른 하나는?

① I think that he is American.
② He knows that she is rich.
③ We don't hope that you will like it.
④ I can't believe that you made this.
⑤ The news that he would not recover worried me.

18 출제율 100%

다음 밑줄 친 부분의 쓰임이 〈보기〉와 같은 것은? (2개)

> I had a lot of work to complete.

① To see is to believe.
② She grew up to become a doctor.
③ Do you have time to play basketball?
④ I went to a mall to buy new shoes.
⑤ Give me a chair to sit on.

19 출제율 90%

다음 우리말과 같도록 주어진 단어를 이용하여 빈칸에 알맞은 말을 쓰시오.

> 우리는 케이크를 구울 더 많은 밀가루가 필요하다.
> (flour / bake)

➡ _____

[20~25] 다음 글을 읽고, 물음에 답하시오.

> ⓐDami gave Seho two basketball tickets. Jihun wanted to go to the basketball game with Seho. Seho dropped one of the tickets _____ⓑ_____ his way to class. Jihun found Seho's ticket in the hallway. Dami saw Seho's ticket in Jihun's hand, and she thought, "He's a bad boy." ⓒJihun gave the ticket back to Seho, and Dami realized _____ⓓ_____ she was _____ⓔ_____. Dami wanted to go to the school basketball game with Jihun. Jihun was really pleased.

20 출제율 85%

위 글의 밑줄 친 ⓐ를 3형식 문장으로 바꿔 쓰시오.

➡ _____

21 출제율 95%

위 글의 빈칸 ⓑ에 알맞은 것은?

① at   ② in
③ to   ④ on
⑤ by

22 출제율 85%

위 글의 밑줄 친 ⓒ를 우리말로 쓰시오.

➡ _____

23 출제율 100%

위 글의 빈칸 ⓓ에 알맞은 것을 쓰시오.

➡ _____

출제율 95%

24 위 글의 빈칸 ⓔ에 다음 영영풀이에 해당하는 단어를 쓰시오.

speaking, acting, or judging in a way that does not agree with the facts or truth

➡ _____

출제율 90%

25 위 글을 읽고, 답할 수 없는 질문은?

① Who did Jihun want to go to the basketball game with?
② What did Seho drop on his way to class?
③ Where did Jihun find Seho's ticket?
④ Why did Dami think Jihun was a bad boy?
⑤ What time is the school basketball game?

[26~30] 다음 글을 읽고, 물음에 답하시오.

_____ ⓐ _____ her way home, Dami saw Jihun. He had the ticket in his hand. Dami got angry and said, "Hey! Why do ①you ...?"

Just then, Jihun saw Seho and shouted, "Seho! ②I found a ticket in the hallway. I think it's ⓑyou."

"Thanks! I was looking _____ ⓒ _____ that!" said Seho.

"③He's not so bad," Dami thought.

"So, what were you saying? Do you have something ⓓsay, Dami?" asked Jihun.

"Um, how about ⓔgo to the school basketball game with ④me this Friday? It's the finals."

Jihun looked really pleased. "⑤I'd love to!"

출제율 90%

26 위 글의 밑줄 친 ①~⑤ 중 지칭하는 대상이 다른 하나는?

①   ②   ③   ④   ⑤

출제율 85%

27 위 글의 빈칸 ⓐ와 ⓒ에 알맞은 말이 바르게 짝지어진 것은?

① On – at   ② In – for
③ At – at   ④ On – for
⑤ In – about

출제율 90%

28 위 글의 밑줄 친 ⓑ를 알맞은 형태로 고쳐 쓰시오. (한 단어로 쓸 것)

➡ _____

출제율 100%

29 위 글의 밑줄 친 ⓓ와 ⓔ를 알맞은 형태로 고쳐 쓰시오.

ⓓ _____   ⓔ _____

출제율 85%

30 Why did Dami think Jihun was not so bad? Answer in Korean.

➡ _____

01 다음 우리말과 같은 뜻이 되도록 빈칸에 알맞은 말을 쓰시오.

> 나는 그 여행이 매우 기대돼.
> ➡ I _____ _____ for the trip.

02 다음 대화의 빈칸에 주어진 말을 이용하여 영어로 쓰시오.

> A: _____ (what / think)
>   (너의 영어 선생님에 대해서 어떻게 생각하니?)
> B: She is kind.

➡ _____

03 다음 대화의 괄호 안의 단어들을 바르게 배열하여 대화를 완성하시오.

> A: When does your summer vacation start?
> B: This Friday. (to / forward / it / looking / I'm).

➡ _____

04 자연스러운 대화가 되도록 (A)~(D)의 순서를 바르게 배열하시오.

> (A) I'll join the soccer club. I like playing soccer.
> (B) The health club? I think it's boring.
> (C) This club looks good for you. What do you think of it?
> (D) Then which club do you want to join?

➡ _____

05 다음 문장에서 어법상 어색한 부분을 찾아 바르게 고쳐 쓰시오.

> I need a pen to write.

_____ ➡ _____

[06~07] 다음 괄호 안에 주어진 어구를 이용하여 우리말을 영어로 옮기시오.

06 (1) 나는 그녀가 선생님이었다는 것을 안다.
   (know / that / teacher)
   ➡ _____

(2) 나는 그가 정직하다고 생각한다.
   (think / that / honest)
   ➡ _____

(3) 그는 그것이 매우 재미있을 것이라고 믿는다.
   (believe / that / a lot of fun)
   ➡ _____

07 (1) 그녀는 가수가 되려는 강한 욕망을 갖고 있다.
   (strong desire, be, singer)
   ➡ _____

(2) 우리는 이야기할 것이 있었다.
   (something, talk about)
   ➡ _____

(3) 나는 쓸 종이를 한 장 원한다.
   (want, write)
   ➡ _____

(4) 제게 뜨거운 마실 것을 좀 주십시오.
   (please, something, drink)
   ➡ _____

ⓐOn her way to home, Dami saw Jihun. He had the ticket in his hand. Dami got angry and said, "Hey! Why do you ...?"

Just then, Jihun saw Seho and shouted, "Seho! I found a ticket in the hallway. ⓑ(I / it's / yours / think / that)."

"Thanks! I was looking for that!" said Seho.

"He's not so bad," Dami thought.

"So, what were you saying? Do you have something to say, Dami?" asked Jihun.

"Um, how about going to the school basketball game with me this Friday? It's the finals."

Jihun looked really ⓒ . "I'd love to!"

08 위 글의 밑줄 친 ⓐ에서 어법상 어색한 부분을 바르게 고쳐 문장을 다시 쓰시오.

➡ _____

09 위 글의 ⓑ 안의 단어들을 순서대로 바르게 배열하시오.

➡ _____

10 When is the school basketball game? Answer in English.

➡ _____

11 위 글의 빈칸 ⓒ에 다음 영영풀이에 해당하는 단어를 주어진 철자로 시작하여 쓰시오.

> feeling happy about something

➡ p_____

_____

This ⓐ means "Nice words for nice words" in English. I will say nice words to others first. Then they will say nice words to me, (A)[too / either]. I believe that I can make lots of good friends ⓑthis way. This year, I will always try (B)[remembering / to remember] this ⓒ and say nice words to others.

12 위 글의 빈칸 ⓐ와 ⓒ에 공통으로 알맞은 것을 다음 영영풀이를 참조하여 주어진 철자로 시작하여 쓰시오.

> an old and well-known phrase that expresses an idea that most people believe is true

➡ s_____

13 위 글의 괄호 (A)와 (B)에서 알맞은 것을 골라 쓰시오.

(A) _____ (B) _____

14 위 글의 밑줄 친 ⓑ가 의미하는 것을 우리말로 쓰시오.

➡ _____
_____

15 위 글의 빈칸에 알맞은 제목을 우리말 속담으로 쓰시오.

➡ _____

01 다음 질문에 각자의 답을 to부정사를 이용하여 〈보기〉와 같이 쓰시오.

┌ 보기 ┐

I want a pair of short pants to wear during the summer.

Q: What do you want for your birthday present? You should mention at least two items.

(1) _____

(2) _____

02 다음 (A), (B), (C)에 주어진 어구를 이용하여 〈보기〉와 같이 문장을 4개 쓰시오. (필요하면 어형을 바꿀 것)

(A)	(B)	(C)
I	know that	Jenny is kind
He	hope that	they need help
She	say that	it's delicious
Tony	think that	many children are hungry
They	hear that	everyone will be happy

┌ 보기 ┐

I hope that everyone will be happy.

(1) _____

(2) _____

(3) _____

(4) _____

03 자신의 경우에 맞게 to부정사를 이용하여 〈보기〉와 같이 지금 필요한 것에 대해 써 보시오.(3 문장 이상)

┌ 보기 ┐

I need something to drink.

(1) _____

(2) _____

(3) _____

(4) _____

단원별 모의고사

01 다음 영영풀이에 해당하는 단어로 알맞은 것은?

> to give food or drink to someone at a meal, in a restaurant, etc.

① wait ② reply
③ hurry ④ serve
⑤ practice

02 다음 중 밑줄 친 우리말 뜻이 잘못된 것은?

① She cut in on our talk.
　　끼어들었다
② It will snow a lot this year.
　　　　　　　올해
③ I happened to hear the news.
　　우연히 들었다
④ After school, I was walking home alone.
　　방과 후에
⑤ I found out about it yesterday.
　　발견했다

03 다음 빈칸에 들어갈 말로 적절하지 않은 것은? (대·소문자 무시)

> • _____ your notes here.
> • Can you tell me how to _____ this problem?
> • I will _____ back the money within three days.
> • Spend time with people that you _____.

① trust ② mean
③ pay ④ solve
⑤ post

04 다음 빈칸에 알맞은 말이 바르게 짝지어진 것은?

> • Look _____ the price tag.
> • Walking in the morning is good _____ the health.

① in – to ② at – for
③ of – for ④ to – at
⑤ for – at

05 다음 빈칸에 공통으로 알맞은 말을 주어진 철자로 시작하여 쓰시오.

> • He is a big baseball f_____.
> • He turned on the f_____ because it was too hot.

06 다음 우리말에 맞도록 빈칸에 알맞은 말을 쓰시오.

> 남의 이야기 중에 끼어드는 것은 무례한 짓이다.
> ➡ It is rude to _____ _____ while others are talking.

07 다음 중 그 의미가 나머지 넷과 다른 하나는?

① I'm looking forward to the game.
② I'm expecting the game.
③ I can't wait to see the game.
④ I'm worried about the game.
⑤ I want to see the game.

[08~12] 다음 대화를 읽고, 물음에 답하시오.

> B: Let's join the School Band club together. ⓐWhat do you think of it?
> G: Okay. I like playing the flute. (①)
> B: I like playing the ukulele.
> G: Let's join the club right now. (②) They practice after school every Tuesday and Thursday. (③)
> B: They're going to have the first concert _____ⓑ_____ July 15. (④)
> G: Great. (⑤)
> B: Me, too. ⓒ나는 콘서트가 매우 기다려져.

08 위 대화의 밑줄 친 ⓐ와 바꿔 쓸 수 없는 것은?

① How do you like it?
② Why don't you think of it?
③ What's your opinion on it?
④ How do you feel about it?
⑤ What do you think about it?

09 위 대화의 ①~⑤ 중 다음 문장이 들어갈 알맞은 곳은?

> I hope to play in the concert.

①   ②   ③   ④   ⑤

10 위 대화의 빈칸 ⓑ에 알맞은 것은?

① at   ② in   ③ on
④ for   ⑤ over

11 위 대화의 밑줄 친 ⓒ의 우리말을 주어진 단어를 이용하여 영작하시오.

> (wait)

➡ _____

12 위 대화의 내용을 다음과 같이 포스터로 만들 때 빈칸에 알맞은 말을 쓰시오.

> **School Band**
> • Practice: after school on _____ and _____
> • First Concert: _____ _____

13 다음 빈칸에 알맞은 것은?

> This is a good story _____.

① read   ② reads
③ to read   ④ reading
⑤ to reading

14 다음 중 밑줄 친 부분의 쓰임이 나머지와 다른 하나는?

① I think that he is handsome.
② He believes that he can be a good doctor.
③ She hopes that there will be no more exams.
④ Do you know that handsome guy over there?
⑤ Professor Kim says that we should save energy.

15 다음 괄호 안에 주어진 단어를 이용하여 우리말에 맞도록 문장을 완성하시오.

> 차가운 마실 것 좀 주세요.
> (something / cold)
> ➡ Give me _____.

16 다음 빈칸에 들어갈 말로 알맞지 않은 것은?

> I think _____.

① it is easy　　　② she is pretty
③ is she busy　　④ that he likes you
⑤ that she is taller than you

17 다음 문장의 괄호 안의 말을 바르게 배열한 것은?

> She needs (paper, on, to write).

① on paper to write
② paper on to write
③ to write paper on
④ paper to write on
⑤ on write to paper

18 다음 〈보기〉의 밑줄 친 부분과 쓰임이 같은 것은?

> ┤ 보기 ├
> This is a question to solve now.

① To study English is interesting.
② I need something to write on.
③ I want to do well this semester.
④ My plan is to travel around the world.
⑤ Where do you plan to spend your holiday?

19 다음 우리말에 맞도록 빈칸에 알맞은 말을 쓰시오.

> Ann은 그 없이는 살 수 없을 것이라는 사실을 몰랐다.
> ➡ Ann _____ _____ _____ she wouldn't be able to live without him.

[20~24] 다음 글을 읽고, 물음에 답하시오.

ⓐOn her way home, Dami saw Jihun. (①) He had the ticket in his hand. (②) Dami got angry and said, "Hey! (A)Why do you ...?"

Just then, Jihun saw Seho and ⓑshouted, "Seho! I found a ticket in the hallway. I think (B)it's yours. (③)"

"Thanks! (④)" said Seho.

"He's not so bad," Dami thought.

"So, what were you saying? Do you have something ⓒsaying, Dami?" asked Jihun.

"Um, how about ⓓgoing to the school basketball game with me this Friday? (C)It's the finals. (⑤)"

Jihun looked really ⓔpleased. "I'd love to!"

20 위 글의 ①~⑤ 중 다음 문장이 들어갈 알맞은 곳은?

> I was looking for that!

①　　②　　③　　④　　⑤

21 위 글의 밑줄 친 (A)에서 생략된 말을 넣어 완전한 문장으로 다시 쓰시오.

➡ _____

22 위 글의 밑줄 친 ⓐ~ⓔ 중 어법상 틀린 것은?

① ⓐ　② ⓑ　③ ⓒ　④ ⓓ　⑤ ⓔ

23 위 글의 밑줄 친 (B)it와 (C)It가 가리키는 것을 각각 쓰시오.

(B) _____
(C) _____

24 위 글의 내용과 일치하면 T, 일치하지 <u>않으면</u> F를 쓰시오.

(1) When Dami saw one of Seho's tickets in Jihun's hand, she was pleased. (   )
(2) Jihun gave the ticket back to Seho, and Dami realized that she was wrong. (   )

[25~27] 다음 글을 읽고, 물음에 답하시오.

At the corner, Seho bumped ___ⓐ___ someone. "Sorry!" he said and continued to run. Just then, Jihun saw something ___ⓑ___ the floor.

"Wait, Seho!" he said, but Seho was not there.

After class, Seho went to Dami and said, "ⓒ(find / of / I / my tickets / can't / one). ⓓ<u>Did you happen to see it?</u>"

"No," she answered.

"Isn't it in your bag?"

"No, it's not there. I think I lost it," said Seho.

25 위 글의 빈칸 ⓐ와 ⓑ에 알맞은 말이 바르게 짝지어진 것은?

① up – over
② to – in
③ into – on
④ with – from
⑤ over – under

26 위 글의 괄호 ⓒ 안의 단어들을 바르게 배열하시오.

➡ _____

27 위 글의 밑줄 친 ⓓ를 우리말로 옮기시오.

➡ _____

[28~30] 다음 글을 읽고, 물음에 답하시오.

"You know what?" Jihun cut in. "Minjun isn't a ___ⓐ___ of basketball. But ①I am!"

"Well, I'll ask him first anyway," replied Seho.

"②He won't go with you. Trust ③me," said Jihun.

"Who is ④<u>this guy</u>?" Dami thought ___ⓑ___ herself, "⑤He wants Minjun's ticket."

"Oh! There's the bell. See you later," said Dami. She hurried ___ⓒ___ class.

"Come on, Jihun," said Seho, and he started to run.

28 위 글의 빈칸 ⓐ에 다음 영영풀이에 해당하는 단어를 쓰시오.

a person who admires someone or something or enjoys watching or listening to someone or something very much

➡ _____

29 위 글의 ①~⑤ 중 지칭하는 대상이 <u>다른</u> 하나는?

① ② ③ ④ ⑤

30 위 글의 빈칸 ⓑ와 ⓒ에 공통으로 알맞은 것을 쓰시오.

➡ _____

I Love My Town!

 의사소통 기능

- 계획 말하기
  I'm planning to volunteer at the library.
- 약속 정하기
  Can you make it at 3 p.m.?

언어 형식

- 조건을 나타내는 접속사 if
  He will get better **if** he gets enough rest.
- 지각동사
  Ryan **heard** the doorbell **ring**.

Words & Expressions

Key Words

- **address** [ədrés] 몡 주소
- **around** [əráund] 젠 ~ 주위에
- **away** [əwéi] 빔 떨어진 곳에
- **block** [blak] 몡 구역, 블록
- **borrow** [bárou] 동 빌리다(↔ lend)
- **brown** [braun] 혭 갈색의
- **build** [bild] 동 짓다, 건축하다
- **butterfly** [bʌtərflài] 몡 나비
- **care** [kɛər] 몡 돌봄, 보살핌
- **chat** [tʃæt] 동 수다를 떨다
- **check** [tʃek] 동 살피다, 확인하다
- **closely** [klóusli] 빔 자세히, 면밀히
- **clothes** [klouz] 몡 옷, 의복
- **cry** [krai] 동 울다(↔ laugh)
- **cut** [kʌt] 몡 상처 동 자르다, 베다
- **cute** [kju:t] 혭 귀여운
- **director** [diréktər] 몡 감독
- **doorbell** [dɔrbel] 몡 초인종
- **elderly** [éldərli] 혭 연세가 드신
- **enough** [inʌf] 혭 충분한
- **exactly** [igzǽktli] 빔 꼭, 정확히
- **feed** [fi:d] 동 먹이를 주다
- **follow** [fálou] 동 따라가다
- **free** [fri:] 혭 무료의, 한가한
- **gate** [geit] 몡 문
- **green** [gri:n] 혭 초록색의
- **guess** [ges] 동 알아맞히다
- **hard** [ha:rd] 빔 열심히

- **hope** [houp] 몡 희망 동 바라다
- **hurry** [hə́:ri] 동 급히[서둘러] 가다
- **inside** [insáid] 빔 안에(↔ outside)
- **leave** [li:v] 동 ~을 두고 오다[가다]
- **lonely** [lóunli] 혭 외로운
- **lost** [lɔ:st] 혭 잃어버린
- **miss** [mis] 동 놓치다, 그리워하다
- **move** [mu:v] 동 이사하다, 옮기다
- **neighbor** [néibər] 몡 이웃
- **nervous** [nə́:rvəs] 혭 긴장되는
- **nod** [nɑd] 동 (고개를) 끄덕이다
- **outside** [áutsáid] 빔 밖에, 밖에서
- **pass** [pæs] 동 지나가다, 통과하다
- **perfect** [pə́:rfikt] 혭 완벽한
- **practice** [prǽktis] 동 연습하다
- **rest** [rest] 몡 휴식(= break)
- **return** [ritə́:rn] 동 돌아오다[가다]
- **sell** [sel] 동 팔다(↔ buy)
- **shape** [ʃeip] 몡 모양
- **special** [spéʃəl] 혭 특별한(↔ general)
- **spot** [spot] 몡 점, 반점
- **stage** [steidʒ] 몡 무대
- **still** [stil] 빔 여전히
- **strange** [streindʒ] 혭 이상한
- **used** [ju:st] 혭 중고의
- **volunteer** [vàləntíər] 몡 자원봉사자 동 자원봉사하다
- **wash** [waʃ] 동 씻다

Key Expressions

- **a pair of** 한 켤레[벌]의
- **be good at** ~을 잘하다
- **be late for** ~에 늦다
- **clean up** 청소하다
- **get better** (병·상황 따위가) 좋아지다, 호전되다
- **get enough rest**: 충분한 휴식을 취하다
- **in front of** ~의 앞쪽에[앞에]
- **in need** 어려움에 처한, 도움이 필요한
- **last month** 지난달
- **look around** 둘러보다

- **look at** ~을 보다
- **look like** ~처럼 보이다
- **over there** 저쪽에
- **prepare for** ~을 준비하다
- **put up** ~을 붙이다
- **run after** ~을 쫓아다니다, ~을 뒤쫓다
- **take A to B** A를 B로 데려가다
- **take a break** 휴식을 취하다
- **take care of** ~을 돌보다
- **thanks to** ~ 덕분에

Word Power

※ 명사에 -ly를 붙여 형용사가 되는 단어

☐ **cost** (비용) → **costly** (비용이 많이 드는)

☐ **coward** (겁쟁이) → **cowardly** (겁 많은)

☐ **friend** (친구) → **friendly** (친한)

☐ **leisure** (여가) → **leisurely** (한가한)

☐ **love** (사랑) → **lovely** (사랑스러운)

☐ **time** (시간) → **timely** (시기적절한)

※ 형용사에 -ly를 붙여 부사가 되는 단어

☐ **easy** (쉬운) → **easily** (쉽게)

☐ **careful** (주의 깊은) → **carefully** (주의 깊게)

☐ **kind** (친절한) → **kindly** (친절하게)

☐ **loud** (소리가 큰) → **loudly** (큰 소리로)

☐ **special** (특별한) → **specially** (특별히)

☐ **sudden** (갑작스러운) → **suddenly** (갑자기)

English Dictionary

☐ **address** 주소
→ details of where someone lives or works and where letters, etc. can be sent
누군가가 살거나 일하는 곳과 편지 등을 보낼 수 있는 곳에 대한 세부 사항

☐ **block** 구역, 블록
→ a group of buildings with streets on all sides
사방에 거리가 있는 건물의 그룹

☐ **borrow** 빌리다
→ to take and use something that belongs to someone else, and return it to them at a later time
다른 사람의 것을 가져와서 사용하고, 나중에 그들에게 돌려주다

☐ **build** 짓다
→ to make something by putting together parts or materials
여러 가지 부품과 재료를 결합하여 어떤 것을 만들다

☐ **butterfly** 나비
→ a flying insect with a long thin body and four large, usually brightly colored wings
길고 얇은 몸과 네 개의 큰 보통은 밝은 색상의 날개들을 가진 날아다니는 곤충

☐ **cut** 상처
→ a wound on a person's body that is made by something sharp
날카로운 것에 의해 사람의 몸에 생긴 상처

☐ **doorbell** 초인종
→ a bell on the outside of a house which you can ring so that the people inside know that you want to see them
당신이 안에 있는 사람들을 보기를 원한다는 것을 알 수 있도록 울릴 수 있는 집 바깥에 있는 종

☐ **feed** 먹이를 주다
→ to give food to a person or an animal
사람이나 동물에게 음식을 주다

☐ **lonely** 외로운
→ unhappy because you have no friends or people to talk to
친구나 대화할 사람이 없기 때문에 불행한

☐ **neighbor** 이웃
→ someone who lives next to you or near you
당신 옆이나 당신 근처에 사는 사람

☐ **nod** (고개를) 끄덕이다
→ to move your head up and down, especially in order to show agreement or understanding
특히 동의나 이해를 보여주기 위해 머리를 위아래로 움직이다

☐ **perfect** 완벽한
→ complete and without faults or weaknesses
완전하고 결점이나 약점이 없는

☐ **rest** 휴식
→ a period of time in which you relax, sleep, or do nothing after you have been active or doing work
활동하거나 일을 한 후에 쉬거나 잠을 자거나 아무 일도 하지 않는 기간

☐ **return** 돌아오다[가다]
→ to come or go to a place again
이떤 장소로 다시 오거나 가다

☐ **volunteer** 자원봉사자
→ a person who does a job without being paid for it
그 일에 대한 대가를 받지 않고 일을 하는 사람

01 다음 중 단어의 성격이 <u>다른</u> 것은?

① lonely   ② friendly

③ lovely   ④ loudly

⑤ cowardly

02 다음 우리말에 맞도록 빈칸에 알맞은 것은?

> 나는 아빠와 함께 공원을 청소할 계획이다.
> ➡ I'm planning to clean _____ the park with my dad.

① up   ② with

③ out   ④ over

⑤ into

03 다음 영영풀이에 해당하는 단어로 알맞은 것은?

> to move your head up and down, especially in order to show agreement or understanding

① feed   ② bend

③ build   ④ nod

⑤ catch

04 다음 짝지어진 두 단어의 관계가 같도록 빈칸에 알맞은 말을 쓰시오.

> hungry : full = lend : _____

05 다음 우리말과 일치하도록 빈칸에 알맞은 말을 쓰시오.

> 나는 네 덕분에 좋은 이웃을 만났다.
> ➡ I met a good _____ thanks to you.

06 다음 빈칸에 알맞은 말이 바르게 짝지어진 것은?

> • Look _____ the pictures on page 229.
> • She is putting _____ a poster on the wall.

① in – about   ② up – over

③ for – with   ④ at – up

⑤ over – on

07 다음 중 짝지어진 단어의 관계가 <u>다른</u> 것은?

① cry : laugh   ② far : near

③ inside : outside   ④ rest : break

⑤ special : general

08 다음 영영풀이에 해당하는 단어를 쓰시오.

> details of where someone lives or works and where letters, etc. can be sent

➡ _____

01 다음 짝지어진 두 단어의 관계가 같도록 빈칸에 알맞은 말을 쓰시오.

(1) delicious : tasty = _____ : break

(2) easy : difficult = borrow : _____

(3) right : wrong = buy : _____

(4) remember : forget = cry : _____

02 다음 우리말에 맞게 빈칸에 알맞은 말을 쓰시오.

(1) 장갑 한 켤레와 커다란 비닐봉지를 가져와라.

➡ Please bring _____ _____ _____ gloves and a big plastic bag.

(2) 오후 2시에 시계탑 앞에서 만나자.

➡ Let's meet at 2 p.m. _____ _____ _____ the clock tower.

03 다음 빈칸에 공통으로 들어갈 말을 〈보기〉에서 골라 쓰시오.

┤ 보기 ├
miss   cut   pass

(1) • She studied hard to _____ the exam.
   • We will _____ through the village.

(2) • He had a small _____ above her left eye.
   • She _____ her finger on a piece of glass.

(3) • I _____ my mom and dad a lot.
   • If she is late, he will _____ the train.

04 다음 빈칸에 들어갈 알맞은 말을 〈보기〉에서 골라 쓰시오.

┤ 보기 ├
lonely   elderly   enough

(1) He needs to take _____ rest.

(2) The girl is very polite to the _____.

(3) He has no friend, so he feels _____.

05 다음 빈칸에 알맞은 말을 〈보기〉에서 골라 쓰시오.

┤ 보기 ├
prepare for   be good at   take care of

(1) I want to _____ math.

(2) They need volunteers to _____ the animals.

(3) He's planning to go to the library to _____ the exam.

06 다음 영영풀이에 해당하는 단어를 주어진 철자로 시작하여 쓰시오.

(1) b_____ : a group of buildings with streets on all sides

(2) p_____ : complete and without faults or weaknesses

(3) v_____ : a person who does a job without being paid for it

Conversation

1 계획 말하기

> **A** What are you planning to do this Saturday? 너는 이번 토요일에 무엇을 할 계획이니?
>
> **B** I'm planning to clean up the park with my dad. 나는 우리 아빠와 함께 공원을 청소할 계획이야.

■ What are you planning to do ~?는 상대방에게 미래의 계획에 대해 물을 때 쓰는 표현이다.

- A: What are you planning to do this weekend? 너는 이번 주말에 뭐 할 계획이니?
  B: I'm planning to go to the movies. 영화 보러 갈 계획이야.

계획을 묻는 표현

- What are you planning[going] to do this weekend? 너는 이번 주말에 무엇을 할 거니?
- What are your plans for this weekend? 이번 주말에 너의 계획은 뭐니?
- What will you do this Sunday? 너는 이번 일요일에 무엇을 할 거니?
- Do you have any plans for this weekend? 너는 이번 주말에 무슨 계획이 있니?

■ 자신의 계획을 말할 때는 be planning to를 사용하여 말할 수 있다.

- A: Do you have any plans for the weekend? 너는 주말에 어떤 계획이라도 있니?
  B: Yes. I'm planning to practice dancing at the youth center.
  응. 나는 청소년 센터에서 춤을 연습할 계획이야.

계획을 말하는 표현

- I'm planning[going] to go hiking. 나는 하이킹을 갈 계획이야.
- I will play baseball with my brothers. 나는 내 동생들과 야구를 할 거야.
- I plan to visit my grandparents. 나는 조부모님을 방문할 계획이야.
- I have a plan to go to the library. 나는 도서관에 갈 계획이야.

핵심 Check

1. 다음 우리말과 일치하도록 빈칸에 알맞은 말을 쓰시오.

   (1) **A:** _____ are you _____ to do this evening? (너는 오늘 저녁에 무엇을 할 거니?)

   B: _____ _____ _____ go shopping with my parents.

   (나는 부모님과 쇼핑하러 갈 거야.)

   (2) **A:** _____ are your _____ for this weekend? (이번 주말에 너의 계획은 뭐니?)

   B: I _____ _____ play soccer with my brother. (남동생과 축구를 할 계획이야.)

② 약속 정하기

> **A** Can you make it at 3 p.m.? 오후 3시에 올 수 있니?
>
> **B** Sure. Let's meet in front of the library. 물론. 도서관 앞에서 만나자.

■ Can you make it at three?는 '3시에 만날 수 있니?'라는 뜻으로 약속을 정할 때 쓰는 표현이다. make it은 '해내다, 성공하다'라는 의미를 갖고 있지만, 시간이나 장소의 표현과 함께 쓰여 '시간에 맞춰 가다' 또는 '도착하다'라는 의미를 갖는다.

약속 정하기 표현

- Can we meet at six? 6시에 만날까?
- Why don't we meet at six?
- How[What] about meeting at six?
- Shall we meet at six?
- Let's meet at six.

약속 정하기에 답하는 표현

(승낙하기)

It's fine with me. / No problem. / Why not? / Sure, I'd love to. / That's a good idea. / (That) Sounds great.

(거절하기)

I'm sorry, I can't. / I'm afraid not. / I'd love to, but I can't. / Not this time, thanks. / Maybe next time.

핵심 Check

2. 다음 우리말과 일치하도록 빈칸에 알맞은 말을 쓰시오.

(1) **A**: Can you _____ _____ at five at the bus stop? (5시에 버스 정류장에서 만날까?)

　　B: _____. See you _____. (물론이지. 그때 보자.)

(2) **A**: _____ _____ _____ to the movie theater tomorrow?

　　(우리 내일 영화관에 가는 게 어때?)

　　B: No _____. (문제없어.)

(3) **A**: _____ _____ soccer this Saturday. (이번 토요일에 농구하자.)

　　B: _____, _____ _____. (미안하지만, 못하겠어.)

A. Start Off - Listen & Talk B

B: ❶What are you going to do this Saturday?

G: ❷I'm planning to clean up the park with my dad.

B: ❸Sounds like a wonderful plan. Can I join you?

G: Sure. ❹Can you make it at the bus stop at 1 p.m.?

B: ❺I'm afraid not. How about 2?

G: Fine with me. ❻Please bring a pair of gloves and a big plastic bag.

B: Okay. See you on Saturday.

B: 이번 토요일에 뭐 할 거니?

G: 아빠와 함께 공원을 청소할 계획이야.

B: 멋진 계획인 것 같구나. 같이 가도 될까?

G: 물론이지. 버스 정류장에서 오후 1시에 만날 수 있니?

B: 안 될 것 같아. 2시는 어때?

G: 난 괜찮아. 장갑 한 켤레와 커다란 비닐봉지를 가져와.

B: 알았어. 토요일에 보자.

❶ What are you going to do ~?: 너는 ~에 무엇을 할 예정이니?(= What are you planning to do ~?

❷ I'm planning to+동사원형 ~: 나는 ~할 계획이야.(= I'm going to + 동사원형 ~) / clean up: ~을 청소하다

❸ sound like + 명사(구): ~처럼 들리다

❹ Can you make it ~?: ~에 만날 수 있니? (약속 시간을 제안하는 표현)

❺ I'm afraid not.: 안 될 것 같아.(제안에 거절하는 표현)

❻ a pair of: 한 켤레의

Check(√) True or False

(1) The boy and the girl will meet at the bus stop at 1 p.m.　　T ☐ F ☐

(2) The boy should bring a pair of gloves and a big plastic bag.　　T ☐ F ☐

B. Step Up - Real-life Scene

Let's Volunteer for a Better Town!

Jina: ❶I'm planning to volunteer at the animal care center this Sunday morning.

Alex: You mean the one near Grand Park, Jina?

Jina: Right. ❷Will you come with me, Alex? ❸They need volunteers to take care of the animals.

Alex: I'd love to join. I like feeding and walking animals. ❹I'm also good at washing them.

Jina: Great. You can bring other friends with you, too.

Alex: Okay. I'll ask my neighbor Nancy. She loves animals, too. ❺What time shall we meet?

Jina: Can you make it at 8 a.m. at the Grand Park bus stop?

Alex: Sure. I'll see you on Sunday.

더 나은 마을을 위해 자원 봉사합시다!

지나: 이번 일요일 아침에 동물 보호 센터에서 자원봉사를 할 계획이야.

Alex: Grand Park 근처에 있는 거 말하는 거니, 지나야?

지나: 맞아. 나랑 같이 갈래, Alex? 그들은 동물들을 돌볼 자원 봉사자들이 필요해.

Alex: 나도 함께하고 싶어. 나는 동물들에게 먹이를 주고 산책시키는 것을 좋아해. 그리고 그들을 씻기는 것도 잘해.

지나: 좋아. 다른 친구들도 데려와도 돼.

Alex: 알았어. 내 이웃인 Nancy에게 물어볼게. 그녀도 동물들을 아주 좋아해. 몇 시에 만날까?

지나: Grand Park 버스 정류장에서 오전 8시에 만날까?

Alex: 알았어. 일요일에 보자.

❶ I'm planning to+동사원형 ~: 나는 ~할 계획이야.(= I'm going to+동사원형 ~)

❷ Will you ~?: ~할래?(= Can you ~?= Would you ~?= Could you ~?)

❸ take care of: ~을 돌보다

❹ be good at: ~을 잘하다 / them = animals

❺ What time shall we meet?: 우리 몇 시에 만날까?(약속 정하기 표현)

Check(√) True or False

(3) The animal care center is near Grand Park.　　T ☐ F ☐

(4) Jina and Alex will meet at Grand Park on Saturday.　　T ☐ F ☐

Get Ready -2

1. B: ❶I'm going to take some pictures in front of the flower gate.
   G: ❷Sounds good. It's over there.
2. B: Hello. It's me, Jamie. I think I'll get there in 20 minutes.
   G: Okay. ❸Let's meet at 2 p.m. in front of the clock tower.
3. B: ❹I'm planning to buy some clothes for a school picnic.
   G Look. They're selling old books and clothes over there.
   B: Great. ❺Let's go and look around.

❶ in front of: ~ 앞에서
❷ sound+형용사: ~하게 들리다 / over there: 저쪽에
❸ Let's meet at ~: ~에서 만나자.
❹ I'm planning to+동사원형 ~: 나는 ~할 계획이야.(= I'm going to+동사원형 ~)
❺ look around: 둘러보다

Start Off - Listen & Talk A

1. G: ❶Do you have any plans for the weekend?
   B: Yes. I'm planning to practice dancing at the youth center.
   G: ❷Sounds great. ❸Can I join you?
   B: ❹Why not?
2. G: I'm planning to go to the library to prepare for the exam.
   B: You mean City Library? I want to study with you.
   G: Great. ❺Can you make it at 3 p.m. tomorrow?
   B: Sure. See you then.

❶ Do you have any plans for~?: ~에 어떤 계획이라도 있니?
❷ sound + 형용사: ~하게 들리다
❸ Can I ~?: 내가 ~해도 될까?(= May I ~?)
❹ Why not?: 왜 안 되겠니?, 그거 좋지.(Okay. = Sure. = Of course. = No problem.)
❺ Can you make it at ~?: ~에 만날 수 있을까?

Start Off - Speak Up - Look and talk.

A: ❶I'm planning to volunteer at the library this Tuesday.
B: Great. ❷Can I come with you?
A: ❸Why not? Can you make it at 3 p.m.?
B: Sure. ❹Let's meet in front of the library.

❶ I'm planning to+동사원형 ~: 나는 ~할 계획이야.(= I'm going to + 동사원형 ~)
❷ Can I ~?: 내가 ~해도 될까?(= May I ~?)
❸ Why not?: 왜 안 되겠니?, 그거 좋지.(Okay. = Sure. = Of course. = No problem.)
❹ Let's+동사원형 ~.: ~하자. / in front of: ~ 앞에서

Express Yourself A

1. M: ❶I'm planning to go to the town festival to watch a dance show.
   W: Sounds interesting. Can I come with you?
   M: Of course. Can you make it at the school gate at 6 p.m.?
   W: ❷No problem. See you then.
2. W: I'm planning to enter a singing contest in my town, but I'm nervous.
   M: Don't worry. ❸If you practice hard, you can win the contest.
   W: Thank you.

❶ I'm planning to+동사원형 ~.: 나는 ~할 계획이다. / to watch: to부정사의 부사적 용법(목적)
❷ No problem.: 물론.(=Okay.=Sure.=Of course.=Why not?)
❸ If+주어+현재시제 ~, 주어+will[can/may]+동사원형 ~.

Check Yourself - Listen & Speak

B: ❶What are you going to do this Friday, Aria?
G: I'm planning to volunteer at the post office.
B: Sounds great!
G: ❷Will you come with me, Eric?
B: Sure. ❸When shall we meet?
G: Can you make it at 3 p.m.?
B: I'm afraid not. ❹How about 4 p.m.?
G: Good. See you then.

❶ What are you going to+동사원형 ~?: 너는 ~에 무엇을 할 예정이니?
❷ Will you ~?: ~할래?(= Can you ~? = Would you ~? = Could you ~?)
❸ When shall we meet?: 우리 언제 만날까?(약속 정하기 표현)
❹ How about ~?: ~는 어때?(=What about ~?)

● 다음 우리말과 일치하도록 빈칸에 알맞은 말을 쓰시오.

Get Ready - 2

1. **B:** I'm _____ _____ _____ some pictures in _____ _____ the flower gate.

   G: _____ good. It's _____ there.

2. **B:** Hello. _____ me, Jamie. I think I'll _____ there in 20 minutes.

   G: Okay. _____ meet _____ 2 p.m. _____ front of the clock tower.

3. **B:** I'm _____ to buy some clothes _____ a school picnic.

   G: Look. They're _____ old books and clothes _____ _____.

   B: Great. _____ go and look _____.

Start Off - Listen & Talk A

1. **G:** Do you have _____ plans _____ the weekend?

   B: Yes. I'm _____ _____ practice _____ at the youth center.

   G: _____ great. _____ I _____ you?

   B: Why _____?

2. **G:** I'm _____ _____ go to the library _____ _____ for the exam.

   B: You _____ City Library? I want to study _____ you.

   G: Great. Can you _____ _____ at 3 p.m. tomorrow?

   B: Sure. See you _____.

Start Off - Listen & Talk B

B: What _____ you _____ _____ do this Saturday?

G: I'm planning to _____ _____ the park _____ my dad.

B: Sounds _____ a wonderful plan. _____ I _____ you?

G: Sure. Can you _____ _____ at the bus stop _____ 1 p.m.?

B: I'm afraid _____. How _____ 2?

G: Fine _____ me. Please bring _____ _____ _____ gloves and a big plastic bag.

B: Okay. _____ you _____ Saturday.

Start Off - Speak Up - Look and talk.

A: I'm _____ _____ volunteer _____ the library this Tuseday.

B: Great. _____ I come _____ you?

A: _____ _____? Can you _____ it at 3 p.m.?

B: Sure. _____ meet in _____ _____ the library.

1. **B:** 꽃문 앞에서 사진 몇 장을 찍을 거야.
   G: 좋은 생각이야. 그것은 저쪽에 있어.
2. **B:** 여보세요. 나야, Jamie. 20분 후에 도착할 것 같아.
   G: 알았어. 오후 2시에 시계탑 앞에서 만나자.
3. **B:** 학교 소풍을 위해 옷을 살 계획이야.
   G: 봐. 저기서 헌 책과 옷을 팔고 있어.
   B: 잘됐다. 가서 둘러보자.

1. **G:** 주말에 무슨 계획 있니?
   B: 응. 청소년 센터에서 춤을 연습하려고 해.
   G: 정말 잘 됐다. 같이 가도 될까?
   B: 물론이지.
2. **G:** 나는 시험을 준비하기 위해 도서관에 갈 계획이야.
   B: 시립 도서관 말하는 거니? 나는 너와 함께 공부하고 싶어.
   G: 좋아. 내일 오후 3시에 만날 수 있니?
   B: 물론. 그럼 그때 봐.

B: 이번 토요일에 뭐 할 거니?
G: 아빠와 함께 공원을 청소할 계획이야.
B: 멋진 계획인 것 같구나. 같이 가도 될까?
G: 물론이지. 버스 정류장에서 오후 1시에 만날 수 있니?
B: 안 될 것 같아. 2시는 어때?
G: 난 괜찮아. 장갑 한 켤레와 커다란 비닐봉지를 가져와.
B: 알았어. 토요일에 보자.

A: 이번 화요일에 도서관에서 자원봉사를 할 계획이야.
B: 멋지다. 같이 가도 될까?
A: 왜 안 되겠니? 오후 3시에 만날 수 있을까?
B: 물론이지. 도서관 앞에서 만나자.

Step Up - Real-life Scene

Let's Volunteer for a Better Town!

Jina: I'm planning _____ _____ at the animal _____ center this Sunday morning.

Alex: You _____ the one _____ Grand Park, Jina?

Jina: Right. _____ you come _____ me, Alex? They need volunteers to _____ _____ _____ the animals.

Alex: I'd _____ to join. I like feeding and _____ animals. I'm also _____ _____ washing them.

Jina: Great. You can _____ other friends _____ you, _____.

Alex: Okay. I'll ask my _____ Nancy. She loves animals, _____. What time _____ we _____?

Jina: Can you _____ it _____ 8 a.m. _____ the Grand Park bus stop?

Alex: Sure. I'll see you _____ Sunday.

Express Yourself A

1. **M:** _____ _____ _____ go to the town festival _____ _____ a dance show.

   W: Sounds _____. Can I come _____ you?

   M: _____ course. _____ you _____ it at the school gate _____ 6 p.m.?

   W: _____ problem. See you _____.

2. **W:** I'm planning _____ _____ a singing contest in my town, but I'm nervous.

   M: _____ worry. If you practice hard, you _____ _____ the contest.

   W: _____ you.

Learning Diary - Listen & Speak

B: What _____ you _____ _____ do this Friday, Aria?

G: I'm _____ to volunteer _____ the post office.

B: Sounds _____!

G: _____ you come _____ me, Eric?

B: Sure. When _____ we _____?

G: Can you _____ _____ at 3 p.m.?

B: I'm _____ not. How _____ 4 p.m.?

G: Good. _____ you _____.

더 나은 마을을 위해 자원 봉사합시다!

지나: 이번 일요일 아침에 동물 보호 센터에서 자원봉사를 할 계획이야.

Alex: Grand Park 근처에 있는 거 말하는 거니, 지나야?

지나: 맞아. 나랑 같이 갈래, Alex? 그들은 동물들을 돌볼 자원 봉사자들이 필요해.

Alex: 나도 함께하고 싶어. 나는 동물들에게 먹이를 주고 산책시키는 것을 좋아해. 그리고 그들을 씻기는 것도 잘해.

지나: 좋아. 다른 친구들도 데려와도 돼.

Alex: 알았어. 내 이웃인 Nancy에게 물어볼게. 그녀도 동물들을 아주 좋아해. 몇 시에 만날까?

지나: Grand Park 버스 정류장에서 오전 8시에 만날까?

Alex: 물론. 일요일에 보자.

1. M: 나는 춤 공연을 보기 위해 마을 축제에 갈 계획이야.
   W: 재미있겠다. 같이 가도 될까?
   M: 물론이지. 오후 6시에 학교 정문에서 만날까?
   W: 그래. 그럼 그때 보자.

2. W: 나는 우리 동네 노래 경연 대회에 나갈 계획인데, 긴장돼.
   M: 걱정하지 마. 열심히 연습하면 너는 대회에서 우승할 수 있어.
   W: 고마워.

B: 이번 금요일에 뭐 할 거니, Aria?
G: 우체국에서 자원봉사를 할 계획이야.
B: 멋지다!
G: 나랑 같이 갈래, Eric?
B: 물론이지. 우리 언제 만날까?
G: 오후 3시에 만날 수 있을까?
B: 안 될 것 같아. 오후 4시는 어때?
G: 좋아. 그때 보자.

[01~02] 다음 대화의 밑줄 친 부분과 바꿔 쓸 수 있는 것을 고르시오.

01

> A: <u>What are you going to do this evening?</u>
> B: I'm going to the park.

① Will you go to the park this evening?
② Do you go to the park this evening?
③ What's your plan for this evening?
④ Can you go to the park this evening?
⑤ Would you like to go to the park this evening?

02

> A: What time should we meet tomorrow?
> B: <u>Can you make it at five?</u>

① Let's go there at five.　　② Let's meet tomorrow.
③ Let's meet at five.　　④ I can't make it at five.
⑤ How about meeting together?

[03~04] 다음 대화의 빈칸에 알맞은 것을 고르시오.

03

> A: _____
> B: I'm planning to go travelling.

travel 여행하다

① What are you doing now?
② What did you do last winter?
③ Are you planning to go travelling?
④ When are you planning to go travelling?
⑤ What are you planning to do this winter?

04

> A: Let's go see a movie tomorrow.
> B: Good idea!
> A: _____
> B: Okay. Let's meet at 5 o'clock.

① Where can we meet?　　② When can you come?
③ How would you like it?　　④ Can you make it at 5?
⑤ What time shall we meet?

[01~04] 다음 대화를 읽고, 물음에 답하시오.

> B: ⓐWhat are you going to do this Saturday? (①)
> G: I'm planning to clean up the park with my dad. (②)
> B: Sounds like a wonderful plan. (③)
> G: Sure. Can you make it at the bus stop at 1 p.m.? (④)
> B: ___ⓑ___ How about 2?
> G: Fine with me. (⑤) Please bring a pair of gloves and a big plastic bag.
> B: Okay. See you on Saturday.

01 위 대화의 ①~⑤ 중 다음 문장이 들어갈 알맞은 곳은?

> Can I join you?

① ② ③ ④ ⑤

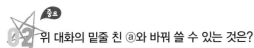
02 위 대화의 밑줄 친 ⓐ와 바꿔 쓸 수 있는 것은?

① What did you do
② Where are you going
③ Where will you go
④ What will you do
⑤ What will you buy

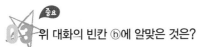
03 위 대화의 빈칸 ⓑ에 알맞은 것은?

① Of course. ② No problem.
③ Good idea. ④ I'm afraid not.
⑤ Sure, why not?

04 위 대화를 읽고, 답할 수 없는 질문은?

① What is the girl planning to do this Saturday?
② Who is the girl planning to clean up the park with?
③ Why can't the boy meet the girl at 1 p.m.?
④ What time will the boy and the girl meet?
⑤ What should the boy bring?

[05~07] 다음 대화를 읽고, 물음에 답하시오.

> G: Do you have any plans for the weekend?
> B: Yes. ⓐI'm planning to practice ⓑdance at the youth center.
> G: Sounds great. Can I join you?
> B: ⓒWhy not?

05 위 대화의 밑줄 친 ⓐ와 바꿔 쓸 수 있는 것은?

① I went to ② I will going to
③ I'm going to ④ I go to
⑤ I was going to

06 위 대화의 밑줄 친 ⓑ를 알맞은 형태로 고쳐 쓰시오.

➡ _____

07 위 대화의 밑줄 친 ⓒ와 바꿔 쓸 수 없는 것은?

① Okay. ② Sure.
③ Of course. ④ Not at all.
⑤ No problem.

[08~14] 다음 대화를 읽고, 물음에 답하시오.

> Jina: I'm planning to volunteer at the animal care center this Sunday morning. (①)
>
> Alex: You mean ⓐthe one near Grand Park, Jina?
>
> Jina: Right. Will you come with me, Alex? They need volunteers to take care ⓑ the animals. (②)
>
> Alex: I'd love to join. I like feeding and walking animals. (③)
>
> Jina: Great. You ⓒcan bring other friends with you, too. (④)
>
> Alex: Okay. I'll ask my neighbor Nancy. (⑤) She loves animals, too. _____ⓓ_____
>
> Jina: ⓔCan you make it at 8 a.m. at the Grand Park bus stop?
>
> Alex: Sure. I'll see you on Sunday.

08 위 대화의 ①~⑤ 중 다음 문장이 들어갈 알맞은 곳은?

> I'm also good at washing them.

①   ②   ③   ④   ⑤

09 위 대화의 밑줄 친 ⓐ가 가리키는 것을 찾아 쓰시오.

➡ _____

10 위 대화의 빈칸 ⓑ에 알맞은 것은?

① for   ② of
③ in   ④ with
⑤ about

11 위 대화의 밑줄 친 ⓒ와 쓰임이 같은 것은?

① Can the rumor be true?
② The child can not walk yet.
③ He can speak German very well.
④ You can go out and play outdoors.
⑤ Can you speak any foreign languages?

12 위 대화의 빈칸 ⓓ에 알맞은 것은?

① When can you come?
② Where should we meet?
③ How would you like it?
④ Can you make it at ten?
⑤ What time shall we meet?

13 위 대화의 밑줄 친 ⓔ를 다음과 같이 바꿔 쓸 때 빈칸에 알맞은 말을 쓰시오.

> _____ _____ meeting at 8 a.m. at the Grand Park bus stop?

14 위 대화를 읽고, 답할 수 없는 질문은?

① What is Jina planning to do this Sunday morning?
② Where is the animal care center?
③ Why does the animal care center need volunteers?
④ How many animals does Alex have?
⑤ Where will Jina and Alex meet?

[01~03] 다음 대화를 읽고, 물음에 답하시오.

B: I'm planning to volunteer at the library this Tuesday.
G: Great. Can I come with you?
B: Why not? ⓐCan you make it at 3 p.m.?
G: Sure. ⓑ도서관 앞에서 만나자.

01 위 대화의 밑줄 친 ⓐ를 다음과 같이 바꿔 쓸 때 빈칸에 알맞은 말을 쓰시오.

How about _____ at 3 p.m.?

02 위 대화의 밑줄 친 ⓑ의 우리말을 주어진 단어를 이용하여 영작하시오.

(front / the library / let's)

➡ _____

03 What is the boy planning to do this Tuesday? Answer in Korean.

➡ _____

04 다음 대화의 순서를 바르게 배열하시오.

(A) Why not?
(B) Yes. I'm planning to practice dancing at the youth center.
(C) Do you have any plans for the weekend?
(D) Sounds great. Can I join you?

➡ _____

[05~08] 다음 대화를 읽고, 물음에 답하시오.

B: ⓐ너는 이번 토요일에 무엇을 할 거니?
G: I'm planning to clean up the park with my dad.
B: Sounds like a wonderful plan. Can I join you?
G: Sure. ⓑ오후 1시에 버스 정류장에서 만날까?
B: I'm afraid not. How about 2?
G: Fine with me. Please bring a pair of gloves and a big plastic bag.
B: Okay. See you ⓒ Saturday.

05 위 대화의 밑줄 친 ⓐ의 우리말을 주어진 단어들을 이용하여 영작하시오.

(going / this)

➡ _____

06 위 대화의 밑줄 친 ⓑ의 우리말과 같도록 할 때, 빈칸에 알맞은 말을 쓰시오.

Can you _____ _____ at the bus stop at 1 p.m.?

07 What time and where will the boy and the girl meet? Answer in English.

➡ _____

08 위 대화의 빈칸 ⓒ에 알맞은 전치사를 쓰시오.

➡ _____

Grammar

1 조건을 나타내는 접속사 if

> - He will get better **if** he gets enough rest. 충분한 휴식을 취하면, 그는 더 좋아질 것이다.
> - **If** I hurry, I will catch the bus. 서두르면, 나는 버스를 탈 것이다.

■ 접속사 if는 두 개의 절을 연결하는 접속사이며, '만약 ~하면'이라는 의미로 조건을 나타낸다. if가 이끄는 종속절은 주절의 앞이나 뒤에 올 수 있다.

  - **If** it's rainy, I will read a book. 비가 내리면, 나는 책을 읽을 것이다.

  - You can win the contest **if** you practice hard. 열심히 연습한다면, 너는 대회에서 우승을 할 수 있다.

■ 조건을 나타내는 접속사 if가 이끄는 절에서는 미래의 일을 나타내는 경우에도 동사는 현재형을 쓴다.

  - **If** it will be sunny tomorrow, I will go swimming. (✗)

  - **If** it is sunny tomorrow, I will go swimming. (○)
    내일 날씨가 맑으면, 나는 수영하러 갈 것이다.

■ '만약 ~하지 않는다면'이라는 의미의 「if+주어+don't[doesn't]+동사원형 ~」은 「unless+주어+동사의 현재형 ~」으로 바꿔 쓸 수 있다.

  - **If** you do **not** read the book, you can't do your homework.
    = **Unless** you read the book, you can't do your homework.

    네가 그 책을 읽지 않으면, 너는 숙제를 할 수 없다.

핵심 Check

1. 다음 괄호 안에서 알맞은 것을 고르시오.

  (1) If I am late, I (miss / will miss) the train.

  (2) (If / Because) I get there on time, I will catch the train.

  (3) If she (takes / will take) the subway, she will be there on time.

  (4) Unless he (studies / doesn't study) hard, he can't get a high score.

② 지각동사

- Ryan **heard** the doorbell **ring**. Ryan은 초인종이 울리는 소리를 들었다.
- I **saw** Amy **read** a book to the children. 나는 Amy가 아이들에게 책을 읽어주는 것을 보았다.

■ 지각동사란 눈으로 보고 귀로 듣는 것과 같이 감각기관을 통하여 우리가 느끼는 것을 표현하는 동사로 see, watch, hear, listen to, feel 등이 있다.

■ 지각동사가 쓰인 5형식 문장은 '주어＋지각동사＋목적어＋목적격 보어(동사원형[분사])' 형태로 나타내며, '목적어가 ~하는 것을 보다[듣다/느끼다]'의 의미를 나타낸다. 이때 목적격 보어 자리에 현재분사 (동사 -ing)를 쓰면, '동작이 진행되는 순간'의 의미가 더 강조된다.

- I **watched** Jane **swim** in the pool. 나는 Jane이 수영장에서 수영하는 것을 보았다.
- I **felt** the ground **shake**. 나는 땅이 흔들리는 것을 느꼈다.
- I **saw** her **crossing** the street. 나는 그녀가 길을 건너고 있는 것을 보았다.
- Peter **heard** Susan **ringing** the bell. Peter는 Susan이 벨을 울리는 것을 들었다.

■ 지각동사의 목적어와 목적격 보어의 관계가 능동일 때는 목적격 보어로 동사원형을, 수동일 때는 과거 분사를 사용한다.

- I felt someone **touch** my bag. 나는 누군가가 내 가방을 만지는 것을 느꼈다.
- I heard my name **called** by her. 나는 내 이름이 그녀에 의해서 불리는 것을 들었다.

핵심 Check

2. 다음 괄호 안에서 알맞은 것을 고르시오.

(1) They saw a monkey (play / played) on a branch.

(2) He heard someone (knocked / knocking) on his door.

(3) They felt thc building (shook / shaking).

(4) She saw the window (broken / breaking) by somebody.

01 다음 우리말에 맞게 〈보기〉에서 골라 빈칸에 알맞은 형태로 고쳐 쓰시오.

┌─── 보기 ───────────────────────────────────┐
│   touch   hear   arrive   see   feel   run   │
└───┘

(1) Tom은 누군가가 그의 등을 만지는 것을 느꼈다.

➡ Tom _____ somebody _____ his back.

(2) 그는 기차가 역에 도착하는 소리를 들었다.

➡ He _____ the train _____ at the station.

(3) 그녀는 소년이 공원에서 달리는 것을 보았다.

➡ She _____ a boy _____ in the park.

02 다음 두 문장을 if를 써서 한 문장으로 나타내시오. (단, 종속절이 주절의 앞에 오는 문장으로 바꿀 것.)

hurry up 서두르다
go on a picnic 소풍가다

(1) Hurry up. You will catch the bus.

➡ _____.

(2) It will be fine tomorrow. We will go on a picnic.

➡ _____.

(3) You are tired. You can sit here.

➡ _____.

03 다음 괄호 안에 주어진 어구를 적당한 위치에 알맞은 형태로 넣어서 문장을 다시 쓰시오.

(1) She watched her husband the wall. (paint)

➡ _____.

(2) The dog heard the baby. (cry)

➡ _____.

(3) The police officer sees a girl a bottle. (pick up)

➡ _____.

04 다음 우리말과 일치하도록 빈칸에 알맞은 말을 넣어 문장을 완성하시오.

(1) 네가 만일 열심히 공부한다면, 너는 그 시험에 합격할 거야.

➡ _____ _____ _____ _____, you'll pass the exam.

(2) 만일 내일 비가 오면, 우리는 집에 있을 것이다.

➡ _____ _____ _____ tomorrow, we'll stay home.

01 다음 우리말에 맞도록 빈칸에 알맞은 것은?

> 선생님은 그들이 열심히 공부하고 있는 것을 보았다.
> ➡ The teacher saw them _____ hard.

① to study   ② studied
③ studying   ④ to studying
⑤ are studying

02 다음 문장의 빈칸에 들어갈 말로 알맞은 것은?

> If we don't start now, we _____ the bus.

① take   ② will miss
③ will take   ④ don't miss
⑤ don't take

 다음 문장의 빈칸에 올 수 없는 것은?

> He watched a lot of people _____.

① sit on the grass
② dancing to the music
③ walk along the street
④ sing along with the band
⑤ to walk toward the park

04 다음 빈칸에 들어갈 말이 바르게 짝지어진 것은?

> If she _____ her cell phone, she _____ her mother.

① found – calls   ② finds – will call
③ found – will call   ④ finds – would call
⑤ will find – will call

서답형

05 다음 우리말과 같도록 빈칸에 알맞은 말을 써서 문장을 완성하시오.

> 만약 이번 일요일에 날씨가 맑으면, 우리는 소풍을 갈 것이다.
> ➡ _____ _____ _____ sunny this Sunday, we _____ _____ on a picnic.

06 다음 빈칸에 알맞은 것을 모두 고르면? (정답 2개)

> Have you ever seen him _____?

① dance   ② dancing
③ danced   ④ to dance
⑤ to dancing

07 다음 밑줄 친 ①~⑤ 중 어법상 어색한 것은?

> ①If ②it ③will snow ④tomorrow, we ⑤ will go out.

①   ②   ③   ④   ⑤

08 다음 빈칸에 알맞은 말이 바르게 짝지어진 것은?

> • Did you see him _____ his room?
> • I heard Ann _____ with her sister.

① cleaning – to talk   ② to clean – talking
③ to clean – to talk   ④ cleaning – talking
⑤ to clean – to talking

09 다음 빈칸에 들어갈 말이 바르게 짝지어진 것은?

> • _____ you get up early, you'll be late for school.
> • I am happy _____ you are always with me.

① When – as　　② Since – as
③ If – because　④ Unless – because
⑤ Although – as

10 다음 문장에서 어법상 틀린 부분을 찾아 고쳐 쓰시오.

> David felt someone touched his head.

_____ ➡ _____

11 다음 중 어법상 틀린 것은?

① Did you hear the girl sang?
② I saw the boy run in the park.
③ I felt somebody touch my back.
④ I heard someone call my name.
⑤ We saw him cleaning the classroom.

12 다음 중 밑줄 친 if의 쓰임이 나머지 넷과 다른 것은?

① If I have enough time, I'll visit my uncle.
② If the weather is fine tomorrow, we'll go on a picnic.
③ He asked me if I needed a pen.
④ If I am rich, I'll help poor people.
⑤ I'll go alone if you are busy.

13 다음 두 문장이 같은 뜻이 되도록 한 문장으로 다시 쓰시오.

> We heard the rain. The rain was falling on the roof.

➡ _____

14 다음 빈칸에 공통으로 알맞은 것은?

> • He _____ the car move.
> • I _____ a bird singing yesterday.
> • I've _____ him laughing loudly with others.

① had　②② got　③ made
④ heard　⑤ wanted

15 다음 우리말과 의미가 같도록 두 문장의 빈칸에 알맞은 말을 쓰시오.

> 만일 네가 너무 많이 먹는 것을 멈추지 않으면, 너는 살찌게 될 것이다.
> ➡ _____ you _____ stop eating too much, you'll get fat.
> ➡ _____ you stop eating too much, you'll get fat.

16 다음 문장의 빈칸에 공통으로 알맞은 것은?

> 너는 Paul이 노래하는 것을 들어본 적이 있니?

① Do you hear Paul sing a song?
② Were you hear Paul singing a song?
③ Have you heard Paul sing a song?
④ Have you heard Paul has sung a song?
⑤ Have you heard Paul is singing a song?

서답형

17 다음 문장에서 어법상 <u>어색한</u> 부분을 찾아 바르게 고쳐 쓰시오.

> If it will rain tomorrow, I will not go there, either.

_____ ➡ _____

18 다음 중 밑줄 친 부분의 의미가 〈보기〉와 <u>다른</u> 하나는?

┌── 보기 ──
| <u>If</u> you want to go there, you have to finish your homework first.
└──

① <u>If</u> she can't, I'll do it instead.
② I can't tell <u>if</u> it will rain or not.
③ <u>If</u> the rumor is true, I'll be very sad.
④ Add more hot water <u>if</u> the soup is too thick.
⑤ I'll go home <u>if</u> he doesn't come out in two minutes.

서답형

19 다음 우리말과 같도록 주어진 단어를 배열하여 문장을 완성하시오.

> 그녀는 누군가가 그녀를 치는 것을 느꼈다.
> (hit / her / somebody / felt)

➡ She _____ .

20 다음 중 어법상 <u>틀린</u> 문장은?

① You'll be able to swim if I teach you.
② If I have a garden, I will make it beautiful.
③ If you don't take this pill, you'll be sick.
④ If he is sick, I'll take him to the hospital.
⑤ They'll go to the zoo if it will be sunny this Sunday.

21 다음 주어진 어구를 이용하여 우리말을 영어로 옮기시오.

> 만약에 네가 티켓을 구한다면, 우리는 콘서트에 갈 수 있다. (get / go to the concert)

➡ _____

22 다음 중 어법상 알맞은 것은?

① Chris felt someone touched his shoulder.
② Rachel heard me called her name.
③ I saw the boy throwing stones at the dog.
④ I felt the ground shook several times.
⑤ Did you see the man stole the wallet?

23 다음 중 빈칸에 <u>lf[if]</u>가 올 수 <u>없는</u> 것은?

① _____ you practice hard, you can win the contest.
② You may go out _____ you finish your homework.
③ _____ you hurry, you can catch the last bus.
④ Subong likes Sumi _____ she is very kind.
⑤ _____ I go shopping, I'll buy some vegetables.

서답형

24 다음 주어진 단어들을 사용하여 우리말 의미에 맞도록 영작하시오.

> 그가 계단을 내려가는 소리가 들리니?
> (you / down / the / him / go / can / stairs / hear)?

➡ _____

01 다음 두 문장을 한 문장으로 연결하시오.

(1) I saw a strange man. + The man entered my house.

➡ _____

(2) I saw my brother. + He was meeting a lady in the bakery.

➡ _____

(3) I felt something. + It crawled up my arm.

➡ _____

(4) I heard the church bells.+They rang out in the distance.

➡ _____

02 다음 괄호 안에 주어진 단어와 접속사 if를 이용하여 문장을 완성하시오.

(1) (sunny / tomorrow)

➡ _____, I will play badminton.

(2) (not / stop / rain)

➡ _____, we won't take a walk in the park.

03 다음 문장에서 어법상 틀린 부분을 찾아 바르게 고쳐 쓰시오.

(1) I saw him to read books in the library.

_____ ➡ _____

(2) Tom heard his brother sang a song.

_____ ➡ _____

04 접속사 if를 사용하여 다음 두 문장을 한 문장으로 고쳐 쓰시오. (단, 종속절이 주절 앞에 오는 문장으로 바꿀 것)

(1) The weather is nice. I always walk to school.

➡ _____

(2) It rains on weekends. We watch TV.

➡ _____

(3) I am late for class. My teacher gets very angry.

➡ _____

05 다음 주어진 어구를 배열하여 문장을 완성하시오.

(1) (baseball / playing / the boys / saw)

➡ I _____.

(2) (hit / felt / her / somebody)

➡ She _____.

06 다음 빈칸에 알맞은 말을 〈보기〉에서 골라 쓰시오. (문장의 앞에 오는 경우 대문자로 쓰시오.)

┌─ 보기 ┤
| when   if   unless |
└─

(1) _____ you don't leave now, you will miss the last train.

(2) We had a big party _____ Sarah came home.

(3) _____ you start now, you'll be late for the meeting.

07 다음 주어진 어구를 이용하여 우리말을 영어로 옮기시오.

> 나는 어제 한 유명한 가수가 무대 위에서 노래하는 것을 들었다. (hear / on the stage)

➡ _____

_____

08 다음 두 문장이 같은 뜻이 되도록 빈칸에 알맞은 말을 쓰시오

(1) If you don't leave now, you will miss the school bus.

➡ _____ _____ _____ now, you will miss the school bus.

(2) Unless it rains tomorrow, I will go camping.

➡ _____ _____ _____ rain tomorrow, I will go camping.

09 다음 주어진 단어들을 이용하여 우리말을 영작하시오.

(1) 나는 아빠가 세차하시는 것을 지켜보았다.
(watch / wash)

➡ _____

(2) 지수는 Tom이 자전거를 타는 것을 보았다.
(see / ride)

➡ _____

(3) 그는 따뜻한 손이 자신의 등에 닿는 것을 느꼈다.
(feel / touch)

➡ _____

10 다음 문장에서 어법상 <u>틀린</u> 부분을 찾아 바르게 고쳐 쓰시오.

(1) If you will have a cold, you had better take a rest.

_____ ➡ _____

(2) If I have gone to France, I will visit the Louvre Museum.

_____ ➡ _____

(2) If I won't send an e-mail tomorrow, call me.

_____ ➡ _____

11 다음 주어진 단어를 바르게 배열하여 문장을 다시 쓰시오.

(1) If you (hurry / you'll / late / don't / up / be)

➡ _____

(2) If you (find / three / supermarket / straight / you / blocks / a / go / will)

➡ _____

_____

12 다음 주어진 어구를 바르게 배열하여 문장을 완성하시오.

(1) (the / I / shake / felt / building)

➡ _____

(2) (never / play / I / piano / my sister / have / heard / the)

➡ _____

Bear and Max

Bear was a black and brown cat with green eyes. He lived with a boy, Ryan. Ryan always thought that "Bear" was a perfect name for the cat because he had a black spot in the shape of a bear. Bear liked to go outside every morning and run after butterflies. He always came home just in time for dinner.

Five blocks away, Max the cat lived with a girl, Sheila. When Sheila moved to this town last month, she was lonely. She had no friends there. But, after Max followed her home, he became a good friend to her.

One day, Sheila saw Max sitting under the desk. He was making a strange sound. "What's wrong?" asked Sheila. She looked at him closely and found a bad cut on his leg. She took him to the animal hospital. The doctor said, "He will get better if he gets enough rest. Keep him inside for a week."

That night, at Ryan's house, there was no Bear. Ryan checked outside, but he couldn't find him. He made posters and put them up around town. A third night passed. Still no Bear.

brown 갈색의
perfect 완벽한
spot 점, 반점
shape 모양
outside 밖에, 밖으로
block 구역, 블록
away 떨어진 곳에
move 이사하다
lonely 외로운
follow 따라가다
strange 이상한
closely 자세히, 면밀히
cut 상처
inside 안에
around ~ 주위에
pass 지나가다
still 여전히

📎 **확인문제**

● 다음 문장이 본문의 내용과 일치하면 T, 일치하지 않으면 F를 쓰시오.

1 Bear had a brown spot in the shape of a bear. ☐

2 Bear went outside every morning and came home late in the evening. ☐

3 Max followed Sheila home and became her friend. ☐

4 Max had a bad cut on his leg. ☐

5 Ryan could find Max after three days. ☐

When Sheila was walking near her house, she saw a poster about
절 ~할 때)   과거진행형

the lost cat. She read it closely, and her eyes got big. "This cat looks
= a poster

exactly like Max. It's so strange." She hurried home. "Come on, Max!
look like: ~처럼 보이다

Let's go!" She took him to the address on the poster. "Ding-Dong."
take A to B: A를 B로 데려가다

When Ryan heard the doorbell ring, he ran to the door and opened it.
지각동사 hear+목적어+동사원형   = the door

"Bear, you're back!" Ryan cried. Max jumped up into Ryan's arms.
be back: 돌아오다   뛰어오르다

"Let me guess," said Sheila. "Your cat comes home only in the
사역동사 let+목적어+동사원형

evenings, doesn't he?" Ryan nodded. "And you lost him last Friday,
부가의문문

didn't you?" Sheila said. "Yes! How did you know?" said Ryan.

"Because this is my cat, too, and he usually comes to my home only
접 ~ 때문에   빈도부사는 일반동사 앞. be동사나 조동사 뒤에 위치   낮 동안에만

during the day."

"Our cat has two families!" said Ryan. "Hey, if you have time, please
                                                         조건을 나타내는 접속사 if(~하면)

come in and have some cookies." "Sure," said Sheila. "Thank you,
먹다 (= eat)

Max," she thought. "I met a good neighbor thanks to you!"
                                                ~ 덕분에

near ~가까이에(서)

exactly 꼭, 정확히

lost 잃어버린

strange 이상한

hurry 급히[서둘러] 가다

address 주소

hear 듣다

doorbell 초인종

cry 울다, 외치다

guess 알아맞히다

nod (고개를) 끄덕이다

lose 잃어버리다

neighbor 이웃

 확인문제

● 다음 문장이 본문의 내용과 일치하면 T, 일치하지 <u>않으면</u> F를 쓰시오.

1   Sheila saw a poster about the lost cat near her house. ☐

2   Sheila took Max to the address on the poster. ☐

3   The cat usually comes to Sheila's home only in the evenings. ☐

4   Ryan lost Max last Thursday. ☐

● 우리말을 참고하여 빈칸에 알맞은 말을 쓰시오.

1 Bear was a black and brown cat _____ green eyes.

2 He lived _____ a boy, Ryan.

3 Ryan _____ _____ that "Bear" was a _____ name for the cat _____ he had a black _____ in the shape of a bear.

4 Bear liked to go _____ every morning and _____ _____ butterflies.

5 He always came home just _____ time _____ dinner.

6 Five blocks _____, Max the cat _____ _____ a girl, Sheila.

7 When Sheila moved _____ this town last month, she was _____.

8 She had _____ friends there.

9 But, _____ Max _____ her home, he became a good friend to her.

10 _____ _____, Sheila saw Max _____ under the desk.

11 He _____ _____ a strange sound.

12 "What's _____?" asked Sheila.

13 She looked _____ him _____ and found a bad _____ on his leg.

14 She _____ him _____ the animal hospital.

15 The doctor said, "He will _____ _____ if he gets _____ rest. Keep him _____ for a week."

16 That night, _____ Ryan's house, there _____ no Bear.

17 Ryan checked _____, but he _____ find him.

18 He made posters and _____ them _____ around town.

19 A _____ night passed. _____ no Bear.

20 _____ Sheila was _____ near her house, she saw a poster about the _____ cat.

1	Bear는 초록색 눈을 가진 검은색과 갈색의 고양이였다.
2	그는 소년 Ryan과 함께 살았다.
3	Ryan은 항상 "Bear"가 곰 모양의 검은 반점이 있기 때문에 그 고양이에게 딱 맞는 이름이라고 생각했다.
4	Bear는 매일 아침 밖으로 나가 나비를 쫓아다니는 것을 좋아했다.
5	그는 항상 저녁 식사 시간에 맞춰 집에 왔다.
6	다섯 블록 떨어진 곳에, 고양이 Max는 Sheila라는 소녀와 함께 살았다.
7	지난달에 Sheila가 이 마을로 이사 왔을 때, 그녀는 외로웠다.
8	그녀는 그곳에 친구가 없었다.
9	하지만 Max가 그녀를 따라 집으로 온 후, 그는 그녀에게 좋은 친구가 되었다.
10	어느 날, Sheila는 책상 밑에 앉아 있는 Max를 보았다.
11	그는 이상한 소리를 내고 있었다.
12	"무슨 일 있니?" Sheila가 물었다.
13	그녀는 그를 자세히 살펴보고 그의 다리에 심한 상처가 난 것을 발견했다.
14	그녀는 그를 동물 병원으로 데려갔다.
15	의사는 "충분한 휴식을 취하면 좋아질 거야. 그를 일주일 동안 안에 있도록 해라."라고 말했다.
16	그날 밤, Ryan의 집에는 Bear가 없었다.
17	Ryan은 바깥을 살폈지만 그를 찾을 수 없었다.
18	그는 포스터를 만들어서 마을을 다니며 그것을 붙였다.
19	세 번째 밤이 지났다. 여전히 Bear는 나타나지 않았다.
20	Sheila가 그녀의 집 근처를 걷고 있었을 때, 그녀는 잃어버린 고양이에 대한 포스터를 보았다.

21 She _____ it closely, and her eyes got _____.

22 "This cat _____ exactly _____ Max. It's so _____."

23 She _____ home.

24 "Come _____, Max! _____ go!"

25 She took him _____ the address _____ the poster.

26 "_____." When Ryan _____ the doorbell _____, he _____ to the door and _____ it.

27 "Bear, you're _____!" Ryan _____.

28 Max _____ _____ into Ryan's arms.

29 "_____ me _____," said Sheila.

30 "Your cat comes home only _____ the evenings, _____ he?"

31 Ryan _____.

32 "And you lost him _____ Friday, _____ _____?" Sheila said.

33 "Yes! _____ did you _____?" said Ryan.

34 "_____ this is my cat, _____, and he usually comes to my home only _____ the day."

35 "_____ cat _____ two families!" said Ryan.

36 "Hey, _____ you have time, please _____ _____ and _____ some cookies."

37 "_____," said Sheila.

38 "_____ you, Max," she _____.

39 "I _____ a good neighbor _____ _____ you!"

● 우리말을 참고하여 본문을 영작하시오.

1 ▶ Bear는 초록색 눈을 가진 검은색과 갈색의 고양이였다.
➡ _____

2 ▶ 그는 소년 Ryan과 함께 살았다.
➡ _____

3 ▶ Ryan은 항상 "Bear"가 곰 모양의 검은 반점이 있기 때문에 그 고양이에게 딱 맞는 이름이라고 생각했다.
➡ _____
_____

4 ▶ Bear는 매일 아침 밖으로 나가 나비를 쫓아다니는 것을 좋아했다.
➡ _____

5 ▶ 그는 항상 저녁 식사 시간에 맞춰 집에 왔다.
➡ _____

6 ▶ 다섯 블록 떨어진 곳에, 고양이 Max는 Sheila라는 소녀와 함께 살았다.
➡ _____

7 ▶ 지난달에 Sheila가 이 마을로 이사 왔을 때, 그녀는 외로웠다.
➡ _____

8 ▶ 그녀는 그곳에 친구가 없었다.
➡ _____

9 ▶ 하지만 Max가 그녀를 따라 집으로 온 후, 그는 그녀에게 좋은 친구가 되었다.
➡ _____

10 ▶ 어느 날, Sheila는 책상 밑에 앉아 있는 Max를 보았다.
➡ _____

11 ▶ 그는 이상한 소리를 내고 있었다.
➡ _____

12 ▶ "무슨 일 있니?" Sheila가 물었다.
➡ _____

13 ▶ 그녀는 그를 자세히 살펴보고 그의 다리에 심한 상처가 난 것을 발견했다.
➡ _____

14 ▶ 그녀는 그를 동물 병원으로 데려갔다.
➡ _____

15 ▶ 의사는 "충분한 휴식을 취하면 좋아질 거야. 그를 일주일 동안 안에 있도록 해라."라고 말했다.
➡ _____

16 ▶ 그날 밤, Ryan의 집에는 Bear가 없었다.
➡ _____

17 ▶ Ryan은 바깥을 살폈지만 그는 그를 찾을 수 없었다.
_____

18 ▶ 그는 포스터를 만들어서 마을을 다니며 그것을 붙였다.
➡ _____

19 ▶ 세 번째 밤이 지났다. 여전히 Bear는 나타나지 않았다.
➡ _____

20 ▶ Sheila가 그녀의 집 근처를 걷고 있었을 때, 그녀는 잃어버린 고양이에 대한 포스터를 보았다.
➡ _____

21 그녀는 그것을 자세히 읽고, 그녀의 눈은 커졌다.

➡ _____

22 "이 고양이는 꼭 Max 같아 보여. 너무 이상해."

➡ _____

23 그녀는 서둘러 집으로 돌아갔다.

➡ _____

24 "자, Max! 가자!"

➡ _____

25 그녀는 그를 포스터에 적힌 주소로 데려갔다.

➡ _____

26 "딩동." Ryan은 초인종이 울리는 소리를 듣고 문으로 달려가 문을 열었다.

➡ _____

27 "Bear야, 돌아왔구나!" Ryan이 외쳤다.

➡ _____

28 Max가 Ryan의 팔 안으로 뛰어올랐다.

➡ _____

29 "내가 맞춰 볼게," Sheila가 말했다.

➡ _____

30 "너의 고양이는 저녁에만 집에 오지, 그렇지?"

➡ _____

31 Ryan은 고개를 끄덕였다.

➡ _____

32 "그리고 너는 지난 금요일에 그를 잃어버렸지, 그렇지 않니?" Sheila가 말했다.

➡ _____

33 "응! "어떻게 알았니?"라고 Ryan은 말했다.

➡ _____

34 "이것은 또한 내 고양이이기 때문이야, 보통 낮에만 우리 집에 오거든."

➡ _____

35 "우리 고양이는 가족이 둘이야!" Ryan이 말했다.

➡ _____

36 이봐, 시간이 있으면 들어와서 쿠키 좀 먹어."

➡ _____

37 "그래," Sheila가 말했다.

➡ _____

38 "고마워, Max." 그녀는 생각했다.

➡ _____

39 "나는 네 덕분에 좋은 이웃을 만났어!"

➡ _____

[01~05] 다음 글을 읽고, 물음에 답하시오.

Bear was a black and brown cat with green eyes. He lived ___ⓐ___ a boy, Ryan. Ryan always thought that "Bear" was a perfect name for the cat ___ⓑ___ he had a black spot in the shape of a bear. Bear liked to go outside every morning and run after butterflies. He always came home just ___ⓒ___ time for dinner.

서답형

01 위 글의 빈칸 ⓐ에 알맞은 전치사를 쓰시오.

➡ _____

중요

02 위 글의 빈칸 ⓑ에 알맞은 것은?

① when   ② until
③ while   ④ before
⑤ because

03 위 글의 빈칸 ⓒ에 알맞은 것은?

① at   ② in
③ for   ④ of
⑤ across

서답형

04 위 글에서 다음 영영풀이에 해당하는 단어를 찾아 쓰시오.

a small area of a surface that is different from other areas

➡ _____

05 위 글을 읽고, 답할 수 없는 질문은?

① What is Bear?
② What color are Bear's eyes?
③ Who did Bear live with?
④ Why did Bear run after butterflies?
⑤ When did Bear always come home?

[06~10] 다음 글을 읽고, 물음에 답하시오.

Five blocks away, Max the cat lived with a girl, Sheila. When Sheila moved to this town last month, she was ___ⓐ___. She had no friends there. ___ⓑ___, after Max followed her home, he became a good friend to her.

One day, ⓒSheila saw Max to sit under the desk. He was making a strange sound. "What's wrong?" asked Sheila. She looked ___ⓓ___ him closely and found a bad cut on his leg. She took him ___ⓔ___ the animal hospital. The doctor said, "He will get better if he gets enough rest. Keep him inside for a week."

중요

06 위 글의 빈칸 ⓐ에 알맞은 것은?

① bored   ② pleased
③ excited   ④ lonely
⑤ disappointed

07 위 글의 빈칸 ⓑ에 알맞은 것은?

① So   ② But
③ Also   ④ Or
⑤ Then

서답형

08 위 글의 밑줄 친 ⓒ에서 어법상 **틀린** 부분을 찾아 바르게 고쳐 쓰시오.

_____ ➡ _____

09 위 글의 빈칸 ⓓ와 ⓔ에 알맞은 말이 바르게 짝지어진 것은?

① up – in
② into – on
③ at – to
④ for – from
⑤ after – in

10 위 글을 읽고, 답할 수 <u>없는</u> 질문은?

① Who did Max live with?
② When did Sheila move to this town?
③ Did Sheila have friends in this town?
④ What did Sheila find on Max's leg?
⑤ Why did Max get hurt?

[11~15] 다음 글을 읽고, 물음에 답하시오.

That night, at Ryan's house, there was no Bear. Ryan checked outside, ___ⓐ___ he couldn't find him. He made posters and put them ___ⓑ___ around town. A third night passed. Still no Bear.

When Sheila was walking near her house, she saw a poster about the lost cat. She read ⓒit closely, and her eyes got big. "This cat looks exactly ___ⓓ___ Max. It's so strange." She hurried home. "Come on, Max! Let's go!" She took him to the address ___ⓔ___ the poster.

11 위 글의 빈칸 ⓐ에 알맞은 것은?

① or
② and
③ so
④ but
⑤ for

12 위 글의 빈칸 ⓑ와 ⓔ에 알맞은 말이 바르게 짝지어진 것은?

① up – on
② on – in
③ out – at
④ down – of
⑤ away – for

서답형

13 위 글의 밑줄 친 ⓒit이 가리키는 것을 영어로 쓰시오.

➡ _____

서답형

14 위 글의 빈칸 ⓓ에 알맞은 전치사를 쓰시오.

➡ _____

15 위 글을 읽고, 답할 수 <u>없는</u> 질문은?

① Was Bear at Ryan's house that night?
② Where did Ryan put up the posters?
③ Why did Ryan lose Bear?
④ When did Sheila see a poster about the lost cat?
⑤ Why did Sheila's eyes get big when she saw the poster?

[16~20] 다음 글을 읽고, 물음에 답하시오.

"Ding-Dong." ⓐWhen Ryan heard the doorbell to ring, he ran to the door and opened it. "Bear, you're back!" Ryan cried. Max jumped ___ⓑ___ into Ryan's arms.

"Let me guess," said Sheila. "Your cat comes home only ___ⓒ___ the evenings, ___ⓓ___ he?" Ryan nodded. "And you lost him last Friday, didn't you?" Sheila said. "Yes! How did you know?" said Ryan. "Because this is my cat, too, and ⓔhe comes usually to my home only during the day."

서답형

16 위 글의 밑줄 친 ⓐ에서 어법상 틀린 부분을 찾아 바르게 고쳐 쓰시오.

_____ ➡ _____

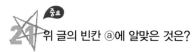

17 위 글의 빈칸 ⓑ와 ⓒ에 알맞은 말이 바르게 짝지어진 것은?

① in – at   ② up – in

③ on – for   ④ at – on

⑤ off – over

서답형

18 위 글의 빈칸 ⓓ에 알맞은 것을 쓰시오.

➡ _____

서답형

19 위 글의 밑줄 친 ⓔ에서 어법상 어색한 부분을 찾아 바르게 고쳐 쓰시오.

_____ ➡ _____

20 위 글을 읽고, 답할 수 없는 질문은?

① Why did Ryan run to the door?

② When does Bear come to Ryan's house?

③ When did Ryan lose Bear?

④ When does Sheila's cat come to her house?

⑤ How did Sheila know Max was Ryan's cat?

[21~22] 다음 글을 읽고, 물음에 답하시오.

Bear was a black and brown cat with green eyes. He lived with a boy, Ryan. Ryan always thought ___ⓐ___ "Bear" was a perfect name for the cat because he had a black spot in the shape of a bear. Bear liked to go outside every morning and run after butterflies. He always came home just in time for dinner.

21 위 글의 빈칸 ⓐ에 알맞은 것은?

① if   ② that

③ though   ④ whether

⑤ because

22 위 글의 Bear에 대한 내용으로 옳지 않은 것은?

① 검은색과 갈색의 고양이이다.

② 초록색 눈을 가지고 있다.

③ 곰 모양의 검은 반점이 있다.

④ 나비를 쫓아다니는 것을 좋아했다.

⑤ 항상 저녁 식사 시간보다 늦게 집에 왔다.

[23~26] 다음 글을 읽고, 물음에 답하시오.

One day, Sheila saw Max sitting under the desk. (①) He was making a strange sound. (②) "What's wrong?" asked Sheila. (③) She looked at him closely and found a bad cut __ⓐ__ his leg. (④) The doctor said, "He will ⓑget better if he gets enough rest. Keep him inside __ⓒ__ a week." (⑤)

23 위 글의 ①~⑤ 중 다음 문장이 들어갈 알맞은 곳은?

> She took him to the animal hospital.

①   ②   ③   ④   ⑤

24 위 글의 빈칸 ⓐ와 ⓒ에 알맞은 말이 바르게 짝지어진 것은?

① in – until   ② on – for
③ at – in   ④ from – by
⑤ over – during

25 위 글의 밑줄 친 ⓑ와 의미가 같은 것은?

① wake   ② suffer
③ develop   ④ improve
⑤ recover

서답형

26 위 글에서 다음 영영풀이에 해당하는 단어를 찾아 쓰시오.

> a wound on a person's body that is made by something sharp

➡ _____

[27~29] 다음 글을 읽고, 물음에 답하시오.

ⓐThat night, at Ryan's house, there were no Bear. Ryan checked outside, but he couldn't find him. He made posters and put them up around town. A third night passed. Still no Bear.

When Sheila was walking near her house, she saw a poster about the lost cat. She read it closely, and her eyes got big. "This cat looks exactly like Max. ⓑIt's so strange." She hurried home. "Come on, Max! Let's go!" She took him to the address on the poster.

서답형

27 위 글의 밑줄 친 ⓐ에서 어법상 틀린 부분을 찾아 바르게 고쳐 쓰시오.

_____ ➡ _____

서답형

28 위 글의 밑줄 친 ⓑ가 의미하는 것을 우리말로 쓰시오.

➡ _____

29 위 글의 내용과 일치하지 <u>않는</u> 것은?

① Ryan은 Bear를 찾기 위해 포스터를 마을 주위에 붙였다.
② 사흘이 지났지만 여전히 Bear는 나타나지 않았다.
③ Sheila는 마을 입구에서 잃어버린 고양이에 대한 포스터를 보았다.
④ Sheila는 포스터에 있는 고양이가 Max와 꼭 닮은 것을 보고 이상하게 여겼다.
⑤ Sheila는 포스터에 적힌 주소로 Max를 데리고 갔다.

[01~04] 다음 글을 읽고, 물음에 답하시오.

Bear was a black and brown cat ⓐ green eyes. He lived with a boy, Ryan. Ryan always thought that "Bear" was a ____ⓑ____ name for the cat because he had a black spot in the shape of a bear. Bear liked to go outside every morning and run after butterflies. He always came home just in time for dinner.

01 위 글의 빈칸 ⓐ에 알맞은 전치사를 쓰시오.

➡ _____

02 What color are Bear's eyes? Answer in English.

➡ _____

03 위 글의 빈칸 ⓑ에 다음 영영풀이에 해당하는 단어를 주어진 철자로 시작하여 쓰시오.

| complete and without faults or weaknesses |

➡ p_____

04 Why did Ryan think that "Bear" was a perfect name for the cat? Answer in English.

➡ _____
_____

[05~08] 다음 글을 읽고, 물음에 답하시오.

"Ding-Dong." ⓐ(the doorbell / when / ring / heard / Ryan), he ran to the door and opened it. "Bear, you're back!" Ryan cried. Max jumped up into Ryan's arms.

"Let me guess," said Sheila. "Your cat comes home only in the evenings, doesn't he?" Ryan nodded. "And you lost him last Friday, ____ⓑ____?" Sheila said. "Yes! How did you know?" said Ryan. "Because this is my cat, too, and he usually comes to my home only during the day."

05 위 글의 괄호 ⓐ 안의 단어들을 순서대로 배열하시오.

➡ _____

06 When did Ryan lose Bear? Answer in English.

➡ _____

07 위 글의 빈칸 ⓑ에 알맞은 부가의문문을 쓰시오.

➡ _____

08 When does Sheila's cat come to her home? Answer in English.

➡ _____

[09~12] 다음 글을 읽고, 물음에 답하시오.

Five blocks away, Max the cat lived with a girl, Sheila. When Sheila moved to this town last month, she was lonely. She had no friends there. But, (A)[before / after] Max followed her home, he became a good friend to her.

One day, Sheila saw Max (B)[sitting / to sit] under the desk. He was making a strange sound. "What's wrong?" asked Sheila. She looked at him closely and found a bad cut on his leg. She took him to the animal hospital. The doctor said, "He will get better if he (C)[gets / will get] enough rest. Keep him inside for a week."

09 When did Sheila move to this town? Answer in English.

➡ _____

10 위 글에서 다음 영영풀이에 해당하는 단어를 찾아 쓰시오.

> unhappy because you have no friends or people to talk to

➡ _____

11 위 글의 괄호 (A)~(C)에서 문맥상 또는 어법상 알맞은 것을 골라 쓰시오.

(A) _____ (B) _____ (C) _____

12 Why did Sheila take Max to the animal hospital? Complete the blank.

> Because _____.

[13~16] 다음 글을 읽고, 물음에 답하시오.

That night, at Ryan's house, there was no Bear. Ryan checked outside, but he couldn't find him. He made posters and put them up around town. A third night passed. Still no Bear.

When Sheila was walking near her house, she saw a poster about the lost cat. She read it ⓐ(close / closely), and her eyes got big. "This cat looks exactly ⓑ(like / alike) Max. It's so strange." She hurried home. "Come on, Max! Let's go!" She took him to the ___ⓒ___ on the poster.

13 What did Ryan do to find Bear? Answer in English.

➡ _____

14 위 글의 괄호 ⓐ와 ⓑ에서 알맞은 것을 골라 쓰시오.

ⓐ _____ ⓑ _____

15 When did Sheila see a poster about the lost cat? Answer in English.

➡ _____

16 위 글의 빈칸 ⓒ에 다음 영영풀이에 해당하는 단어를 쓰시오.

> details of where someone lives or works and where letters, etc. can be sent

➡ _____

해석

Express Yourself C1~C2

C1: Do you want to watch a magic show? If you visit the town festival on
조건을 나타내는 접속사 if(~하면)

Monday, you will see Harry do magic tricks. Have fun at the festival!
on + 요일   지각동사 see+목적어+동사원형

C2: Do you want to watch an outdoor movie? If you visit the town festival on

Friday, you will hear Mr. Jackson, a director talk about his new movie. It
지각동사 hear + 목적어 + 동사원형

will be fun!

구문해설 • magic: 마술의 • magic trick: 마술 묘기 • festival: 축제 • outdoor: 야외의

• director: 영화감독

C1: 마술쇼를 보고 싶니? 월요일에 마을 축제에 가면, Harry가 마술 묘기를 부리는 것을 볼 수 있을 거야. 축제 잘 보내!

C2: 야외 영화 보고 싶니? 금요일에 마을 축제에 가면, 너는 영화감독 Jackson 씨가 그의 새 영화에 대해 이야기하는 것을 들을 거야. 그것은 재미있을 거야!

Project - Step 2

This is my favorite *tteokbokki* restaurant in my town. If you go there, you will
조건을 나타내는 접속사 if(~하면)

see many students eating *tteokbokki* and chatting.
지각동사 see + 목적어 + 현재분사

This is a small but beautiful park near the school. If you want to take a nice
take a break 휴식을 취하다

break, please visit it. You can hear birds singing in the trees.
지각동사 hear + 목적어 + 현재분사

구문해설 • favorite: 가장 좋아하는 • chat: 수다를 떨다 • near: ~에서 가까이

이곳은 우리 동네에서 내가 제일 좋아하는 떡볶이 식당이다. 그곳에 가면, 너는 많은 학생들이 떡볶이를 먹으면서 수다를 떨고 있는 것을 볼 수 있을 것이다.

이곳은 학교 근처에 있는 작지만 아름다운 공원이다. 편안한 휴식을 취하고 싶다면, 꼭 이곳을 방문해라. 너는 나무에서 새들이 지저귀는 소리를 들을 수 있다.

Link to the World

Let's make a better town!

In the U.S., there is a volunteer project to build houses for families in need.
There is + 단수 명사 ~: ~이 있다   도움이 필요한

Many people are joining the project to give them hope.
현재진행형   수여동사 give + 간접목적어 + 직접목적어

It's a little free library in Canada. If you want to read books together with
작은   무료의   in + 국가 명 조건을 나타내는 접속사 if(~하면)   ~와 함께

your neighbors, make one in front of your house!
~ 앞에

It's a special refrigerator in Germany. People can leave food in this

refrigerator for people in need.
도움이 필요한

구문해설 • build: 짓다 • hope: 희망 • free: 무료의 • special: 특별한 • refrigerator: 냉장고

• leave: ~을 두고 오다[가다]

더 나은 마을을 만들자!

미국에서는 도움이 필요한 가정을 위해 집을 짓는 자원봉사 프로젝트가 있다. 많은 사람들이 그들에게 희망을 주기 위해 이 프로젝트에 참여하고 있다.

이것은 캐나다에 있는 작은 무료 도서관이다. 만약 여러분이 여러분의 이웃과 함께 책을 읽고 싶다면, 여러분의 집 앞에 그것을 만들어라!

이것은 독일에 있는 특별한 냉장고다. 사람들은 도움이 필요한 사람들을 위해 이 냉장고 안에 음식을 두고 갈 수 있다.

영역별 핵심문제

Words & Expressions

01 다음 영영풀이에 해당하는 단어로 알맞은 것은?

> a small round area that has a different color or feels different from the surface it is on

① cut   ② care

③ block   ④ spot

⑤ shape

02 다음 중 짝지어진 단어의 관계가 <u>다른</u> 것은?

① sell : buy   ② inside : outside

③ lost : missing   ④ ask : reply

⑤ remember : forget

03 다음 빈칸에 공통으로 알맞은 것은?

> • Let's _____ a break for ten minutes.
> • He loves to _____ care of animals.

① make   ② get

③ have   ④ take

⑤ keep

04 다음 우리말과 같도록 빈칸에 알맞은 말을 주어진 철자로 시작하여 쓰시오.

> 이상한 소리에 그는 잠을 깼다.
> ➡ A s_____ noise broke his sleep.

05 다음 빈칸에 공통으로 알맞은 것을 쓰시오.

> • She always sends money to children _____ need.
> • There is a young boy _____ front of the door.

06 다음 영영풀이에 해당하는 단어를 쓰시오.

> a flying insect with a long thin body and four large, usually brightly colored, wings

➡ _____

Conversation

07 다음 대화의 빈칸에 알맞은 것은?

> A: What are you planning to do this vacation?
> B: _____

① I visited my grandmother.

② I went to America.

③ Yes. I have a plan to go to America.

④ I have a plan to go to Australia.

⑤ No. I'm not going to America.

08 다음 대화의 빈칸에 알맞은 것은?

> A: Can you make it at two?
> B: _____ Let's meet at the school gym.

① You're welcome.　② No problem.
③ I don't know.　④ You're right.
⑤ I'm afraid not.

09 다음 대화의 순서를 바르게 배열하시오.

> (A) No problem. See you then.
> (B) Sounds interesting. Can I come with you?
> (C) Of course. Can you make it at the school gate at 6 p.m.?
> (D) I'm planning to go to the town festival to watch a dance show.

➡ _____

10 다음 짝지어진 대화 중 어색한 것은?

① A: What time should we meet?
　 B: Let's meet at 5.
② A: Can you make it at 6?
　 B: Sure. See you then.
③ A: How about meeting in front of the museum?
　 B: That museum was great.
④ A: Where should we meet?
　 B: Can we meet at the bus stop?
⑤ A: Do you want to go skateboarding?
　 B: Sure. That sounds like fun.

[11~14] 다음 대화를 읽고, 물음에 답하시오.

> B: ⓐ너는 이번 토요일에 무엇을 할 계획이니?
> G: I'm planning to clean up the park with my dad.
> B: Sounds like a wonderful plan. ____ⓑ____
> G: Sure. Can you ____ⓒ____ it at the bus stop at 1 p.m.?
> B: I'm afraid not. How about 2?
> G: Fine with me. Please bring a pair of gloves and a big plastic bag.
> B: Okay. See you on Saturday.

11 위 대화의 밑줄 친 ⓐ의 우리말에 맞도록 주어진 단어를 이용하여 영작하시오. (필요하면 어형을 바꿀 것)

> (plan / this Saturday)

➡ _____

12 위 대화의 빈칸 ⓑ에 알맞은 것은?

① Can I help you?
② Can I join you?
③ Where do you play?
④ What sport do you like?
⑤ What time shall we meet?

13 위 대화의 빈칸 ⓒ에 알맞은 단어를 쓰시오.

➡ _____

14 위 대화를 읽고, 다음 질문에 완전한 문장으로 답하시오.

> Q: What time and where will the boy and the girl meet?
> A: _____

15 다음 문장의 빈칸에 알맞은 것은?

> She _____ at the station.

① arrive heard the train
② the train heard arrive
③ heard the train arrives
④ heard the train arrive
⑤ heard arriving the train

16 다음 우리말에 맞게 빈칸에 알맞은 것은?

> 만일 그가 내일 여기에 도착하면, 내가 너에게
> 전화할게.
> ➡ _____, I'll call you.

① If he arrives here tomorrow
② If he doesn't arrive here tomorrow
③ If he will arrive here tomorrow
④ Unless he will arrive here tomorrow
⑤ Unless he arrives here tomorrow

17 다음 문장에서 어법상 틀린 부분을 찾아 바르게 고쳐 쓰시오.

> I saw a boy to get on the train.

_____ ➡ _____

18 다음 빈칸에 공통으로 알맞은 것은?

> • You will get one free _____ you buy this.
> • I wonder _____ she is really a middle school student.

① as   ② if
③ that   ④ since
⑤ whether

19 다음 문장에서 어법상 어색한 부분을 찾아 바르게 고쳐 쓰시오.

> If you won't clean your room, I won't let you go out.

_____ ➡ _____

20 다음 중 어법상 어색한 문장은?

① I felt the ground move under me.
② She saw Daniel cleaning the window.
③ I heard someone calling my name.
④ We see Jenny shopping at the mart.
⑤ I heard a cat cried in the park.

21 다음 중 밑줄 친 if의 쓰임이 〈보기〉와 다른 것은?

> ┤ 보기 ├
> Don't wait for me if I'm late this evening.

① I can help you if you want.
② You will miss the train if you don't hurry up.
③ If it snows tomorrow, I will go out.
④ I don't know if he will leave for Busan tomorrow.
⑤ If you read the book again, you can understand it.

22 다음 우리말에 맞게 주어진 단어들을 바르게 배열하시오.

> 나는 어떤 노인이 기차에서 내리는 것을 보았다.
> (get off / saw / the train / I / an old man)

➡ _____

23 다음 두 문장을 한 문장으로 바꿔 쓰시오.

> Susan does not get up now. She will miss the train.

➡ _____
_____
_____

24 다음 문장의 밑줄 친 ①~⑤ 중 어법상 어색한 것은?

> ①The boy ②watched ③a man ④to turn off ⑤the faucet.

①   ②   ③   ④   ⑤

25 다음 빈칸에 들어갈 말이 나머지 넷과 다른 것은?

① Mike will stay at home _____ it is cold.

② You can stay at home _____ you're tired.

③ She'll watch TV _____ she finishes her work early.

④ He'll buy a necktie for his dad _____ he goes shopping.

⑤ I think _____ Anderson won't come back.

26 다음 주어진 단어를 이용하여 우리말을 영어로 옮기시오.

> Kate는 누군가가 그녀를 향해 소리치는 것을 들었다. (heard / someone)

➡ _____

[27~32] 다음 글을 읽고, 물음에 답하시오.

Bear was a black and brown cat ___ⓐ___ green eyes. He lived with a boy, Ryan. Ryan always thought ⓑthat "Bear" was a perfect name for the cat ___ⓒ___ he had a black spot in the shape of a bear. Bear liked to go outside every morning and run after butterflies. He always came home just in time for dinner.

Five ___ⓓ___ away, Max the cat lived with a girl, Sheila. When Sheila moved to this town last month, she was lonely. She had no friends there. But, ___ⓔ___ Max followed her home, he became a good friend to her.

27 위 글의 빈칸 ⓐ에 알맞은 것은?

① of   ② on

③ into   ④ with

⑤ from

28 위 글의 밑줄 친 ⓑ와 쓰임이 다른 하나는?

① I think that the movie was terrible.

② I know that Sally doesn't have a job.

③ I think that bag is yours.

④ I hope that he will be my boyfriend.

⑤ I know that she will go abroad to study.

29 위 글의 빈칸 ⓒ에 알맞은 것은?

① if   ② so

③ when   ④ because

⑤ though

30 위 글의 빈칸 ⓓ에 다음 영영풀이를 참조하여 알맞은 단어를 쓰시오.

> a group of buildings with streets on all sides

➡ _____

31 위 글의 빈칸 ⓔ에 알맞은 것은?

① while   ② before

③ after   ④ until

⑤ although

32 위 글을 읽고, 답할 수 <u>없는</u> 질문은?

① What color was Bear?

② Did Bear like to go outside?

③ When did Bear always come home?

④ Why did Sheila move to this town?

⑤ Why was Sheila lonely?

[33~37] 다음 글을 읽고, 물음에 답하시오.

One day, Sheila saw Max ____ⓐ____ under the desk. He was making a strange sound. "What's wrong?" asked Sheila. She looked at him ⓑ <u>close</u> and found a bad cut ____ⓒ____ his leg. She took him to the animal hospital. The doctor said, "He will get better if he will get enough rest. Keep him inside for a week."

That night, at Ryan's house, there was no Bear. Ryan checked outside, but he couldn't find him. He made posters and put them ____ⓓ____ around town. A third night passed. Still no Bear.

33 위 글의 빈칸 ⓐ에 알맞은 것은?

① sat   ② to sit

③ sitting   ④ to sitting

⑤ is sitting

34 위 글의 밑줄 친 ⓑ를 올바른 형태로 고쳐 쓰시오.

➡ _____

35 위 글의 빈칸 ⓒ와 ⓓ에 알맞은 말이 바르게 짝지어진 것은?

① in – off   ② at – over

③ for – in   ④ from – on

⑤ on – up

36 위 글에서 다음 영영풀이에 해당하는 단어를 찾아 쓰시오.

> a period of time in which you relax, sleep, or do nothing after you have been active or doing work

➡ _____

37 위 글을 읽고, 답할 수 <u>없는</u> 질문은?

① Where was Max sitting?

② What did Sheila find on his leg after looking at Max closely?

③ Was the animal hospital near Sheila's housc?

④ Was Bear at Lyan's house that night?

⑤ Why did Lyan put up posters around town?

단원별 예상문제

01 다음 영영풀이에 해당하는 것은?

> a wound on a person's body that is made by something sharp

① hit
② cut
③ hide
④ hurt
⑤ lose

02 다음 빈칸에 공통으로 알맞은 것을 쓰시오.

> • She put _____ a notice on a board.
> • After cleaning _____ his room, he sat at his desk.

➡ _____

03 다음 빈칸에 공통으로 알맞은 것은?

> • I hope you'll _____ better soon.
> • I didn't _____ enough rest during the weekend.

① do
② get
③ take
④ have
⑤ become

04 다음 우리말에 맞도록 빈칸에 알맞은 말을 쓰시오.

> 밖으로 나가서 도시를 둘러보아라.
> ➡ Go outside and _____ _____ the city.

05 다음 빈칸에 들어갈 말로 적절하지 <u>않은</u> 것은?

> • I'll ask my _____ Nancy.
> • He was making a _____ sound.
> • He felt really _____ before the interview.
> • She has such beautiful _____ eyes.

① strange
② brown
③ neighbor
④ used
⑤ nervous

06 다음 우리말에 맞도록 빈칸에 알맞은 단어를 주어진 철자로 시작하여 쓰시오.

> 영화감독 Jackson 씨는 그의 새 영화에 대해 이야기할 것이다.
> ➡ Mr. Jackson, a movie d_____, will talk about his new movie.

07 다음 대화의 빈칸에 알맞은 것은?

> A: Let's go to the concert this Saturday.
> B: Sounds good. _____
> A: Fine with me.

① Can I join you?
② May I go to the concert?
③ How about going to the concert?
④ Do you like the concert?
⑤ Can you make it at 3?

08 다음 대화의 빈칸에 <u>어색한</u> 것은?

> A: What are you going to do this Sunday?
> B: _____

① I'm planning to go to the zoo.

② I can go to the zoo.

③ I'm going to go to the zoo.

④ I plan to go to the zoo.

⑤ I have a plan to go to the zoo.

[09~12] 다음 대화를 읽고, 물음에 답하시오.

> B: What are you going to do this Friday, Aria?
> (①)
> G: I'm planning to ___ⓐ___ at the post office.
> (②)
> B: Sounds great! (③)
> G: Will you come with me, Eric? (④)
> B: Sure. When shall we meet?
> G: ⓑ(it / you / 3 p.m. / can / make / at / ?)
> B: I'm afraid not. (⑤)
> G: Good. See you then.

09 위 대화의 ①~⑤ 중 다음 문장이 들어갈 알맞은 곳은?

> How about 4 p.m.?

①　　　②　　　③　　　④　　　⑤

10 위 대화의 빈칸 ⓐ에 다음 영영풀이에 해당하는 단어를 쓰시오.

> to offer to do something without expecting any reward

➡ _____

11 위 대화의 괄호 ⓑ 안의 단어들을 바르게 배열하여 완성하시오.

➡ _____

12 위 대화를 읽고, 다음 질문에 완전한 문장으로 답하시오.

> Q: What time will Aria and Eric meet?
> A: _____

13 다음 우리말과 같도록 할 때, 빈칸에 알맞은 것은?

> 만약 내일 그가 오지 않으면, 나는 매우 슬플 것이다.
> ➡ _____, I will feel very sad.

① If he comes tomorrow

② If he won't come tomorrow

③ If he doesn't come tomorrow

④ Unless he won't come tomorrow

⑤ Unless he doesn't come tomorrow

14 다음 빈칸에 알맞은 것을 <u>모두</u> 고르면? (정답 2개)

> Susan saw Chris _____ down the street.

① run　　　　　② runs

③ ran　　　　　④ has run

⑤ running

출제율 95%

15 다음 문장에서 어법상 어색한 부분을 바르게 고쳐 쓰시오.

> I heard a cat to cry in the park.

_____ ➡ _____

[16~17] 다음 중 어법상 어색한 문장을 고르시오.

출제율 90%

16 ① If you eat too much, you'll get fat.
② If you're thirsty, have some water.
③ If I will pass the test, I'll be very happy.
④ If it rains outside, I usually stay at home.
⑤ If school finishes early today, I'll go shopping.

출제율 95%

17 ① I watched my mother cooking.
② She heard the birds sing.
③ He saw his brother hit the ball.
④ We can hear his father shouting.
⑤ I felt the ground to move under me.

출제율 85%

18 다음 두 문장의 의미가 같도록 빈칸에 알맞은 말을 쓰시오.

> If you don't like the food, you don't have to pay.
> ➡ _____, you don't have to pay.

[19~24] 다음 글을 읽고, 물음에 답하시오.

"Ding-Dong." When Ryan heard the doorbell ①ring, he ran to the door and opened it. "Bear, you're back!" Ryan cried. Max jumped up into Ryan's arms.

"Let me ②guess," said Sheila. "Your cat comes home only in the evenings, ③did he?" Ryan nodded. "And you lost him last Friday, didn't you?" Sheila said. "Yes! How did you know?" said Ryan. "____ⓐ____ this is my cat, ④too, and he usually comes to my home only ____ⓑ____ the day."

"Our cat has two families!" said Ryan. "Hey, ____ⓒ____ you have time, please come in and ⑤have some cookies." "Sure," said Sheila. "Thank you, Max," she thought. "I met a good neighbor thanks ____ⓓ____ you!"

출제율 85%

19 위 글의 밑줄 친 ①~⑤ 중 어법상 틀린 것은?

①   ②   ③   ④   ⑤

출제율 90%

20 위 글의 빈칸 ⓐ에 알맞은 것은?

① If   ② That
③ Though   ④ Because
⑤ Whether

출제율 100%

21 위 글의 빈칸 ⓑ와 ⓓ에 알맞은 말이 바르게 짝지어진 것은?

① for – of   ② for – by
③ during – to   ④ during – for
⑤ for – from

출제율 95%

22 위 글의 빈칸 ⓒ에 알맞은 것은?

① as   ② if
③ that   ④ while
⑤ when

출제율 90%

23 위 글에서 다음 영영풀이에 해당하는 단어를 찾아 쓰시오. (원형으로 쓸 것)

> to move your head up and down, especially in order to show agreement or understanding

➡ _____

출제율 90%

24 위 글을 읽고, 다음 질문에 완전한 문장으로 답하시오.

> Q: When does Max come to Ryan's home?
> A: _____

[25~29] 다음 글을 읽고, 물음에 답하시오.

Bear was a black and brown cat with green eyes. He lived with a boy, Ryan. Ryan always thought _____ⓐ_____ "Bear" was a perfect name for the cat (A)[because / because of] he had a black spot in the _____ⓑ_____ of a bear. Bear liked to go outside every morning and run _____ⓒ_____ butterflies. He always came home just in time for dinner.

Five blocks away, Max the cat lived with a girl, Sheila. When Sheila moved to this town last month, she was lonely. She had no friends there. But, (B)[before / after] Max followed her home, he became a good friend to her.

출제율 90%

25 위 글의 빈칸 ⓐ에 알맞은 것은?

① as   ② if
③ that   ④ while
⑤ when

출제율 85%

26 위 글의 빈칸 ⓑ에 다음 영영풀이에 해당하는 단어를 쓰시오.

> the form or outline of an object

➡ _____

출제율 100%

27 위 글의 괄호 (A)와 (B)에서 알맞은 것을 골라 쓰시오.

(A) _____   (B) _____

출제율 90%

28 위 글의 빈칸 ⓒ에 알맞은 것은?

① off   ② over
③ down   ④ after
⑤ into

출제율 85%

29 위 글의 내용과 일치하지 <u>않는</u> 것은?

① Bear는 초록색 눈을 가진 검은색과 갈색의 고양이었다.
② Bear는 곰 모양의 검은색 반점이 있다.
③ Bear는 가끔 저녁 시간에 맞춰 Ryan의 집에 왔다.
④ Sheila는 Ryan의 집에서 다섯 블록 떨어진 곳에 살았다.
⑤ Sheila는 지난달에 Ryan의 마을로 이사 왔다.

서술형 실전문제

01 다음 주어진 단어를 이용하여 대화를 완성하시오.

> G: What are your plans for the weekend?
> B: _____
> (plan / visit / my grandparents)

02 다음 주어진 문장과 같은 의미가 되도록 빈칸에 알맞은 말을 쓰시오.

> What will you do on New Year's day?
> ➡ What _____ on New Year's day?
> ➡ What _____ on New Year's day?

[03~04] 다음 대화를 읽고, 물음에 답하시오.

> B: I'm planning to see a movie this Sunday. Do you want to come with me?
> G: Sure. ⓐ우리 몇 시에 만날까?
> B: ⓑCan you make it at the bus stop at 9 a.m.?
> G: Okay. See you then.

03 위 대화의 밑줄 친 ⓐ의 우리말을 주어진 단어를 이용하여 영작하시오.

> (shall)

➡ _____

04 위 대화의 밑줄 친 ⓑ를 다음과 같이 바꿔 쓸 때 빈칸에 알맞은 말을 쓰시오.

> Can we _____ at the bus stop at 9 a.m.?

05 다음 문장에서 어법상 어색한 부분을 찾아 고쳐 쓰시오. (한 군데)

(1) I heard someone to play the trumpet last night.

_____ ➡ _____

(2) If she will go tomorrow, I will go, too.

_____ ➡ _____

(3) I watched my sister drew a picture.

_____ ➡ _____

06 다음 두 문장의 뜻이 같도록 빈칸에 알맞은 말을 쓰시오.

> If you don't hurry up, you will miss the bus.
> ➡ _____ you hurry up, you will miss the bus.

07 다음 우리말과 같도록 주어진 어휘들을 바르게 배열하시오.

> Hana는 그녀의 고양이가 벽을 올라가는 것을 보았다.
> (saw / cat / her / the / climbing / wall / Hana).

➡ _____

08 다음 괄호 안에 주어진 표현을 이용하여 우리말과 같은 뜻이 되도록 영작하시오.

> 만약 네가 시간을 어기지 않고 도착한다면, 네 친구가 너를 기다릴 필요가 없을 것이다.
> (on time, have to)

➡ _____

_____

That night, at Ryan's house, there was no Bear. Ryan checked outside, but he couldn't find him. ⓐHe made posters and put up them around town. A third night passed. Still no Bear.

When Sheila was walking near her house, she saw a poster about the lost cat. She read it closely, and her eyes got big. "ⓑ이 고양이는 꼭 Max처럼 보인다. It's so strange." She hurried home. "Come on, Max! Let's go!" She took him to the address on the poster.

09 위 글의 밑줄 친 ⓐ에서 어법상 어색한 부분을 고쳐 문장을 다시 쓰시오.

➡ _____

10 위 글에서 다음 영영풀이에 해당하는 단어를 찾아 쓰시오.

> happening or existing before now and continuing into the present

➡ _____

11 위 글의 밑줄 친 ⓑ의 우리말에 맞게 주어진 단어들을 바르게 배열하시오.

> (like / this / Max / exactly / looks / cat)

➡ _____

12 Where did Sheila take Max? Answer in English.

➡ _____

One day, ⓐSheila는 Max가 책상 밑에 앉아 있는 것을 보았다. He was making a strange sound. "What's wrong?" asked Sheila. She looked at him closely and found a bad __ⓑ__ on his leg. She took him to the animal hospital. The doctor said, "ⓒHe will get better if he gets enough rest. Keep him inside for a week."

13 위 글의 밑줄 친 ⓐ의 우리말에 맞게 주어진 단어를 바르게 배열하시오.

> (the desk / sitting / Sheila / under / Max / saw)

➡ _____

14 위 글의 빈칸 ⓑ에 다음 영영풀이에 해당하는 단어를 주어진 철자로 쓰시오.

> a wound on a body that is made by something sharp

➡ c_____

15 Where did Sheila take Max? Answer in English.

➡ _____

16 위 글의 밑줄 친 ⓒ를 우리말로 쓰시오.

➡ _____

창의사고력 서술형 문제

01 다음 〈보기〉와 같이 주어진 단어를 이용하여 문장을 만드시오. (3문장)

┌── 보기 ──┐
│ I saw Mom wash[washing] the dishes.   │
└───┘

(A)	(B)	(C)
heard	somebody	touch my leg
saw	a man	ring
felt	a phone	plant trees

(1) _____
(2) _____
(3) _____

02 다음과 같은 상황이 벌어진다면 어떨지 상상하여 〈보기〉와 같이 쓰시오.

┌──┐
│ • go to China   │
│ • get an A on the math test   │
│ • it is sunny tomorrow   │
│ • find an abandoned dog on the street   │
└──┘

┌── 보기 ──┐
│ If I go to China, I can see the Great Wall.   │
└───┘

(1) _____
(2) _____
(3) _____

03 다음 〈보기〉의 지각동사를 이용하여 문장을 4개 쓰시오. (필요시 어형을 바꿀 것)

┌── 보기 ──┐
│   feel   watch   hear   see   │
└───┘

(1) _____
(2) _____
(3) _____
(4) _____

단원별 모의고사

01 다음 중 짝지어진 단어의 관계가 나머지 넷과 <u>다른</u> 것은?

① ask : answer

② laugh : cry

③ lend : borrow

④ gate : door

⑤ forget : remember

02 다음 빈칸에 알맞은 말이 바르게 짝지어진 것은?

> • I'll take care _____ the dog.
> • Thanks _____ your help, I was able to do it.

① in – to

② at – for

③ of – for

④ of – to

⑤ for – at

03 다음 빈칸에 공통으로 알맞은 것을 주어진 철자로 시작하여 쓰시오.

> • Hurry up, or we'll m_____ the train.
> • They m_____ their homes, their friends, and family.

04 다음 중 영영풀이가 <u>잘못된</u> 것은?

① sell: to exchange something for money

② move: to go to a different place to live

③ feed : to give food to a person or an animal

④ rcturn: to come or go to a place again

⑤ borrow: to give something to someone to be used for a period of time and then returned

05 다음 빈칸에 알맞은 말이 바르게 짝지어진 것은?

> • Let's _____ a break under this tree.
> • He _____ up pictures of his favorite flowers.

① have – turn

② take – put

③ keep – pick

④ get – set

⑤ make – post

06 다음 빈칸에 우리말에 맞도록 알맞은 말을 쓰시오.

(1) 그들은 저쪽에서 헌 책과 옷을 팔고 있다.

➡ They're selling old books and clothes _____ there.

(2) 그는 또한 어려움에 처한 사람들을 돕는 것을 좋아한다.

➡ He also likes to help people _____ need.

07 다음 대화의 빈칸에 알맞은 말을 <u>모두</u> 고르면? (2개)

> A: What are you going to do this Sunday?
> B: _____

① I will be busy this Saturday.

② I'm planning to go camping.

③ I visited my unclc ycsterday.

④ I'm going to the museum now.

⑤ I'm going to play basketball with my friends.

[08~12] 다음 대화를 읽고, 물음에 답하시오.

Jina: I'm planning to volunteer at the animal care center this Sunday morning. (①)

Alex: You mean the one near Grand Park, Jina?

Jina: Right. (②) Will you come with me, Alex? ⓐThey need volunteers to take care ____ⓑ____ the animals.

Alex: I'd love to join. I like feeding and walking animals. I'm also good ____ⓒ____ washing them.

Jina: Great. (③)

Alex: Okay. I'll ask my neighbor Nancy. She loves animals, too. What time shall we meet? (④)

Jina: ⓓGrand Park 버스 정류장에서 오전 8시에 만날 수 있을까?

Alex: Sure. I'll see you on Sunday. (⑤)

08 위 대화의 ①~⑤ 중 다음 문장이 들어갈 알맞은 곳은?

> You can bring other friends with you, too.

①   ②   ③   ④   ⑤

09 위 대화의 밑줄 친 ⓐ가 가리키는 것을 우리말로 쓰시오.

➡ _____

10 위 대화의 빈칸 ⓑ와 ⓒ에 알맞은 말이 바르게 짝지어진 것은?

① in – for   ② about – in
③ for – up   ④ of – at
⑤ of – about

11 위 대화의 밑줄 친 ⓓ의 우리말과 같도록 빈칸에 알맞은 말을 쓰시오.

> Can you ____ ____ ____ 8 a.m. at the Grand Park bus stop?

12 위 대화를 읽고, 답할 수 <u>없는</u> 질문은?

① When is Jina planning to volunteer at the animal care center?
② What kind of animal does Jina have?
③ Is Alex good at washing animals?
④ Whose neighbor is Nancy?
⑤ What day will Jina and Alex meet?

13 다음 대화의 빈칸에 알맞은 것은?

> A: John is sick, so he can't come.
> B: No way! I saw him ____ tennis yesterday.

① plays   ② play
③ to play   ④ played
⑤ to playing

14 다음 중 어법상 <u>어색한</u> 문장은?

① If I get an A on the exam, I will be happy.
② If you will go by bus, it will be cheaper.
③ If she comes back to Korea, her husband will be pleased.
④ If my brother comes home early, my dad won't be angry.
⑤ If you speak too fast, Mike will not understand you.

15 다음 문장에서 어법상 <u>어색한</u> 부분을 찾아 바르게 고쳐 문장을 다시 쓰시오.

> If Mary will sleep early, we will go to the theater at night.

➡ _____

_____

16 다음 중 어법상 <u>틀린</u> 것은?

① Did you feel the train stopping?

② I heard this song sung on TV.

③ I saw a horse run on the road.

④ Nobody noticed you leave the classroom.

⑤ I heard your number calling out a few minutes ago.

17 다음 문장에서 어법상 <u>어색한</u> 곳을 찾아 바르게 고쳐 쓰시오.

(1) I watched the tree cutting down.

_____ ➡ _____

(2) I saw something to burn.

_____ ➡ _____

18 다음 중 밑줄 친 부분의 쓰임이 <u>다른</u> 하나는?

① I don't know <u>if</u> he will come soon.

② Can you tell me <u>if</u> the test is on Friday?

③ He wanted to know <u>if</u> she had a broken bone.

④ Do you know <u>if</u> he will have dinner with us?

⑤ I will go out <u>if</u> it is fine tomorrow.

[19~22] 다음 글을 읽고, 물음에 답하시오.

(①) One day, Sheila saw Max sitting under the desk. (②) "@What's wrong?" asked Sheila. She looked at him closely and found a bad cut on his leg. (③) She took him to the animal hospital. (④) The doctor said, "ⓑHe will get better if he will get enough rest. Keep him inside for a week." (⑤)

19 위 글의 ①~⑤ 중 다음 문장이 들어갈 알맞은 곳은?

> He was making a strange sound.

①   ②   ③   ④   ⑤

20 위 글의 밑줄 친 @와 바꿔 쓸 수 <u>없는</u> 것은?

① What's the matter?

② Is anything wrong?

③ What's wrong with you?

④ What happened?

⑤ Why are you so scared?

21 위 글의 밑줄 친 ⓑ에서 어법상 <u>틀린</u> 부분을 고쳐 문장을 다시 쓰시오.

➡ _____

22 위 글에서 다음 영영풀이에 해당하는 단어를 찾아 쓰시오.

> as many or as much as is needed or wanted

➡ _____

[23~26] 다음 글을 읽고, 물음에 답하시오.

"Ding-Dong." _____ ⓐ _____ Ryan heard the doorbell ring, he ran to the door and opened it. "Bear, you're back!" Ryan cried. Max jumped up into Ryan's arms.

" _____ ⓑ _____ me guess," said Sheila. "Your cat comes home only in the evenings, doesn't he?" Ryan nodded. "And you lost him last Friday, _____ ⓒ _____ ?" Sheila said. "Yes! How did you know?" said Ryan. "Because this is my cat, _____ ⓓ _____ , and he usually comes to my home only during the day."

23 위 글의 빈칸 ⓐ에 들어갈 알맞은 것은?

① If   ② Since
③ Though   ④ When
⑤ Because

24 위 글의 빈칸 ⓑ에 들어갈 알맞은 것은?

① Be   ② Don't
③ Have   ④ Let
⑤ Let's

25 위 글의 빈칸 ⓒ에 알맞은 부가의문문을 쓰시오.

➡ _____

26 위 글의 빈칸 ⓓ에 알맞은 것은?

① also   ② too
③ then   ④ either
⑤ neither

[27~30] 다음 글을 읽고, 물음에 답하시오.

That night, at Ryan's house, there was no Bear. Ryan checked outside, _____ ⓐ _____ he couldn't find him. He made posters and put ⓑ them up around town. A third night passed. Still no Bear.

When Sheila was walking near her house, she saw a poster _____ ⓒ _____ the lost cat. She read it closely, and her eyes got big. "This cat looks exactly like Max. It's so strange." She hurried home. "Come on, Max! Let's go!" She took him to the address _____ ⓓ _____ the poster.

27 위 글의 빈칸 ⓐ에 알맞은 것은?

① but   ② so   ③ and
④ for   ⑤ when

28 위 글의 밑줄 친 ⓑ가 가리키는 것을 찾아 영어로 쓰시오.

➡ _____

29 위 글의 빈칸 ⓒ와 ⓓ에 알맞은 말이 바르게 짝지어진 것은?

① of – in   ② for – from
③ at – with   ④ about – on
⑤ on – over

30 위 글의 내용과 일치하지 <u>않는</u> 것은?

① Ryan put up posters around town to find Bear.
② The third night passed, but Bear still did not show up.
③ Sheila saw a poster about a lost cat on her way to school.
④ Sheila was surprised to see that the cat on the poster looked like Max.
⑤ Sheila took Max to the address on the poster.

Lesson 3

Be Active, Be Safe!

 의사소통 기능

- 경험 묻고 답하기
  A: Have you ever heard of beach safety rules?
  B: Yes, I have.

- 금지하기
  You shouldn't swim too far.

언어 형식

- 현재완료
  I **have visited** a selfie museum before.

- 접속사 though
  Though the boys are not really riding horses, it looks like they are.

Words & Expressions

Key Words

- **active**[金ktiv] 형 활동적인, 활발한
- **actually**[金ktʃuəli] 부 실제로, 정말로
- **advice**[ædváis] 명 조언(= tip), 충고
- **alone**[əlóun] 부 혼자
- **back**[bæk] 명 등 부 뒤로, 다시
- **balance**[bǽləns] 명 균형, 평형
- **beach**[bi:tʃ] 명 해변, 바닷가
- **before**[bifɔ́:r] 전 ~하기 전에 부 전에, 앞에
- **behind**[biháind] 전 ~ 뒤에 부 뒤에
- **bite**[bait] 동 (이빨로) 물다, 베어 물다
- **careful**[kɛ́ərfəl] 형 조심하는, 주의 깊은(↔ careless)
- **chat**[tʃæt] 명 담소, 이야기 동 담소하다, 채팅하다
- **climb**[klaim] 동 오르다, 올라가다
- **climber**[kláimər] 명 등반가
- **close**[klouz] 형 가까운, 친한
- **clothes**[klouz] 명 옷, 의복
- **create**[kriéit] 동 창조하다, 만들다
- **dangerous**[déindʒərəs] 형 위험한(↔ safe)
- **direction**[dirékʃən] 명 방향, (주로 복수로) 지시
- **during**[djúəriŋ] 전 ~ 동안[내내], (~하는) 중에
- **else**[els] 부 또[그 밖의] 다른, 다른
- **even**[í:vən] 부 ~도[조차], 심지어
- **exist**[igzíst] 동 ~에 있다, 존재하다
- **far**[fa:r] 형 먼(↔ near) 부 멀리
- **festival**[féstəvəl] 명 축제
- **figure**[fígjər] 명 인물, 모습
- **following**[fálouiŋ] 형 다음에 나오는, 그 다음의
- **fun**[fʌn] 명 재미 형 재미있는
- **grass**[græs] 명 풀, 잔디
- **harmony**[há:rməni] 명 조화, 화합
- **helmet**[hélmit] 명 헬멧
- **information**[ìnfərméiʃən] 명 정보
- **join**[dʒɔin] 동 함께하다, 가입하다

- **kind**[kaind] 명 종류
- **later**[léitər] 부 나중에, 후에
- **loose**[lu:s] 형 헐거워진, 풀린, 헐렁한(↔ tight)
- **mirror**[mírə] 명 거울
- **museum**[mju:zí:əm] 명 박물관, 미술관
- **painter**[péintər] 명 화가, 칠장이
- **past**[pæst] 명 과거, 지난날
- **place**[pleis] 명 곳, 장소
- **pose**[pouz] 명 포즈[자세] 동 포즈[자세]를 취하다
- **practice**[prǽktis] 동 연습하다
- **princess**[prínsis] 명 공주(↔ prince)
- **probably**[prábəbli] 부 아마
- **push**[puʃ] 동 밀다(↔ pull)
- **real**[rí:əl] 형 진짜의, 현실적인
- **remember**[rimémbər] 동 기억하다(↔ forget)
- **ride**[raid] 동 타다
- **rock**[rak] 명 바위, 암석
- **rule**[ru:l] 명 규칙
- **safe**[seif] 형 안전한
- **safety**[séifti] 명 안전, 안전성
- **scenery**[sí:nəri] 명 경치, 풍경
- **search**[sə:rtʃ] 동 찾다, 수색하다
- **selfie**[selfi:] 명 셀피(스마트폰으로 찍은 자신의 사진)
- **sign**[sain] 명 표지판, 간판
- **skill**[skil] 명 기술, 기량
- **someday**[sʌmdei] 부 언젠가, 훗날
- **special**[spéʃəl] 형 특별한, 특수한(↔ general)
- **street**[stri:t] 명 길, 거리, 도로
- **teenage**[tineidʒ] 형 십대의
- **touch**[tʌtʃ] 동 만지다, 건드리다
- **trick**[trik] 명 비결, 요령, 속임수
- **without**[wiðáut] 전 ~ 없이, ~하지 않고
- **yet**[jet] 부 아직

Key Expressions

- **be good for** ~에 좋다
- **for example** 예를 들면, 예를 들어
- **for the first time** 처음으로
- **go up** 오르다
- **hang up** 전화를 끊다
- **hear of** ~에 대해 듣다

- **in front of** ~ 앞에
- **keep ~ in mind** ~을 명심하다, ~을 잊지 않다
- **look at** ~을 보다
- **lots of** 수많은
- **make noise** 떠들다, 소란 피우다
- **over there** 저쪽에, 저기에서

Word Power

※ 명사에 형용사 어미 -ful 이 붙으면 형용사가 되는 단어들이 있다. 이때 철자가 변하는 것도 있으므로 주의해야 한다.

- ☐ **care**(주의) – **careful**(주의 깊은)
- ☐ **help**(도움) – **helpful**(도움이 되는)
- ☐ **color**(색) – **colorful**(다채로운)

- ☐ **sorrow**(슬픔) – **sorrowful**(슬픈)
- ☐ **beauty**(아름다움) – **beautiful**(아름다운)
- ☐ **harm**(해) – **harmful**(해로운)

English Dictionary

☐ **active** 활동적인, 활발한
→ moving around a lot or doing a lot of things
많이 움직이거나 많은 일을 하는

☐ **advice** 조언, 충고
→ what you think someone should do in a particular situation
당신이 생각하기에 누군가가 특정한 상황에서 해야 하는 것

☐ **beach** 해변, 바닷가
→ an area of sand or stones beside the sea
바다 옆의 모래나 돌이 있는 지역

☐ **careful** 조심하는, 주의 깊은
→ giving serious attention to what you are doing, in order to avoid harm, damage, or mistakes
해나 손상 또는 실수를 피하기 위해 당신이 하고 있는 일에 심각한 주의를 기울이는

☐ **chat** 담소[이야기]하다
→ to talk to each other in an informal and friendly way
비형식적이고 친근한 태도로 서로 이야기하다

☐ **climb** 오르다, 올라가다
→ to move towards the top of something such as a tree, mountain, or ladder
나무, 산, 사다리 같은 것의 꼭대기 쪽으로 움직이다

☐ **clothes** 옷, 의복
→ the things that people wear, such as shirts, coats, trousers, and dresses
셔츠, 코트, 바지, 드레스와 같은 사람들이 입는 옷들

☐ **dangerous** 위험한
→ able or likely to hurt or harm you
당신을 다치게 하거나 해를 끼칠 수 있는

☐ **helmet** 헬멧
→ a hat made of a strong material which you wear to protect your head
당신의 머리를 보호하기 위해 당신이 착용하는 튼튼한 재료로 만들어진 모자

☐ **mirror** 거울
→ a flat piece of glass which reflects light, so that when you look at it you can see yourself reflected in it
빛을 반사하는 납작한 유리조각으로, 그것을 볼 때 당신은 그 안에 반사된 자신을 볼 수 있다

☐ **painter** 화가
→ an artist who paints pictures
그림을 그리는 화가

☐ **past** 과거
→ the time before the present, and the things that have happened
현재 이전의 시간과 현재까지 일어난 일들

☐ **princess** 공주
→ a female member of a royal family, usually the daughter of a king or queen
왕가의 여성 일원으로 왕이나 왕비의 딸

☐ **push** 밀다
→ to use force to make something move away from you or away from its previous position
어떤 것을 당신에게서 멀어지게 하거나 이전의 위치에서 멀어지게 하기 위해 힘을 사용하다

☐ **ride** 타다
→ sit on a horse or bike and control its movements
말이나 자전거에 앉아 그 움직임을 통제하다

☐ **rock** 바위, 암석
→ the hard substance which the Earth is made of
지구가 구성되어 있는 단단한 물질

☐ **street** 길, 도로
→ a road in a city, town, or village, usually with houses along it
대개 그것을 따라 집들이 있는, 도시나 읍 또는 마을의 도로

☐ **tcenage** 십대의
→ aged between thirteen and nineteen years old
열세 살에서 열아홉 살 사이의 나이인

01 다음 중 나머지 넷을 대표할 수 있는 단어는?

① coats   ② shirts
③ trousers   ④ dresses
⑤ clothes

02 다음 빈칸에 알맞은 말이 바르게 짝지어진 것은?

> • We met _____ the first time five years ago.
> • What are you looking _____?

① of – at   ② for – at
③ on – for   ④ at – for
⑤ to – over

03 다음 영영풀이에 해당하는 단어로 알맞은 것은?

> a road in a city, town, or village, usually with houses along it

① yard   ② ground
③ stadium   ④ street
⑤ garden

서답형

04 다음 짝지어진 두 단어의 관계가 같도록 빈칸에 알맞은 말을 쓰시오.

> remember : forget = careful : _____

05 다음 우리말에 맞게 빈칸에 알맞은 것은?

> 저기에 주유소가 있네요.
> ➡ There's a gas station _____ there.

① up   ② on
③ over   ④ from
⑤ along

서답형

06 다음 영영풀이에 해당하는 단어를 쓰시오.

> aged between thirteen and nineteen years old

➡ _____

서답형

07 다음 우리말에 맞게 빈칸에 알맞은 말을 쓰시오.

> 교실 안에서 소란 피우지 말아요.
> ➡ Don't _____ noise in the classroom.

08 다음 빈칸에 공통으로 알맞은 것은?

> • He took some coins out _____ his pocket.
> • We had lots _____ fun at the party.

① in   ② of
③ up   ④ about
⑤ at

01 다음 짝지어진 두 단어의 관계가 같도록 빈칸에 알맞은 말을 쓰시오.

(1) care : careful = color : _____

(2) actor : actress = prince : _____

(3) dangerous : _____ = strong : weak

02 다음 우리말에 맞게 빈칸에 알맞은 말을 쓰시오.

(1) 예를 들면, 인도에서는 어떤 동전은 사각형이다.

➡ In India, _____ _____, some coins have square sides.

(2) 우리는 Sarah의 파티에서 아주 재미있게 보냈다.

➡ We _____ a lot of _____ at Sarah's party.

(3) 너의 앨범을 보아도 좋으니?

➡ May I _____ _____ your album?

03 다음 빈칸에 들어갈 알맞은 말을 〈보기〉에서 골라 쓰시오.

┌─── 보기 ───┐

even someday during following

(1) My grandfather died _____ the war.

(2) _____ a child can understand it.

(3) Answer the _____ questions.

(4) I hope you will visit here _____.

04 다음 괄호 안의 단어를 문맥에 맞게 고쳐 쓰시오.

(1) It's not _____ raining now. (actual)

(2) Follow your doctor's _____. (advise)

(3) The traffic here is very _____ for children. (danger)

05 다음 빈칸에 알맞은 말을 〈보기〉에서 골라 쓰시오.

┌─── 보기 ───┐

keep in mind look for
hear of good at

(1) Nancy is _____ dancing.

(2) I was surprised to _____ his failure.

(3) You had better _____ your dog at the park.

(4) Please _____ what I said.

06 다음 영영풀이에 해당하는 단어를 주어진 철자로 시작하여 쓰시오.

(1) r_____ : sit on a horse or bike and control its movements

(2) c_____ : to move towards the top of something such as a tree, mountain, or ladder

(3) p_____ : the time before the present, and the things that have happened

교과서

Conversation

① 경험 묻고 답하기

A Have you heard of beach safety rules? 넌 해변 안전 규칙에 대해 들어본 적 있니?
B Yes, I have. 응, 있어.

■ **경험 묻기**
'~해 본 적이 있나요?'라고 과거부터 현재까지의 상대방의 경험을 물을 때는 「Have you (ever)+과거분사 ~?」 형태인 현재완료 의문문으로 물을 수 있다.

경험에 대한 물음에 대답하기

- 경험이 있으면 Yes, I have. / Yes, I have+과거분사. 등으로 한다.
- 경험이 없으면 No, I haven't. / No, I have never+과거분사. / Not yet. 등으로 한다.

- A: Have you ever seen a bear? 너는 곰을 본 적이 있니?
  B: Yes, I have. / No, I haven't. 응, 본 적이 있어. / 아니, 본 적이 없어.

cf. '~에 가본 적 있니?'라고 묻는 표현은 Have you ever gone to ~?가 아니라 Have you ever been to ~?임에 주의한다.

- have been to: ~에 가본 적이 있다(경험) / ~에 다녀 왔다(완료)

- have gone to: ~에 가버렸다(결과)

■ 경험을 나타낼 때는 다음과 같은 부사(구)를 함께 쓰는 경우가 많다. ever(지금까지), never(~한 적 없는), before(이전에), once(한 번), twice(두 번), 「숫자+times(~번, ~차례)」, many times(여러 번), often(자주)

- She has made fried rice many times. 그녀는 볶음밥을 여러 번 만든 적이 있다.

핵심 Check

1. 다음 우리말과 일치하도록 빈칸에 알맞은 말을 쓰시오.

(1) **A:** _____ you ever _____ *Les Miserables*? (너 '레미제라블' 읽어 봤니?)

   B: Yes, I _____ . (응, 있어.)

(2) **A:** _____ you _____ of Rock Boys? (너는 Rock Boys에 대해 들어 봤니?)

   B: No, I _____ . (아니, 나는 못 들어 봤어.)

② 금지하기

> **A** May I swim in this lake? 이 호수에서 수영해도 돼요?
>
> **B** Okay, Mike, but you shouldn't swim too far. 그래, Mike야, 하지만 너무 멀리까지 수영하면 안 된다.

■ You should not ~은 '~하면 안 돼.'라는 뜻으로 어떤 일을 하지 말아야 함을 이야기할 때 사용하는 금지의 표현이다.

- A: Tony, you should not run when you cross the street. Tony, 길을 건널 때 뛰면 안 돼.
  B: Okay, I see. 응, 알겠어.

■ You should ~는 '~해야 한다.'라는 뜻으로 상대방에게 제안이나 충고를 할 때 사용한다.

- You should have breakfast every day. 너는 매일 아침식사를 해야 한다.

금지를 나타내는 표현

- You should not take pictures at the museum. 박물관에서는 사진을 찍으면 안 돼.

  = You must not take pictures at the museum.

  = Don't[Do not] take pictures at the museum.

  = You can't take pictures at the museum.

  = You'd better not take pictures at the museum.

  = You're not supposed[allowed/permitted] to take pictures at the museum.

핵심 Check

2. 다음 우리말과 일치하도록 빈칸에 알맞은 말을 쓰시오.

(1) **A:** Excuse me. You _____ _____ your cell phone here.

(실례합니다. 이곳에서 휴대 전화를 사용하시면 안 됩니다.)

B: Oh, I'm _____. (오, 죄송합니다.)

(2) **G:** Wait. _____ jump into the water yet. (잠깐만. 아직 물속으로 뛰어들지 마.)

B: Why _____? (왜 안 돼?)

G: You _____ swim without a life jacket. (구명조끼 없이 수영하면 안 돼.)

(3) **A:** I _____ I've got a _____. (나 감기에 걸린 것 같아.)

B: You'd _____ _____ _____ cold water. (너는 차가운 물을 마시지 않는 게 좋겠어.)

A. Start Off - Listen & Talk B

B: ❶Have you heard of bird watching?

M: Sure. I tried it when I was a child.

B: That's nice. ❷Actually, I'm doing it for the first time this Saturday.

M: Are you? You should bring warm clothes and something to eat.

B: Okay. What else should I keep in mind?

M: ❸You shouldn't make any noise when you watch the birds.

B: I'll keep that in mind. Thanks, Dad.

B: 새 관찰에 대해 들어보셨어요?
M: 물론이지. 어렸을 때 해 봤어.
B: 그거 멋지네요. 사실, 전 이번 주 토요일에 처음으로 그것을 할 거예요.
M: 그래? 넌 따뜻한 옷과 먹을 것을 가져가야 해.
B: 알았어요. 그 밖에 또 무엇을 명심해야 하나요?
M: 너는 새들을 관찰할 때 아무 소리도 내지 말아야 해.
B: 그것을 명심할게요. 고마워요, 아빠.

❶ Have you heard of ~?: ~에 대해 들어본 적이 있나요?(경험을 묻는 표현)
❷ I'm doing ~: 현재진행형이 미래의 일을 나타내는 경우 / it=bird watching
❸ You shouldn't ~: 너는 ~해서는 안 된다(금지를 나타내는 표현)

Check(√) True or False

(1) The boy's father tried bird watching when he was a child.　　T ☐ F ☐

(2) The boy may make some noise when he watches the birds.　　T ☐ F ☐

 B. Step Up - Real-life Scene

Video Chat with Minjun from Jeju

A: Hello, Somin! It's me! Can you see me?

B: Oh, hi, Minjun! What's up?

A: ❶This is so cool, isn't it? We can video chat on the phone! Have you heard of Jeju *Olle*?

B: Yes, I have. I really want to go there someday.

A: ❷Guess what? I'm on it now. Actually, I'm going to go up Seongsan Ilchulbong now.

B: That's great!

A: ❸Don't hang up. Enjoy the beautiful scenery with me.

B: Be careful! ❹You shouldn't use your cell phone while you're walking.

A: Oh, right. Thank you. I'll send you photos later.

제주에서 걸려 온 민준과의 화상 채팅
A: 여보세요, 소민아! 나야! 나를 볼 수 있니?
B: 오, 안녕, 민준아! 무슨 일이니?
A: 이거 정말 멋지지 않니? 전화로 화상 채팅도 할 수 있어! 너 제주 올레에 대해 들어 본 적이 있니?
B: 응, 있어. 나는 언젠가 꼭 가 보고 싶어.
A: 그거 알아? 나 지금 올레에 있어. 사실은, 지금 성산 일출봉에 올라가려고 해.
B: 멋지다!
A: 끊지 마. 나와 함께 아름다운 경치를 즐겨.
B: 조심해! 걸을 때는 휴대폰을 사용해서는 안 돼.
A: 아, 맞다. 고마워. 나중에 사진 보여 줄게.

❶ This is so cool, isn't it?: 부가의문문에서 This는 it으로 받는다.
❷ Guess what?: 있잖아., 그거 알아?(어떤 것에 대해 말을 꺼낼 때 쓰는 관용적인 표현)
❸ hang up: 전화를 끊다
❹ while: ~하는 동안

Check(√) True or False

(3) Minjun is going to go up Seongsan Ilchulbong.　　T ☐ F ☐

(4) Somin wants to enjoy the beautiful scenery with Minjun.　　T ☐ F ☐

Get Ready -2

1. G: Look at that boy. He's great.
   B: ❶He's riding an MTB. Do you know about it?
   G: No. What is it?
   B: ❷It's a special bike for riding on a mountain.
2. G: Wait. Don't jump into the water yet.
   B: ❸Why not?
   G: You shouldn't swim without a life jacket.
3. G: Look at the beautiful flowers over there! ❹ I'd like to take a selfie in front of them.
   B You shouldn't go over there.
   G: Oh, okay.
4. B: ❺I want to watch the birds in the trees.
   G: You shouldn't go up too close to the birds.
   B: All right, thanks.

❶ MTB: mountain bike
❷ for riding a mountain: 산을 오르기 위한
❸ Why not?=Why can't I jump into the water?
❹ I'd like to: ~하고 싶다 / in front of: ~ 앞에서
❺ in the trees: 나무에 있는(the birds를 수식하는 형용사구)

 Start Off - Listen & Talk A

1. G: ❶Dad, have you ever heard of Kim Soyun, the rock climber?
   M: Yes, I've seen her on TV.
   G: ❷She's teaching rock climbing at a camp this Saturday. I want to join the camp.
   M: Okay, Miso, but you shouldn't climb up too high.
   G: ❸All right. Thanks, Dad.
2. G: Have you heard of Rock Boys?
   M: No, I haven't.
   G: ❹It's my favorite band. There's a concert this Saturday. Can I go?
   M: Okay, Minju, but you shouldn't come home too late.
   G: All right. Thanks, Dad.

❶ Kim Soyun과 the rock climber는 동격 관계이다.
❷ She's teaching=She will teach
❸ All right.: 알았어요., 좋아요.
❹ It = Rock Boys

 Start Off - Speak Up - Look and talk.

A: Have you heard of safety rules for mountain hiking?
B: Yes. But I don't know much about them.
A: ❶Let me tell you one. You shouldn't walk too fast.
B: ❷Oh, I see.

❶ Let me ~: 내가 ~할게 / one=a safety rule for mountain hiking
❷ I see.: 알겠어.

 Express Yourself A

1. G: Have you heard of Elvis Presley?
   B: No, I haven't. Who is he?
   G: He was a famous American singer and actor. ❶We can see a figure of Elvis here.
   B: ❷Sounds interesting. I want to take pictures with it.
   G: Okay. Let's go.
2. W: You shouldn't take selfies here. Van Gogh's painting is behind you.
   B: Don't worry, Mom. It's not his real painting. ❸So I can take selfies in front of it.
   W: Really? Sounds interesting. Can I take selfies here, too?
   B: ❹Why not?

❶ a figure of Elvis: Elvis의 모형
❷ Sounds interesting.: 흥미롭게 들린다.
❸ so: 그래서 / in front of: ~의 앞에
❹ Why not?: 물론 되고말고.

 Check Yourself - Listen & Speak

1. B: Wait, Jimin.
   G: Why?
   B: Look at that sign. ❶You shouldn't take a photo here.
   G: Oh, okay.
2. B: ❷This place is good for bike riding.
   G: Look, there's a sign. You shouldn't ride a bike here.

❶ You shouldn't ~.: 너는 ~ 해서는 안 된다.
❷ be good for: ~에 좋다

● 다음 우리말과 일치하도록 빈칸에 알맞은 말을 쓰시오.

 해석

Get Ready - 2

1. G: Look _____ that boy. He's _____.

   B: He's _____ an MTB. Do you _____ about it?

   G: No. _____ is it?

   B: It's a _____ bike for _____ on a mountain.

2. G: Wait. _____ jump _____ the water yet.

   B: _____ not?

   G: You _____ swim _____ a life jacket. _____ it _____.

3. G: _____ at the beautiful flowers _____ there! I'd _____ to _____ a selfie in _____ of them.

   B: You shouldn't go _____ there.

   G: Oh, _____.

4. B: I want to _____ the birds _____ the trees.

   G: You shouldn't go _____ too close to the _____.

   B: All _____, thanks.

1. G: 저 소년을 봐. 그는 대단하다.
   B: 그는 MTB를 타고 있어. 넌 그것에 대해 알고 있니?
   G: 아니. 그게 뭐지?
   B: 그것은 산에서 타는 특별한 자전거야.

2. G: 기다려. 아직 물속으로 뛰어들지 마.
   B: 왜 안 돼?
   G: 구명조끼 없이 수영하면 안 돼. 이것을 입어.

3. G: 저기 있는 아름다운 꽃들을 봐! 그 꽃들 앞에서 셀피를 찍고 싶어.
   B: 거기 가면 안 돼.
   G: 아, 알았어.

4. B: 나는 나무에 있는 새들을 보고 싶어.
   G: 새들에게 너무 가까이 가지 마.
   B: 알았어, 고마워.

Start Off - Listen & Talk A

1. G: Dad, have you _____ heard of Kim Soyun, the rock _____?

   M: Yes, I've _____ her _____ TV.

   G: She's teaching rock _____ at a _____ this Saturday. I want to _____ the camp.

   M: Okay, Miso, _____ you shouldn't _____ up too high.

   G: All _____. Thanks, Dad.

2. G: _____ you _____ of Rock Boys?

   M: No, I _____.

   G: It's my _____ band. There's a _____ this Saturday. _____ I go?

   M: Okay, Minju, but you _____ come home _____ late.

   G: All _____. Thanks, Dad.

1. G: 아빠, 암벽 등반가인 김소윤에 대해 들어 본 적 있으세요?
   M: 응, TV에서 봤어.
   G: 그녀가 이번 토요일에 캠프에서 암벽 등반을 가르쳐요. 저는 캠프에 참가하고 싶어요.
   M: 알았어, 미소야, 하지만 너무 높이 올라가면 안 돼.
   G: 알았어요. 고마워요, 아빠.

2. G: Rock Boys에 대해 들어보셨어요?
   M: 아니, 듣지 못했다.
   G: 그건 제가 제일 좋아하는 밴드에요. 이번 토요일에 콘서트가 있어요. 가도 돼요?
   M: 좋아, 민주야, 하지만 너무 늦게 집에 오면 안 돼.
   G: 알았어요. 고마워요, 아빠.

Start Off - Listen & Talk B

B: Have you _____ _____ bird watching?

M: Sure. I tried it _____ I was a child.

B: That's nice. Actually, I'm _____ it _____ the first time this Saturday.

M: Are you? You _____ _____ warm clothes and something to eat.

B: Okay. What else _____ I _____ in mind?

M: You _____ make any noise _____ you watch the birds.

B: I'll keep that _____ _____. Thanks, Dad.

Step Up - Real-life Scene

Video Chat with Minjun from Jeju

A: Hello, Somin! _____ me! Can you _____ me?

B: Oh, _____, Minjun! What's _____?

A: This is so cool, _____ it? We can video _____ on the phone! Have you _____ of Jeju *Olle*?

B: Yes, I have. I really _____ to go there someday.

A: _____ what? I'm on it now. Actually, I'm _____ to go up Seongsan Ilchulbong now.

B: That's _____!

A: Don't hang _____. Enjoy the beautiful _____ with me.

B: _____ careful! You shouldn't _____ your cell phone _____ you're walking.

A: Oh, _____. _____ you. I'll _____ you photos _____.

Express Yourself A

1. **G:** Have you _____ of Elvis Presley?

   B: No, I _____. _____ is he?

   G: He was a famous American _____ and _____. We can see a _____ of Elvis here.

   B: _____ interesting. I want to _____ pictures with it.

   G: Okay. _____ go.

2. **W:** You shouldn't _____ selfies here. Van Gogh's _____ is behind you.

   B: Don't _____, Mom. It's not his _____ painting. _____ I can take selfies in _____ of it.

   W: Really? Sounds interesting. _____ I take _____ here, too?

   B: Why _____?

해석

B: 새 관찰에 대해 들어보셨어요?
M: 물론이지. 어렸을 때 해 봤어.
B: 그거 멋지네요. 사실, 전 이번 주 토요일에 처음으로 그것을 할 거예요.
M: 그래? 넌 따뜻한 옷과 먹을 것을 가져가야 해.
B: 알았어요. 그 밖에 또 무엇을 명심해야 하나요?
M: 너는 새들을 관찰할 때 아무 소리도 내지 말아야 해.
B: 그것을 명심할게요. 고마워요, 아빠.

제주에서 걸려온 민준과의 화상 채팅
A: 여보세요, 소민아! 나야! 나를 볼 수 있니?
B: 오, 안녕, 민준아! 무슨 일이니?
A: 이거 정말 멋지지 않니? 전화로 화상 채팅도 할 수 있어! 너 제주 올레에 대해 들어 본 적이 있니?
B: 응, 있어. 나는 언젠가 꼭 가 보고 싶어.
A: 그거 알아? 나 지금 올레에 있어. 사실은, 지금 성산 일출봉에 올라가려고 해.
B: 멋지다!
A: 끊지 마. 나와 함께 아름다운 경치를 즐겨.
B: 조심해! 걸을 때는 휴대폰을 사용해서는 안 돼.
A: 아, 맞다. 고마워. 나중에 사진 보내줄게.

1. G: 엘비스 프레슬리에 대해 들어 본 적 있니?
   B: 아니, 없어. 그는 누구인데?
   G: 그는 유명한 미국 가수이자 배우였어. 우리는 여기서 엘비스의 모형을 볼 수 있어.
   B: 재미있을 것 같다. 그것과 함께 사진을 찍고 싶어.
   G: 좋아. 가자.
2. W: 넌 여기서 셀피를 찍으면 안 돼. 반 고흐의 그림이 네 뒤에 있어.
   B: 엄마, 걱정하지 마세요. 그건 그의 진짜 그림이 아니에요. 그래서 그 앞에서 셀피를 찍을 수 있어요.
   W: 정말이지? 재미있겠다. 나도 여기서 셀피를 찍을 수 있을까?
   B: 물론이죠.

01 다음 두 문장의 의미가 같은 뜻이 되도록 빈칸에 알맞은 말을 쓰시오.

> You shouldn't swim too far.
> = You had _____ _____ swim too far.

02 다음 대화의 밑줄 친 우리말에 해당하는 것은?

> A: Jina, I'm going to Vietnam with my family this winter.
> B: Wow. That sounds like fun.
> A: 너 전에 그곳에 가 본 적 있니?
> B: No, I haven't.

① Were you there before?
② Had you been there before?
③ Have you been there before?
④ Have you gone there before?
⑤ When did you go there before?

03 다음 대화의 빈칸에 알맞은 것은?

stay 머물다
inside 안에

> A: It's going to rain. _____
> B: Okay. If it rains, I'll stay inside.

① You will go outside.   ② You shouldn't go outside.
③ You would go outside.   ④ You might not go outside.
⑤ You can go outside.

04 다음 대화의 빈칸에 알맞은 것은?

> A: Have you eaten this food?
> B: No, _____.

① I don't   ② I didn't
③ I haven't   ④ I hadn't
⑤ I have eaten it

01 다음 대화의 밑줄 친 부분과 바꿔 쓸 수 있는 것은?

> A: Is it okay to eat chocolate?
> B: Sure, but don't eat too much.

① you can eat too much
② you don't have to eat too much
③ you won't eat too much
④ you should eat too much
⑤ you'd better not eat too much

서답형

02 다음 대화의 빈칸에 알맞은 말을 쓰시오.

> A: _____ you _____ tried kimchi, Ann?
> B: Yes, I _____. It was very tasty.

03 다음 대화를 의미가 통하도록 알맞게 배열한 것은?

> (A) Why not?
> (B) Really? Sounds interesting. Can I take selfies here, too?
> (C) You shouldn't take selfies here. Van Gogh's painting is behind you.
> (D) Don't worry, Mom. It's not his real painting. So I can take selfies in front of it.

① (A) – (D) – (B) – (C)
② (B) – (C) – (D) – (A)
③ (C) – (D) – (B) – (A)
④ (D) – (B) – (C) – (A)
⑤ (D) – (C) – (B) – (A)

04 다음 대화의 빈칸에 가장 알맞은 것은?

> A: Have you seen the movie, *Avatar*, Sue?
> B: No, I haven't. _____
> A: Yes, it's my favorite movie.

① Do you?   ② Will you?
③ Had you?   ④ Have you?
⑤ What do you want to see?

05 다음 대화의 빈칸에 들어갈 말로 알맞은 것은?

> A: You should not _____.
> B: Oh, I'm sorry. I won't do that again.

① walk to school
② recycle plastics
③ reuse gift boxes
④ leave computers on
⑤ take a short shower

[06~09] 다음 대화를 읽고, 물음에 답하시오.

> G: Dad, have you ever ⓐhear of Kim Soyun, the rock climber?
> M: Yes, I've seen her ⓑ TV.
> G: She's teaching rock climbing at a camp this Saturday. I want to join the camp.
> M: Okay, Miso, but you ⓒ climb up too high.
> G: All right. Thanks, Dad.

서답형

06 위 대화의 밑줄 친 ⓐ를 알맞은 형으로 고치시오.

➡ _____

07 위 대화의 빈칸 ⓑ에 알맞은 것은?

① in   ② on   ③ by

④ with   ⑤ from

08 위 대화의 빈칸 ⓒ에 들어갈 수 <u>없는</u> 것은? (2개)

① don't   ② must not

③ need not   ④ shouldn't

⑤ had better not

09 위 대화의 내용과 일치하지 <u>않는</u> 것은?

① 미소의 아버지는 김소윤을 알고 있다.

② 김소윤은 암벽 등반가이다.

③ 김소윤은 캠프에서 이번 토요일에 암벽 등반을 강의할 것이다.

④ 미소는 캠프에 참여하기를 원한다.

⑤ 미소의 아버지는 미소가 암벽 등반하는 것을 반대했다.

[10~14] 다음 대화를 읽고, 물음에 답하시오.

A: Hello, Somin! It's me! Can you see me?

B: Oh, hi, Minjun! What's _____ⓐ_____?

A: This is so cool, _____ⓑ_____? We can video chat on the phone! Have you heard of Jeju *Olle*?

B: Yes, I have. I really want to go there someday.

A: Guess what? I'm on it now. ⓒ<u>Actual</u>, I'm going to go up Seongsan Ilchulbong now.

B: That's great!

A: Don't hang up. Enjoy the beautiful _____ⓓ_____ with me.

B: Be careful! You shouldn't use your cell phone while you're walking.

A: Oh, right. Thank you. I'll send you photos later.

10 위 대화의 빈칸 ⓐ에 알맞은 것은?

① on   ② to

③ at   ④ up

⑤ for

11 위 대화의 빈칸 ⓑ에 알맞은 것은?

① is this   ② does it

③ isn't this   ④ doesn't it

⑤ isn't it

서답형

12 위 대화의 밑줄 친 ⓒ를 알맞은 어형으로 고치시오.

➡ _____

서답형

13 위 대화의 빈칸 ⓓ에 다음 영영풀이에 해당하는 단어를 쓰시오.

> the land, water, or plants that you can see around you

➡ _____

14 위 대화를 읽고, 답할 수 <u>없는</u> 질문은?

① Can Somin see Minjun?

② Where is Minjun now?

③ Where does Somin want to go someday?

④ Is Minjun going to go up Seongsan Ilchulbong?

⑤ How many photos will Minjun send to Somin?

[01~02] 다음 대화의 빈칸에 알맞은 말을 쓰시오.

01

> G: Wait. Don't jump into the water yet.
> B: Why not?
> G: You _____ swim without a life jacket.

02 중요

> G: _____ you ever slept in a tent?
> B: No, I _____.

03 다음 대화를 의미가 통하도록 알맞게 배열하시오.

> (A) It's a special bike for riding on a mountain.
> (B) Look at that boy. He's great.
> (C) He's riding an MTB. Do you know about it?
> (D) No. What is it?

➡ _____

[04~06] 다음 대화를 읽고, 물음에 답하시오.

> G: Have you heard of Rock Boys?
> M: ⓐNo, I have.
> G: ⓑIt's my favorite band. There's a concert this Saturday. Can I go?
> M: Okay, Minju, ⓒ _____ you shouldn't come home too late.
> G: All right. Thanks, Dad.

04 중요 위 대화의 밑줄 친 ⓐ에서 어법상 어색한 것을 고치시오.

_____ ➡ _____

05 위 대화의 밑줄 친 ⓑ가 가리키는 것을 영어로 쓰시오.

➡ _____

06 위 대화의 빈칸 ⓒ에 알맞은 접속사를 쓰시오.

➡ _____

[07~08] 다음 대화를 읽고, 물음에 답하시오.

> G: Have you heard of Elvis Presley?
> B: No, I haven't. Who is he?
> G: He was a famous American singer and _____ⓐ_____. We can see a figure of Elvis here.
> B: Sounds interesting. I want to take pictures with ⓑit.
> G: Okay. Let's go.

07 중요 위 대화의 빈칸 ⓐ에 다음 정의에 해당하는 단어를 쓰시오.

> someone whose job is acting in plays or films

➡ _____

08 위 대화의 밑줄 친 ⓑ가 가리키는 것을 우리말로 쓰시오.

➡ _____

Grammar

1 현재완료

- I **have visited** a selfie museum before. 나는 전에 셀피 박물관을 방문한 적이 있다.
- **Have** you ever **heard** of beach safety rules? 너는 해변 안전 규칙에 대해 들어본 적이 있니?

■ **현재완료의 형태**
'have[has]+과거분사'의 형태를 취한다.

- It **has been** such a long time. 정말 오랜만이다.
- I **have had** many different jobs. 나는 많은 다양한 직업을 가져왔다.

cf. yesterday, two days ago, last Sunday 등과 같이 특정한 과거 시점을 나타내는 표현이 오면 현재
완료시제로 쓰지 않고 과거시제로 써야 한다.

- I read the book yesterday.　　(○) 나는 어제 그 책을 읽었다.
- I have read the book yesterday. (✕)

■ **현재완료의 용법**
현재완료는 경험, 계속, 완료, 결과의 용법이 있다.

분류	용법	예문
경험	과거부터 현재까지의 경험 before, ever, never, often 등과 쓰임	I **have** never **been** to Rome. (나는 로마에 가 본 적이 없다.)
계속	과거의 일이 지금까지 계속됨 'since+특정 시점', 'for+기간' 등과 쓰임	I **have known** him since I was a little child. (나는 어릴 때부터 그를 알아 왔다.)
완료	과거에 시작된 일이 이제 막 완료됨 just, already, yet 등과 쓰임	He **has** just **finished** his homework. (그는 방금 숙제를 끝냈다.)
결과	과거의 일이 현재의 결과를 가져옴 '~해서 (지금) …하다'의 의미임	They **have gone** to Madrid. (그들은 마드리드에 가고 없다.)

■ **현재완료의 부정문**
'have[has]와 과거분사 사이에 not을 넣는다.

- He **has not written** the letter yet. 그는 아직 그 편지를 쓰지 않았다.

■ **현재완료의 의문문**
'Have[Has]+주어+과거분사 ~?'의 형태를 취한다.

- **Have** you ever **seen** a lion? 너는 사자를 본 적이 있니?

핵심 Check

1. 다음 괄호 안에서 알맞은 것을 고르시오.

(1) Ann has just (did / done) her homework.

(2) They (have / do) not (ate / eaten) the pizza.

(3) He (lived / has lived) in this town since he was seven.

(4) I have known her (for / since) three years.

❷ 접속사 though

> • **Though** there's a fire, you can be safe. 비록 화재가 나도 너는 안전할 수 있다.
>
> • **Though** the boys are not riding horses, it looks like they are.
>   비록 그 소년들은 말을 타고 있지 않지만, 말을 타고 있는 것처럼 보인다.
>
> • **Though** it was raining, the children played outside.
>   비록 비가 오고 있었지만 아이들은 밖에서 놀았다.

■ 접속사 though는 '비록 ~이지만'의 의미로 사용되며 양보의 부사절을 이끄는 접속사이다.

  • **Though** it was cold, she wasn't wearing a coat. 비록 날씨가 추웠지만, 그녀는 코트를 입고 있지 않았다.

  • **Though** I'm on a diet, I'll eat every hamburger here.
    비록 나는 다이어트를 하고 있지만, 여기에 있는 모든 햄버거를 먹겠다.

■ though 대신 although나 even though를 써도 같은 의미가 된다.

  • **Though** they are so poor, they seem happy. 그들은 아주 가난하지만, 행복해 보인다.
    = **Alhough** they are so poor, they seem happy.
    = **Even though** they are so poor, they seem happy.

  • **Though** you do not like it, you must do it. 너는 그것을 좋아하지 않아도 해야 한다.
    = **Alhough** you do not like it, you must do it.
    = **Even though** you do not like it, you must do it.

■ 종속접속사 though 대신 등위접속사 but을 써서 같은 뜻의 문장으로 바꿔 쓸 수 있다.

  • **Though** I like tennis, I'm not very good at it. 나는 테니스를 좋아하지만, 그것을 별로 잘하지 못한다.
    = I like tennis, **but** I'm not very good at it. 나는 테니스를 좋아한다. 그러나 그것을 별로 잘하지 못한다.

핵심 Check

2. 다음 괄호 안에서 알맞은 것을 고르시오.

(1) (Though / Because) they were rich, they weren't very happy.

(2) (As / Though) the man was very old, he was strong.

(3) (If / Though) I like baseball, I am not a good player.

(4) (Although / While) it was cold, Frank didn't wear a coat.

Grammar 시험대비 기본평가

01 다음 괄호 안에서 알맞은 것을 고르시오.

> reach 도착하다

(1) Jane (was / has been) busy since last week.

(2) How often have you (gone / been) to the United States?

(3) He (has finished / finished) reading a book two hours ago.

(4) He (has just finished / just finishes) his homework.

(5) We (arrived / have arrived) here yesterday.

(6) When (have you reached / did you reach) here?

02 다음 문장에서 어법상 어색한 것을 찾아 고쳐 쓰시오.

> thin 마른

(1) Because Jenny is so thin, she is strong.

_____ ➡ _____

(2) We lost the game since everyone played well.

_____ ➡ _____

(3) As the sun was shining, it wasn't very warm.

_____ ➡ _____

03 다음 괄호 안에 주어진 단어를 어법상 알맞은 형태로 바꾸어 문장을 다시 쓰시오.

> sick 아픈
> newspaper 신문

(1) He (be) sick in bed since last Friday.

➡ _____

(2) How long (you know) Miss Smith?

➡ _____

(3) (you ever read) the Christmas Carol?

➡ _____

(4) My father (not read) the newspaper yet.

➡ _____.

중요
01 다음 두 문장을 한 문장으로 만들 때 빈칸에 알맞은 것은?

> I moved here two years ago. I still live here.
> ➡ I _____ here for two years.

① live
② lived
③ will live
④ am living
⑤ have lived

[02~03] 다음 문장의 빈칸에 알맞은 것을 고르시오.

02
> _____ the car is old, it still runs well.

① As
② If
③ Unless
④ Because
⑤ Though

중요
03
> Ted is hungry because he _____ nothing since this morning.

① eat
② eats
③ ate
④ has eaten
⑤ had eaten

서답형
04 다음 빈칸에 공통으로 알맞은 말을 쓰시오.

> • _____ the service was slow, the waiters were kind.
> • His speech was very good. It was a little too long, _____.

서답형
05 다음 빈칸에 공통으로 알맞은 말을 쓰시오.

> • Sorry to _____ kept you waiting. I _____ been to the station.
> • We _____ known each other since our childhood.

중요
06 다음 문장의 빈칸에 들어갈 수 없는 것은? (2개)

> _____ I met the girl once, I can't remember her name.

① Whether
② Though
③ Although
④ As though
⑤ Even though

07 다음 문장의 빈칸에 알맞지 않은 것은?

> They have been to England _____.

① once
② twice
③ before
④ never
⑤ many times

서답형
08 다음 우리말과 일치하도록 주어진 단어를 바르게 배열하시오.

> 비록 교통체증이 심했지만 우리는 제시간에 도착했다.
> (we, was, the, on, traffic, time, though, heavy, arrived).

➡ _____

_____

09 다음 괄호 안에 주어진 단어를 어법상 바르게 쓴 것은?

> I know some good restaurants here because I (live) in this town for five years.

① live   ② lived

③ is living   ④ have lived

⑤ had lived

10 다음 우리말과 같은 뜻이 되도록 빈칸에 알맞은 것은?

> 내일 비가 올지라도, 나는 집에 있지 않을 것이다.
> ➡ _____ it rains tomorrow, I won't stay home.

① As   ② Since

③ While   ④ Although

⑤ Because

서답형

11 다음 빈칸에 알맞은 말을 쓰시오.

> My mother has gone shopping. She is _____ here.

12 다음 두 문장의 뜻이 같도록 할 때 빈칸에 알맞은 것은?

> Though Mike likes dogs, his wife doesn't.
> ➡ Mike likes dogs, _____ his wife doesn't.

① and   ② so

③ but   ④ for

⑤ because

서답형

13 다음 두 문장의 의미가 같도록 빈칸에 알맞은 말을 쓰시오.

> We have been married for ten years.
> ➡ Ten years have passed _____ we got married.

14 다음 문장의 빈칸에 가장 알맞은 것은?

> _____, I tried not to fall asleep.

① Although I was sleepy

② Though I tried my best

③ Even though we played well

④ Although my family was poor

⑤ Even though my sister was young

15 다음 대화의 빈칸에 알맞은 것은?

> A: Have you ever heard the news?
> B: No, I _____ the news.

① heard   ② have not heard

③ was not heard   ④ did not hear

⑤ had not heard

서답형

16 다음 문장의 밑줄 친 부분을 어법에 맞도록 고쳐 문장을 다시 쓰시오.

> <u>While</u> he played well, he lost the soccer game.

➡ _____

_____

17 다음 두 문장의 뜻이 같도록 할 때 빈칸에 알맞은 것은?

> Though the boy was sick, he went to school.
> ➡ _____ the boy was sick, he went to school.

① So　　　　　② Such
③ Although　　④ Therefore
⑤ Whatever

18 다음 중 어법상 <u>어색한</u> 문장은?

① I have had a fever since last Friday.
② Two years have passed since I came here.
③ We have known each other for many years.
④ He has been seventy years old when he died.
⑤ It has been a long time since I saw you.

19 다음 중 문맥상 <u>어색한</u> 문장은?

① I waited until he came.
② He couldn't buy the camera though he had no money.
③ He has played soccer since he was a boy.
④ Although he was tired, he studied hard.
⑤ Though I was tired, I had to do my homework.

서답형
20 다음 대화의 빈칸에 알맞은 말을 쓰시오.

> A: How long has she been absent from school?
> B: She _____ _____ _____ from school since this Wednesday.

서답형
21 다음 빈칸에 공통으로 알맞은 말을 쓰시오.

> • Have you done your homework _____?
> • She hasn't come home _____.

22 다음 빈칸에 알맞은 것을 순서대로 바르게 짝지은 것은?

> • _____ they were poor, they were very happy.
> • _____ you are late, you must hurry up.

① If – Because
② Though – As
③ When – Even though
④ Unless – Since
⑤ Because – Although

23 다음 밑줄 친 부분의 쓰임이 나머지 넷과 <u>다른</u> 하나는?

① I <u>have seen</u> the movie before.
② My uncle <u>has</u> never <u>lived</u> in China before.
③ How many times <u>have</u> they <u>been</u> to England?
④ Mr. Smith <u>has gone</u> to Berlin on business.
⑤ Sora and Minjun <u>have been</u> to America once.

01 다음 우리말과 같도록 문장을 완성하시오.

(1) 그들은 이미 프로젝트를 끝마쳤다.
➡ They _____ already _____ the project.

(2) 그는 아직 런던에서 돌아오지 않았다.
➡ He _____ _____ _____ from London yet.

(3) 죄송하지만, 그녀는 회의에 가고 없습니다.
➡ I'm sorry, but she _____ _____ _____ a meeting.

02 다음 두 문장의 뜻이 같도록 빈칸에 알맞은 말을 쓰시오.

(1) Even though Kathy couldn't concentrate well, she did her homework.
➡ _____ Kathy couldn't concentrate well, she did her homework.

(2) She doesn't come, but I will finish the work.
➡ I will finish the work _____ she doesn't come.

03 다음 문장에서 어법상 어색한 것을 찾아 바르게 고쳐 쓰시오.

(1) She has gone to Bangladesh last Friday.
_____ ➡ _____

(2) My father hasn't left Seoul already.
_____ ➡ _____

04 다음 빈칸에 공통으로 알맞은 말을 쓰시오.

- _____ he is rich, he has few friends.
- I didn't buy that cap; I liked it, _____.

05 다음 문장에서 어법상 어색한 것을 찾아 바르게 고쳐 쓰시오.

(1) Jack has seen the koala last year.
_____ ➡ _____

(2) The weather is good for ten days.
_____ ➡ _____

06 다음 주어진 단어를 바르게 배열하여 문장을 완성하시오.

(1) (Italy / many / he / to / been / times / has)
➡ _____

(2) (very / days / I / busy / these / been / have)
➡ _____

(3) (have / Paris / before / I / visited / never)
➡ _____

07 다음 보기에서 알맞은 말을 골라 빈칸에 쓰시오.

┌─── 보기 ───┐
since / if / that / though /
because / before
└──────────┘

(1) Take a bath _____ you go to bed.

(2) He was so tired _____ he went to bed early.

(3) Mike has known Mary _____ he was a baby.

(4) Tim couldn't finish the project _____ he was very busy.

(5) I won't go on a picnic _____ it rains tomorrow.

(6) Ann isn't good at swimming _____ she lives near the river.

08 다음 문장에서 어법상 어색한 부분을 바르게 고쳐 문장을 다시 쓰시오.

(1) I have been to London four years ago.
  ➡ _____

(2) When have you seen a white lion?
  ➡ _____

(3) I have often played with her when I was a child.
  ➡ _____

(4) He has been ill in bed last month.
  ➡ _____

09 다음 문장에서 어법상 어색한 부분을 고치시오.

(1) Because the boy is so young, he is very wise.
  _____ ➡ _____

(2) I failed the exam as I studied hard.
  _____ ➡ _____

10 다음 주어진 단어를 이용하여 우리말을 영어로 옮기시오.

(1) 그는 1970년 이래로 뉴욕에서 살았다.
  (live, since)
  ➡ _____

(2) 너는 이 이야기를 벌써 다 읽었니?
  (finish, this, story, yet)
  ➡ _____

(3) 나는 그 영화를 한 번 본 적이 있다.
  (see, once)
  ➡ _____

11 다음 우리말과 뜻이 같도록 빈칸에 주어진 철자로 시작하는 알맞은 말을 쓰시오.

┌────────────────────────┐
비록 과일이 건강에 좋다고 해도, 그는 과일을 좋아하지 않는다.

➡ A_____ fruit is good for his health, he doesn't like it.
└────────────────────────┘

A Selfie Show

Have you ever heard of a "selfie"? When you take a photograph
of yourself, it's a selfie. The students from Minji's photo club have
searched for information about selfies for one month. Here are some of
their presentations about selfies.

Selfies in the Past – Minji

Did people in the past take selfies? Though it wasn't easy at that
time, the answer is yes. Look at this photo of Princess Anastasia. She
used a mirror to take a picture of herself. She looks nervous. Can you
guess why? Well, I think it was her first selfie. And it was probably the
world's first teenage selfie ever.

Fun Places for Selfies – Yunho

You can take selfies at world-famous places like Big Ben and the
Leaning Tower of Pisa. To take great pictures, just do fun poses and
use camera tricks.

You can also visit special museums to take fun selfies. For example,
there is a famous selfie museum in the Philippines. It has special spots
to take selfies. You can touch the paintings and even step inside them.
Look at the following pictures. Though the boys are not really riding
horses, it looks like they are. Though the man is just holding a big
brush, it looks like he is painting the Mona Lisa. Selfie museums exist
in Korea, too.

selfie 셀피
search 찾다
presentation 프레젠테이션, 발표
past 과거
nervous 초조한
mirror 거울
probably 아마
teenage 10대의
fun 재미; 재미있는
pose 포즈, 자세
for example 예를 들면
touch 손을 대다
exist 있다, 존재하다

● 다음 문장이 본문의 내용과 일치하면 T, 일치하지 않으면 F를 쓰시오.

1 Minji belongs to the photo club. ☐

2 People in the past didn't take selfies. ☐

3 Princess Anastasia took pictures of herself several times. ☐

4 There is a famous selfie museum in the Philippines. ☐

5 There aren't any selfie museums in Korea. ☐

I have visited one in Chuncheon before. Why don't you go there
경험을 나타내는 현재완료   ~하지 그래요?
yourself?
주어를 강조하는 재귀대명사

Selfie Safety – Jihun

These selfies look great, but were they a good idea? I don't think
look+형용사: ~해 보이다   = these selfies
so. They don't look safe. You should take special care when you take
= they were a good idea   ~ 해야 한다   ~할 때 - 때를 나타내는 접속사
selfies in the wild or at high places like these. A monkey could bite you
야생에서   ~와 같은   ~할 수 있다: 가능성
at any time, or you could fall. Here are some safety tips:
some+복수 명사

1. Don't take selfies while you're walking.
   부정명령문   ~하는 동안 -때를 나타내는 접속사

2. Do not pose with or near wild animals.
   = Don't: 부정명령문   ~ 가까이에서: 전치사

3. Never take selfies in dangerous places.
   결코 ~하지 마라: 부정명령문

Selfies for a Better School Life – Soyun

I think we can use selfies to make a better school life. We can do good
앞에 접속사 that이 생략   good의 비교급
things at school and take selfies. Then we can post the photos on our
do와 함께 can에 연결됨
school website. I've watered the plants and flowers at school for one
= have watered: 계속을 나타내는 현재완료
month. I've also helped the teacher at the school library many times.
경험을 나타내는 현재완료   여러 번
Look at my selfies of those things. How about joining me to create a
How about -ing?: ~하는 게 어때?
better school life?

before 전에
safety 안전
safe 안전한
special 특별한
care 관심
wild 야생: 야생의
place 장소, 곳
bite 물다
at any time 언제고
while: ~하는 동안
dangerous 위험한
post 올리다, 게재하다
plant 식물
create 창조하다, 만들어 내다

확인문제

● 다음 문장이 본문의 내용과 일치하면 T, 일치하지 <u>않으면</u> F를 쓰시오.

1 There is a selfie museum in Chuncheon. ☐

2 You should take special care when you take selfies in dangerous places. ☐

3 A monkey doesn't bite you. ☐

4 Selfies can be used to make a better school life. ☐

5 Soyun has watered the plants and flowers at school for a year. ☐

● 우리말을 참고하여 빈칸에 알맞은 말을 쓰시오.

1 _____ you ever _____ of a "selfie"?

2 When you _____ a photograph of _____, it's a selfie.

3 The students from Minji's photo _____ have searched _____ information about selfies _____ one month.

4 _____ are some of their presentations _____ selfies.

5 Did _____ in the past _____ selfies?

6 _____ it wasn't easy at that time, the _____ is yes.

7 _____ at this photo of Princess Anastasia.

8 She _____ a mirror to take a picture of _____.

9 She looks _____.

10 Can you guess _____?

11 Well, I _____ it was her _____ selfie.

12 And it was _____ the world's first _____ selfie ever.

13 You can _____ selfies at world-famous places _____ Big Ben and the Leaning Tower of Pisa.

14 To _____ great pictures, just do fun poses and use camera _____.

15 You can _____ visit special museums to take _____ selfies.

16 For _____, there is a _____ selfie museum in the Philippines.

17 It has _____ spots to _____ selfies.

18 You can _____ the paintings and _____ step inside them.

19 Look at the _____ pictures.

20 _____ the boys are not really _____ horses, it looks _____ they are.

1	여러분은 "셀피"에 대해 들어 본 적이 있나요?
2	여러분 자신의 사진을 찍을 때 그것이 셀피에요.
3	민지의 사진 동아리 학생들은 한 달 동안 셀피에 대한 정보를 찾았습니다.
4	여기 셀피에 대한 그들의 발표 내용이 있습니다.
5	과거의 사람들은 셀피를 찍었나요?
6	그 때는 셀피를 찍는 것이 쉽지는 않았지만. 답은 '그렇다'입니다.
7	아나스타샤 공주의 이 사진을 보세요.
8	그녀는 거울을 사용하여 자신의 사진을 찍었습니다.
9	그녀는 긴장되어 보입니다.
10	왜인지 추측할 수 있나요?
11	글쎄. 나는 그것이 그녀의 첫 번째 셀피였다고 생각해요.
12	그리고 그것은 아마도 세계 최초의 10대 소녀의 셀피였을 거예요.
13	여러분은 빅벤과 피사의 사탑과 같은 세계적으로 유명한 장소에서 셀피를 찍을 수 있습니다.
14	멋진 사진을 찍기 위해서, 단지 재미있는 포즈를 취하고 카메라 기술을 이용하세요.
15	여러분은 또한 재미있는 셀피를 찍기 위해 특별한 박물관을 방문할 수 있습니다.
16	예를 들어, 필리핀에는 유명한 셀피 박물관이 있습니다.
17	그곳은 셀피를 찍기 위한 특별한 장소들이 있습니다.
18	여러분은 그림들을 만질 수 있고 심지어 그림들 안으로 들어갈 수도 있어요.
19	다음 사진들을 보세요.
20	비록 그 소년들은 말을 타고 있는 것은 아니지만, 말을 타고 있는 것처럼 보입니다.

21 Though the man is _____ holding a big _____, it looks like he is _____ the Mona Lisa.

22 Selfie museums _____ in Korea, too.

23 I have _____ one in Chuncheon _____.

24 Why _____ you go there _____?

25 These selfies _____ great, _____ were they a good idea?

26 I don't think _____.

27 They don't look _____.

28 You _____ take special care _____ you take selfies in the wild or at high _____ like these.

29 A monkey _____ bite you at any _____, or you could _____.

30 Here are some _____ tips:

31 1. Don't _____ selfies _____ you're walking.

32 2. Do not _____ with or near _____ animals.

33 3. _____ take selfies in dangerous _____.

34 I think we can _____ selfies to make a _____ school life.

35 We can do good _____ at school and _____ selfies.

36 Then we can _____ the photos on our school _____.

37 I've _____ the plants and flowers at _____ for one month.

38 I've _____ helped the teacher _____ the school library many _____.

39 Look _____ my selfies of _____ things.

40 How _____ joining me to _____ a better school life?

21 비록 그 남자는 단지 커다란 붓을 잡고 있지만, 모나리자를 그리고 있는 것처럼 보입니다.

22 한국에도 셀피 박물관이 있습니다.

23 나는 전에 춘천에 있는 한 박물관을 방문한 적이 있습니다.

24 여러분도 직접 그곳에 가는 게 어때요?

25 이 셀피들은 멋져 보이지만, 그것들은 좋은 생각이었나요?

26 난 그렇게 생각하지 않아요.

27 그것들은 안전해 보이지 않습니다.

28 여러분은 야생이나 이와 같이 높은 곳에서 셀피를 찍을 때 특별한 주의를 기울여야 합니다.

29 원숭이가 언제든지 당신을 물거나 또는 당신은 떨어질 수 있습니다.

30 여기 몇 가지 안전 수칙이 있습니다.

31 1. 걸으면서 셀피를 찍지 마세요.

32 2. 야생 동물들과 함께 또는 가까이에서 포즈를 취하지 마세요.

33 3. 위험한 곳에서는 절대 셀피를 찍지 마세요.

34 나는 우리가 더 나은 학교생활을 만들기 위해 셀피를 이용할 수 있다고 생각해요.

35 우리는 학교에서 좋은 일을 할 수 있고 셀피를 찍을 수도 있습니다.

36 그리고 나서 우리는 학교 웹사이트에 사진을 올릴 수 있어요.

37 나는 한 달 동안 학교에서 식물과 꽃에 물을 주었습니다.

38 나는 또한 학교 도서관에서 선생님을 여러 번 도왔습니다.

39 그런 것들에 대한 내 셀피를 보세요.

40 저와 함께 더 나은 학교생활을 만들어 보는 건 어떨까요?

● 우리말을 참고하여 본문을 영작하시오.

1 여러분은 "셀피"에 대해 들어 본 적이 있나요? 여러분 자신의 사진을 찍을 때 그것이 셀피에요.

➡ _____

2 민지의 사진 동아리 학생들은 한 달 동안 셀피에 대한 정보를 찾았습니다.

➡ _____

3 여기 셀피에 대한 그들의 발표 내용이 있습니다.

➡ _____

4 과거의 사람들은 셀피를 찍었나요?

➡ _____

5 그 때는 셀피를 찍는 것이 쉽지는 않았지만. 답은 '그렇다'입니다.

➡ _____

6 아나스타샤 공주의 이 사진을 보세요. 그녀는 거울을 사용하여 자신의 사진을 찍었습니다.

➡ _____

7 그녀는 긴장되어 보입니다. 왜인지 추측할 수 있나요?

➡ _____

8 글쎄, 나는 그것이 그녀의 첫 번째 셀피였다고 생각해요.

➡ _____

9 그리고 그것은 아마도 세계 최초의 10대 소녀의 셀피였을 거예요.

➡ _____

10 여러분은 빅벤과 피사의 사탑과 같은 세계적으로 유명한 장소에서 셀피를 찍을 수 있습니다.

➡ _____

11 멋진 사진을 찍기 위해서, 단지 재미있는 포즈를 취하고 카메라 기술을 이용하세요.

➡ _____

12 여러분은 또한 재미있는 셀피를 찍기 위해 특별한 박물관을 방문할 수 있습니다.

➡ _____

13 예를 들어, 필리핀에는 유명한 셀피 박물관이 있습니다.

➡ _____

14 그곳은 셀피를 찍기 위한 특별한 장소들이 있습니다.

➡ _____

15 여러분은 그림들을 만질 수 있고 심지어 그림들 안으로 들어갈 수도 있어요.

➡ _____

16 다음 사진들을 보세요.

➡ _____

17 비록 그 소년들은 말을 타고 있는 것은 아니지만, 말을 타고 있는 것처럼 보입니다.

➡ _____

18 비록 그 남자는 단지 커다란 붓을 잡고 있지만, 모나리자를 그리고 있는 것처럼 보입니다.

➡ _____

19 한국에도 셀피 박물관이 있습니다. 나는 전에 춘천에 있는 한 박물관을 방문한 적이 있습니다.

➡ _____

20 여러분도 직접 그곳에 가는 게 어때요? 이 셀피들은 멋져 보이지만, 그것들은 좋은 생각이었나요?

➡ _____

21 난 그렇게 생각하지 않아요. 그것들은 안전해 보이지 않습니다.

➡ _____

22 여러분은 야생이나 이와 같이 높은 곳에서 셀피를 찍을 때 특별한 주의를 기울여야 합니다.

➡ _____

23 원숭이가 언제든지 당신을 물거나 또는 당신은 떨어질 수 있습니다.

➡ _____

24 여기 몇 가지 안전 수칙이 있습니다.

➡ _____

25 걸으면서 셀피를 찍지 마세요.

➡ _____

26 야생 동물들과 함께 또는 가까이에서 포즈를 취하지 마세요.

➡ _____

27 위험한 곳에서는 절대 셀피를 찍지 마세요.

➡ _____

28 나는 우리가 더 나은 학교생활을 만들기 위해 셀피를 이용할 수 있다고 생각해요.

➡ _____

29 우리는 학교에서 좋은 일을 할 수 있고 셀피를 찍을 수도 있습니다.

➡ _____

30 그리고 나서 우리는 학교 웹사이트에 사진을 올릴 수 있어요.

➡ _____

31 나는 한 달 동안 학교에서 식물과 꽃에 물을 주었습니다.

➡ _____

32 나는 또한 학교 도서관에서 선생님을 여러 번 도왔습니다.

➡ _____

33 그런 것들에 대한 내 셀피를 보세요.

➡ _____

34 저와 함께 더 나은 학교생활을 만들어 보는 건 어떨까요?

➡ _____

[01~04] 다음 글을 읽고, 물음에 답하시오.

A Selfie Show

 Have you ever heard of a "selfie"? ⓐ you take a photograph of yourself, it's a selfie. The students from Minji's photo club have searched   ⓑ   information about selfies   ⓒ   one month. ⓓHere are some of their presentations about selfies.

01 위 글의 빈칸 ⓐ에 알맞은 것은?

① What ② How
③ When ④ Because
⑤ While

02 위 글의 빈칸 ⓑ와 ⓒ에 공통으로 알맞은 것은?

① of ② to
③ with ④ for
⑤ along

03 위 글의 밑줄 친 ⓓ와 문형이 같은 것은?

① Mike likes music very much.
② The man is strong.
③ Birds fly in the sky.
④ The news made her glad.
⑤ Jane sent me a birthday card.

04 위 글의 뒤에 이어질 내용으로 가장 알맞은 것은?

① 셀피의 의미
② 셀피의 유래
③ 셀피를 찍는 이유
④ 민지의 사진 동아리 학생들이 찍은 여러 가지 셀피들
⑤ 민지의 사진 동아리 학생들이 모은 셀피에 대한 여러 가지 정보

[05~07] 다음 글을 읽고, 물음에 답하시오.

Selfies in the Past – Minji

 Did people in the past take selfies? (①) Though it wasn't easy at that time, the answer is yes. (②) ⓐShe used a mirror to take a picture of her. (③) She looks nervous. (④) ⓑCan you guess why? (⑤) Well, I think it was her first selfie. And it was probably the world's first teenage selfie ever.

05 위 글의 ①~⑤ 중 다음 주어진 문장이 들어갈 알맞은 곳은?

> Look at this photo of Princess Anastasia.

①   ②   ③   ④   ⑤

서답형

06 위 글의 밑줄 친 ⓐ에서 어법상 어색한 것을 고치시오.

_____ ➡ _____

서답형

07 위 글의 밑줄 친 ⓑ를 why의 의미가 구체적으로 드러나도록 우리말로 옮기시오.

➡ _____

[08~11] 다음 글을 읽고, 물음에 답하시오.

(①) You can take selfies at world-famous places ⓐlike Big Ben and the Leaning Tower of Pisa. (②) To take great pictures, just do fun poses and use camera tricks. (③)

You can also visit special museums to take fun selfies. (④) _____ⓑ_____ , there is a famous selfie museum in the Philippines. (⑤)

08 위 글의 ①~⑤ 중 다음 주어진 문장이 들어갈 알맞은 곳은?

> It has special spots to take selfies.

①   ②   ③   ④   ⑤

09 위 글의 밑줄 친 ⓐ와 같은 용법으로 쓰인 것은?

① Do you like apples?
② I like to watch baseball on TV.
③ How do you like this movie?
④ I like to walk in the park on Sundays.
⑤ I want to buy a hat like yours.

10 위 글의 빈칸 ⓑ에 알맞은 것은?

① However   ② For example
③ Therefore   ④ At last
⑤ As a result

11 위 글의 주제로 가장 알맞은 것은?

① 세계적으로 유명한 장소들
② 셀피를 찍는 요령
③ 셀피를 찍기 위한 재미있는 장소
④ 세계의 유명한 박물관들
⑤ 필리핀의 관광 명소

[12~15] 다음 글을 읽고, 물음에 답하시오.

You can touch the paintings and even step inside them. Look at the following pictures. __ⓐ__ the boys are not really riding horses, it looks like they are. __ⓑ__ the man is just holding a big brush, it looks like he is painting the Mona Lisa. Selfie museums ⓒare in Korea, too. I have visited one in Chuncheon before. __ⓓ__ don't you go there yourself?

12 위 글의 빈칸 ⓐ와 ⓑ에 공통으로 알맞은 것은? (2개)

① Though   ② If
③ When   ④ Although
⑤ Since

13 위 글의 밑줄 친 ⓒ와 바꿔 쓸 수 있는 것은?

① fix   ② join
③ exist   ④ stay
⑤ belong

서답형

14 위 글의 빈칸 ⓓ에 알맞은 말을 쓰시오.

➡ _____

15 위 글의 내용과 일치하지 않는 것은?

① 여러분은 그림들을 만질 수 있다.
② 소년들은 실제로 말을 타고 있다.
③ 남자는 모나리자를 그리고 있는 것처럼 보인다.
④ 셀피 박물관은 한국에도 있다.
⑤ 글쓴이는 춘천에 있는 셀피 박물관을 방문한 적이 있다.

[16~19] 다음 글을 읽고, 물음에 답하시오.

Selfie Safety - Jihun

(①) These selfies look great, ⓐ_____ were they a good idea? (②) I don't think so. (③) ⓑYou should take special care when you take selfies in the wild or at high places like these. (④) A monkey could bite you at any time, or you could fall. (⑤) Here are some safety tips:

1. Don't take selfies ⓒ_____ you're walking.
2. Do not pose with or near wild animals.
3. Never take selfies in dangerous places.

16 위 글의 ①~⑤ 중 다음 주어진 문장이 들어갈 알맞은 곳은?

> They don't look safe.

①   ②   ③   ④   ⑤

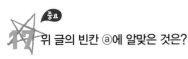

위 글의 빈칸 ⓐ에 알맞은 것은?

① and ② but
③ or ④ so
⑤ for

18 위 글의 밑줄 친 ⓑ를 우리말로 옮기시오.

➡ _____

_____

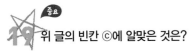

위 글의 빈칸 ⓒ에 알맞은 것은?

① if ② though
③ because ④ since
⑤ while

[20~24] 다음 글을 읽고, 물음에 답하시오.

Selfies for a Better School Life - Soyun

I think we can use selfies ⓐto make a better school life. We can do good things at school and take selfies. ⓑThen we can post the photos on our school website. I've watered the plants and flowers at school ⓒ_____ one month. I've also helped the teacher at the school library many times. Look at my selfies of those things. ⓓHow about joining me to create a better school life?

20 위 글의 밑줄 친 ⓐ와 같은 용법으로 쓰인 것은?

① My hope is to work as a doctor in Africa.
② It's time to go to bed now.
③ My job is to report the news.
④ The boys hoped to find the hidden treasure.
⑤ Kate went to a shopping mall to buy clothes.

서답형

21 위 글의 밑줄 친 ⓑ를 우리말로 옮기시오.

➡ _____

중요

위 글의 빈칸 ⓒ에 알맞은 것은?

① for ② during
③ from ④ since
⑤ while

서답형

23 위 글의 밑줄 친 ⓓ 대신 쓸 수 있는 것을 쓰시오.

➡ _____

24 위 글의 내용으로 보아 대답할 수 <u>없는</u> 질문은?

① What can Soyun use to make a better school life?

② Does Soyun take selfies at school?

③ Where can Soyun post the photos?

④ How long has Soyun watered the plants at school?

⑤ Why did Soyun help the teacher at the school library?

[25~26] 다음 글을 읽고, 물음에 답하시오.

A Selfie Show

Have you ever heard ___ⓐ___ a "selfie"? When you take a photograph ___ⓑ___ yourself, it's a selfie. The students from Minji's photo club ⓒ<u>have searched</u> for information about selfies for one month. Here are some of their presentations about selfies.

25 위 글의 빈칸 ⓐ와 ⓑ에 공통으로 알맞은 것은?

① of   ② for

③ about   ④ into

⑤ from

26 위 글의 밑줄 친 ⓒ와 용법이 같은 것은? (2개)

① I <u>have been</u> in this country since last month.

② Yumi <u>has seen</u> this movie many times.

③ Mike <u>has</u> just <u>cleaned</u> his room.

④ Lisa <u>has had</u> this cat for ten years.

⑤ She <u>has gone</u> out and this room is cold.

[27~30] 다음 글을 읽고, 물음에 답하시오.

Selfies in the Past - Minji

Did people in the past take selfies? ___ⓐ___ it wasn't easy at that time, the answer is yes. Look ___ⓑ___ this photo of Princess Anastasia. ⓒ그녀는 자신의 사진을 찍기 위해 거울을 사용했다. She looks nervous. Can you guess why? Well, I think it was her first selfie. And it was probably the world's first teenage selfie ever.

27 위 글의 빈칸 ⓐ에 알맞은 것은?

① If   ② For

③ Though   ④ When

⑤ Since

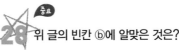
28 위 글의 빈칸 ⓑ에 알맞은 것은?

① at   ② in

③ to   ④ for

⑤ on

서답형
29 위 글의 밑줄 친 ⓒ를 주어진 단어를 이용하여 영어로 옮기시오.

(use, mirror, take, picture, herself)

➡ _____

30 위 글의 내용과 일치하지 <u>않는</u> 것은?

① 옛날 사람도 셀피를 찍었다.

② Anastasia 공주는 자신의 셀피를 찍었다.

③ Anastasia 공주는 종종 셀피를 찍었다.

④ Anastasia 공주는 초조해 보인다.

⑤ 민지는 Anastasia 공주가 찍은 이 셀피가 세계에서 십대의 첫 번째 셀피라고 생각한다.

[01~05] 다음 글을 읽고, 물음에 답하시오.

Fun Places for Selfies - Yunho

ⓐYou can take selfies at world-famous places like Big Ben and the Leaning Tower of Pisa. To take great pictures, just do fun ⓑ_____ and use camera tricks.

You can also visit special museums to take fun selfies. ⓒ_____ example, there is a famous selfie museum in the Philippines. ⓓIt has special spots to take selfies. You can touch the paintings and even step inside them.

01 위 글의 밑줄 친 ⓐ를 우리말로 옮기시오.

➡ _____

_____

02 위 글의 빈칸 ⓑ에 다음 정의에 해당하는 단어를 쓰시오. 필요하면 어형 변화를 할 것.

> a particular way that you stand, sit, or lie, for example when you are being photographed or painted

➡ _____

03 위 글의 빈칸 ⓒ에 알맞은 전치사를 쓰시오.

➡ _____

04 위 글의 밑줄 친 ⓓ가 가리키는 것을 우리말로 쓰시오.

➡ _____

05 Where can you go to take fun selfies? Answer in English.

➡ _____

[06~09] 다음 글을 읽고, 물음에 답하시오.

Look ⓐ_____ the following pictures. ⓑThough the boys are not really riding horses, it looks like they are. Though the man is just holding a big brush, it looks like he is painting the Mona Lisa. Selfie museums exist in Korea, too. I have visited ⓒone in Chuncheon before. Why don't you go there ⓓyou?

06 위 글의 빈칸 ⓐ에 알맞은 전치사를 쓰시오.

➡ _____

07 위 글의 밑줄 친 ⓑ를 우리말로 옮기시오.

➡ _____

_____

08 위 글의 밑줄 친 ⓒ가 가리키는 것을 영어로 쓰시오.

➡ _____

09 위 글의 밑줄 친 ⓓ를 알맞은 어형으로 고치시오.

➡ _____

[10~14] 다음 글을 읽고, 물음에 답하시오.

Selfie Safety - Jihun

These selfies look great, but were they a good idea? I don't think ⓐso. ⓑThey don't look safely. You should take special care when you take selfies in the wild or at high places like these. A monkey could bite you _____ⓒ_____ any time, or you could fall. Here are some safety tips:

1. Don't take selfies while you're walking.
2. Do not pose with or near wild animals.
3. Never take selfies in ⓓdanger places.

10 위 글의 밑줄 친 ⓐ가 가리키는 것을 영어로 쓰시오.

➡ _____

11 위 글의 밑줄 친 ⓑ에서 어법상 어색한 것을 고치시오.

_____ ➡ _____

12 위 글의 빈칸 ⓒ에 알맞은 전치사를 쓰시오.

➡ _____

13 위 글의 밑줄 친 ⓓ를 알맞은 어형으로 고치시오.

➡ _____

14 Why should you take special care when you take selfies in the wild or at high places? Answer in Korean.

➡ _____

[15~18] 다음 글을 읽고, 물음에 답하시오.

Selfie for a Better School Life - Soyun

ⓐI think we can use selfies to make a better school life. We can do good things at school and take selfies. Then we can post the photos on our school website. I've ⓑwater the plants and flowers at school _____ⓒ_____ one month. I've also helped the teacher at the school library many times. Look at my selfies of those things. How _____ⓓ_____ joining me to create a better school life?

15 위 글의 밑줄 친 ⓐ를 우리말로 옮기시오.

➡ _____
_____

16 위 글의 밑줄 친 ⓑ를 알맞은 어형으로 고치시오.

➡ _____

17 위 글의 빈칸 ⓒ에 알맞은 단어를 쓰시오.

➡ _____

18 위 글의 빈칸 ⓓ에 알맞은 단어를 쓰시오.

➡ _____

해석

Fun Time

A: You shouldn't push others when you go swimming.
~해서는 안 된다   = other people

B: Okay. Thank you for your advice.
thank A for B: A에 대해서 B에게 감사하다

구문해설 • push: 밀다   • advice: 충고

A: 수영하러 갈 때 다른 사람들을 밀면 안 돼.
B: 알았어. 충고 고마워.

Express Yourself - C

Have you heard of the pyramids in Egypt? Though I have never been to
= Although: 비록 ~이지만   ~에 다녀오다, ~에 가 본 적이 있다
Egypt before, I'm standing in front of a pyramid in this picture. I took it at the
현재진행형
selfie museum.

구문해설 • before: 전에   • in front of: ~ 앞에

여러분은 이집트의 피라미드에 대해 들어 본 적이 있나요? 나는 전에 이집트에 가 본 적이 없지만, 이 사진에서 나는 피라미드 앞에 서 있어요. 나는 이 사진을 셀피 박물관에서 찍었어요.

Project - Step 2

Fire Safety Rules

Have you heard of fire safety rules? Though there's a fire, you can be safe.

You shouldn't take the elevator. You should follow the teacher's directions.
should not의 축약형: 금지의 표현   = must: ~해야 한다

구문해설 • safety: 안전   • rule: 규칙, 수칙   • safe:: 안전한   • follow: 따르다   • direction: 지시

화재 안전 수칙

당신은 화재 안전 수칙에 대해 들어 본 적이 있습니까? 불이 났지만, 당신은 안전할 수 있어요. 엘리베이터를 타지 마세요. 선생님의 지시에 따라야 해요.

Link to the World

BMX Bike Riding

Riding a BMX bike is very exciting. You can try lots of skills. You can turn
동명사 주어   동명사 주어는 단수 취급 excited(X)   많은(=many = a lot of)
the bike freely and even jump with the bike. Though it's not easy, it's very
접 비록 ~이지만
exciting. You can start with standing skills. When you try standing skills,
접 ~할 때
balancing is very important. But be careful! You should wear a helmet and
명령문: 동사원형 ~
gloves. Also, you shouldn't go too fast when you're riding.
shouldn't+동사원형: ~해서는 안 된다

구문해설 • exciting: 흥미진진한, 신나는   • try: 시도하다   • freely: 자유롭게   • even: ~도[조차]
• easy: 쉬운   • skill: 기술   • balancing: 균형(잡기)   • important: 중요한
• careful: 조심하는, 주의 깊은

BMX 자전거 타기

BMX 자전거를 타는 것은 매우 흥미롭다. 여러분은 많은 기술을 시도할 수 있다. 여러분은 자전거를 자유롭게 돌릴 수 있고 심지어 자전거와 함께 점프할 수도 있다. 쉽지는 않지만, 매우 흥미롭다. 여러분은 서 있는 기술과 함께 시작하면 된다. 서 있는 기술을 시도할 때, 균형을 잡는 것이 매우 중요하다. 하지만 조심해라! 헬멧과 장갑을 착용해야 한다. 또한, 자전거를 탈 때는 너무 빨리 가지 말아야 한다.

01 다음 중 짝지어진 단어의 관계가 나머지와 <u>다른</u> 것은?

① loose – tight   ② advice – tip

③ kind – unkind   ④ birth – death

⑤ remember – forget

02 다음 빈칸에 들어갈 말로 적절하지 <u>않은</u> 것은?

- Kate didn't receive a letter from him _____.
- He turned and looked _____.
- He found the place _____ difficulty.
- What _____ did he say?

① else   ② without

③ other   ④ yet

⑤ back

03 다음 빈칸에 알맞은 단어를 쓰시오.

_____ : present : future

04 다음 문장의 빈칸에 알맞은 것은?

Vegetables are good _____ health.

① in   ② on

③ to   ④ for

⑤ with

05 다음 영영풀이에 해당하는 단어는?

an action that is intended to deceive someone

① object   ② joke

③ humor   ④ plan

⑤ trick

06 다음 문장의 빈칸에 공통으로 들어갈 말을 쓰시오.

- I went to London _____ the first time.
- I like juicy fruits, _____ example, watermelons.

07 다음 우리말에 맞게 빈칸에 알맞은 말을 쓰시오.

전화 끊기 전에 나도 그녀에게 말하게 해 줘.

➡ Let me speak to her before you _____ _____.

08 다음 대화의 빈칸에 알맞은 말을 쓰시오.

A: _____ you visited a selfie museum before?

B: Yes, I _____. It was very interesting.

09 다음 대화에서 밑줄 친 부분의 의도로 알맞은 것은?

> A: Can you take a picture of me?
> B: Sure.
> A: You'd better not use the flash here, David. The baby animals will wake up.
> B: I see.

① 질문하기
② 요청하기
③ 금지하기
④ 허락하기
⑤ 칭찬하기

[10~15] 다음 대화를 읽고, 물음에 답하시오.

> A: Hello, Somin! It's me! Can you see me?
> B: Oh, hi, Minjun! What's __ⓐ__?
> A: ⓑThis is so cool, isn't this? We can video chat on the phone! Have you heard of Jeju *Olle*?
> B: Yes, I have. I really want to go there someday.
> A: Guess __ⓒ__? I'm on it now. Actually, I'm going to go up Seongsan Ilchulbong now.
> B: That's great!
> A: Don't hang __ⓓ__. Enjoy the beautiful scenery with me.
> B: Be ⓔcare! You shouldn't use your cell phone __ⓕ__ you're walking.
> A: Oh, right. Thank you. I'll send you photos later.

10 위 대화의 빈칸 ⓐ와 ⓓ에 공통으로 들어갈 것은?

① on
② to
③ with
④ up
⑤ for

11 위 대화의 밑줄 친 ⓑ에서 어법상 어색한 것을 고치시오.

_____ ➡ _____

12 위 대화의 빈칸 ⓒ에 알맞은 말을 쓰시오.

➡ _____

13 위 대화의 밑줄 친 ⓔ를 알맞은 어형으로 고치시오.

➡ _____

14 위 대화의 빈칸 ⓕ에 알맞은 것은?

① if
② that
③ though
④ because
⑤ while

15 위 대화의 내용과 일치하지 <u>않는</u> 것은?

① 소민과 민준은 화상 채팅을 하고 있다.
② 소민은 제주 올레에 관해 들은 적이 있다.
③ 민준은 지금 성산 일출봉을 오르려고 한다.
④ 소민은 민준과 아름다운 경치를 즐길 것이다.
⑤ 민준은 나중에 소민에게 사진들을 보낼 것이다.

16 다음 문장의 빈칸에 알맞은 것은?

> I _____ never seen such a beautiful mountain.

① be　　　　② did
③ have　　　④ was
⑤ must

17 다음 문장의 빈칸에 알맞은 것은?

> _____ I live near the sea, I'm not good at swimming.

① As　　　　② Since
③ Unless　　④ Though
⑤ Because

18 다음 괄호 안에 주어진 단어를 어법상 바르게 쓴 것은?

> Jack (want) this video game since last year.

① wants　　　② want
③ wanted　　　④ has wanted
⑤ is wanting

19 다음 우리말과 일치하도록 주어진 단어를 바르게 배열하시오.

> 날씨가 추웠지만, 공원에는 사람들이 많이 있었다.
> (was, a lot of, cold, although, were, in the park, people, there, it).

➡ _____
_____

20 다음 중 어법상 어색한 것은?

① He has been sick in bed for a week.
② How long have you stayed in America?
③ I have climbed that mountain last week.
④ You have already walked 100 kilometers.
⑤ I have never been to America.

21 다음 우리말을 영어로 바르게 옮긴 것은?

> 그녀는 비록 돈이 많지만, 행복하지 않다.

① Since she has plenty of money, she is not happy.
② So she has plenty of money, she is not happy.
③ While she has plenty of money, she is not happy.
④ Although she has plenty of money, she is not happy.
⑤ Even although she has plenty of money, she is not happy.

22 다음 문장과 뜻이 가장 가까운 것은?

> Jack's father has gone to Rome.

① Jack's father is going to Rome.
② Jack's father went to Rome.
③ Jack's father went to Rome but he is here now.
④ Jack's father went to Rome and he isn't here now.
⑤ Jack's father went to Rome and he has just come back.

23 다음 〈보기〉의 밑줄 친 부분과 같은 용법으로 사용된 것은?

┌─── 보기 ───┐

Nancy has read the novel three times.

① I have lived here since last year.
② Ted has seen a panda before.
③ My mother has finished washing the dishes.
④ Jack has wanted to have a cat for a long time.
⑤ Mrs. Brown has lost her purse somewhere.

24 다음 중 문맥상 어색한 문장은?

① My mother often sings as she works.
② As it started to rain, we stopped playing baseball.
③ I went home early though I felt sick.
④ My camera can take good pictures though it is very old.
⑤ Though it was very warm, she didn't take off her coat.

25 다음 중 밑줄 친 부분의 쓰임이 올바르지 않은 것은?

① I've been to Madrid ten years ago.
② Kate has lived in Seoul for five years.
③ Mike has been sick in hospital since last Monday.
④ She has never seen such a beautiful lake.
⑤ How often have you been to Paris?

26 다음 두 문장의 의미가 같도록 빈칸에 알맞은 말을 쓰시오.

Though you fall from a high tree, I will catch you.

➡ _____ _____ you fall from a high tree, I will catch you.

Reading

[27~30] 다음 글을 읽고, 물음에 답하시오.

BMX Bike Riding

Riding a BMX bike is very ⓐexcite. You can try ⓑlots of skills. You can turn the bike freely and even jump with the bike. Though it's not easy, it's very exciting. You can start with standing skills. When you try standing skills, balancing is very important. But be careful. You should wear a helmet and gloves. Also, you shouldn't go too fast ⓒ_____ you're riding.

27 위 글의 밑줄 친 ⓐ를 알맞은 어형으로 고치시오.

➡ _____

28 위 글의 밑줄 친 ⓑ 대신 쓸 수 있는 것은?

① much   ② little
③ enough   ④ many
⑤ several

29 위 글의 빈칸 ⓒ에 알맞은 것은?

① if   ② because
③ when   ④ although
⑤ since

30 위 글의 내용으로 보아 알 수 <u>없는</u> 것은?

① BMX 자전거 타는 것은 재미있다.
② BMX 자전거는 값이 비싸다.
③ BMX 자전거를 타려면 많은 기술이 필요하다.
④ BMX 자전거를 타고 점프할 수 있다.
⑤ BMX 자전거를 탈 때는 안전에 주의해야 한다.

[31~35] 다음 글을 읽고, 물음에 답하시오.

You can also visit special museums to take fun selfies. ⓐ example, there is a famous selfie museum in the Philippines. ⓑIt has special spots to take selfies. You can touch the paintings and even step inside them. Look at the following pictures. Though the boys are not really riding horses, it looks like they are. ⓒThough the man is just holding a big brush, it looks like he is painting the Mona Lisa. Selfie museums exist in Korea, too. I have visited one in Chuncheon before. ⓓ don't you go there yourself?

31 위 글의 빈칸 ⓐ에 알맞은 것은?

① To   ② In
③ As   ④ For
⑤ With

32 위 글의 밑줄 친 ⓑ가 가리키는 것을 영어로 쓰시오.

➡ _____

33 위 글의 밑줄 친 ⓒ를 우리말로 옮기시오.

➡ _____
_____

34 위 글의 빈칸 ⓓ에 알맞은 것은?

① Why   ② How
③ What   ④ When
⑤ Where

35 위 글의 내용과 일치하지 <u>않는</u> 것은?

① 재미있는 셀피를 찍기 위해 특별한 박물관을 방문할 수 있다.
② 필리핀에는 유명한 셀피 박물관이 있다.
③ 필리핀의 셀피 박물관에서는 그림에 손을 댈 수 없다.
④ 한국에도 셀피 박물관이 있다.
⑤ 글쓴이는 춘천에 있는 셀피 박물관을 다녀온 적이 있다.

[36~37] 다음 글을 읽고, 물음에 답하시오.

Have you heard of fire ⓐsafe rules? ⓑ there's a fire, you can be safe. You shouldn't take the elevator. You should follow the teacher's directions.

36 위 글의 밑줄 친 ⓐ를 알맞은 형으로 고치시오.

➡ _____

37 위 글의 빈칸 ⓑ에 알맞지 <u>않은</u> 것은? (2개)

① Though   ② Since
③ Although   ④ As though
⑤ Even though

01 출제율 95%

다음 중 짝지어진 단어의 관계가 <u>다른</u> 것은?

① king : queen
② husband : wife
③ uncle : aunt
④ child : kid
⑤ prince : princess

02 출제율 90%

다음 빈칸에 공통으로 알맞은 것은?

- I was fond _____ sports when I was young.
- The bus stops right in front _____ our house.

① in
② of
③ from
④ with
⑤ onto

03 출제율 85%

다음 짝지어진 두 단어의 관계가 같도록 빈칸에 알맞은 말을 쓰시오.

advise : advice = arrive : _____

04 출제율 90%

다음 중 영영풀이가 <u>잘못된</u> 것은?

① alone: without any other people
② clothes: the things that people wear, such as shirts, coats, trousers, and dresses
③ painter: an artist who paints pictures
④ pull: to use force to make something move away from you or away from its previous position
⑤ mirror: a flat piece of glass which reflects light, so that when you look at it you can see yourself reflected in it

05 출제율 100%

다음 우리말에 맞게 빈칸에 알맞은 말을 쓰시오.

그는 이제 더 이상 네 친구가 아니란 걸 명심해.

➡ Keep _____ _____ that he is not your friend anymore.

06 출제율 85%

다음 대화의 밑줄 친 부분의 의도로 알맞은 것은?

B: I want to watch the birds in the trees.
G: <u>You shouldn't go up too close to the birds.</u>
B: All right, thanks.

① 요청하기
② 비난하기
③ 제안하기
④ 금지하기
⑤ 칭찬하기

07 출제율 90%

다음 대화의 빈칸에 알맞은 것은?

A: _____
B: No, I haven't, but I've heard of it many times.

① How often have you been to Haeundae?
② Did you go to Haeundae?
③ When did you go to Haeundae?
④ Have you ever been to Haeundae?
⑤ How many times did you visit Haeundae?

B: Have you heard of bird watching?

M: Sure. I tried ⓐit when I was a child. (①)

B: That's nice. Actually, I'm doing it ⓑ ___ the first time this Saturday. (②)

M: Are you? You should bring warm clothes and something to eat. (③)

B: Okay. (④)

M: You shouldn't ⓒ ___ any noise when you watch the birds. (⑤)

B: I'll keep ⓓthat in mind. Thanks, Dad.

08 위 대화의 ①~⑤ 중 다음 주어진 문장이 들어갈 알맞은 곳은?

> What else should I keep in mind?

① ② ③ ④ ⑤

09 위 대화의 밑줄 친 ⓐ가 가리키는 것을 영어로 쓰시오.

➡ _____

10 위 대화의 빈칸 ⓑ에 알맞은 것은?

① on ② to
③ for ④ in
⑤ with

11 위 대화의 빈칸 ⓒ에 알맞은 것은?

① get ② make
③ do ④ bring
⑤ take

12 위 대화의 밑줄 친 ⓓ가 가리키는 것을 우리말로 쓰시오.

➡ _____

13 위 글의 내용과 일치하지 <u>않는</u> 것은?

① 소년의 아버지는 들새 관찰을 해 본 적이 있다.
② 소년은 이번 토요일에 들새 관찰을 할 예정이다.
③ 소년은 따뜻한 옷과 먹을 것을 가져가야 한다.
④ 들새 관찰을 할 때에는 조용해야 한다.
⑤ 소년의 취미는 들새 관찰이다.

14 다음 문장의 빈칸에 알맞지 <u>않은</u> 것은?

> Jenny has seen the movie ___.

① once ② twice
③ never ④ before
⑤ many times

15 다음 문장의 빈칸에 알맞은 것은?

> ___ Tom's family is poor, they are always happy.

① If ② As
③ Since ④ Unless
⑤ Although

16 다음 밑줄 친 단어의 올바른 형태를 쓰시오. (출제율 85%)

> Jane <u>lived</u> in England since she was ten years old.

➡ _____

17 다음 문장에서 어법상 어색한 부분을 바르게 고쳐 문장을 다시 쓰시오. (출제율 95%)

> I didn't see him since I was eleven.
>
> ➡ _____

18 다음 두 문장의 뜻이 같도록 할 때 빈칸에 알맞은 것은? (출제율 85%)

> Though I looked for your pencil, I couldn't find it.
> = I looked for your pencil, _____ I couldn't find it.

① so   ② but
③ and   ④ for
⑤ because

19 다음 〈보기〉 문장과 뜻이 가장 가까운 것은? (출제율 85%)

┌─── 보기 ───┐
Tom has lost his watch.
└──────────┘

① Tom lost his watch.
② Tom lost his watch and he forgot it.
③ Tom lost his watch, but he found it.
④ Tom lost his watch, and he hasn't found it yet.
⑤ Tom lost his watch, so he is going to buy a new one.

20 다음 문장 중 밑줄 친 부분이 어색한 것은? (출제율 100%)

① I think <u>that</u> your answer is right.
② It was snowing <u>when</u> I got up.
③ I often sing <u>while</u> I'm taking a shower.
④ <u>Although</u> the boy was sick, he went to school.
⑤ <u>Because</u> Mozart's life was short, he changed music history.

21 다음 밑줄 친 부분의 쓰임이 나머지 넷과 다른 하나는? (출제율 90%)

① Jenny <u>has seen</u> the actor before.
② My grandfather <u>has</u> never <u>visited</u> Seoul.
③ Mr. Lincoln <u>has gone</u> to Berlin on business.
④ How many times <u>have</u> they <u>been</u> to China?
⑤ They <u>have been</u> to Italy three times.

[22~25] 다음 글을 읽고, 물음에 답하시오.

> **Selfies in the Past - Minji**
> Did people in the past take selfies? Though ⓐit wasn't easy at that time, the answer is yes. (①) Look at this photo of Princess Anastasia. (②) She used a mirror ⓑto take a picture of herself. (③) She looks nervous. (④) Well, I think it was her first selfie. (⑤) And it was probably the world's first teenage selfie ever.

22 위 글의 ①~⑤ 중 다음 주어진 문장이 들어갈 알맞은 곳은? (출제율 90%)

> Can you guess why?

①   ②   ③   ④   ⑤

23 위 글의 밑줄 친 ⓐ가 가리키는 것을 우리말로 쓰시오.

➡ _____

24 위 글의 밑줄 친 ⓑ와 용법이 같은 것은?

① We decided to visit the house.
② He has no friends to play with.
③ Do you want to go skating now?
④ I had no house to live in.
⑤ He worked hard to support his family.

25 민지는 Anastasia가 왜 긴장하고 있다고 생각하는지 우리말로 간단히 쓰시오.

➡ _____
_____

[26~31] 다음 글을 읽고, 물음에 답하시오.

ⓐRiding a BMX bike is very excited. You can try ⓑ많은 skills. You can turn the bike freely and even jump with the bike. ⓒThough it's not easy, it's very exciting. (①) You can start with standing skills. (②) ⓓ you try standing skills, balancing is very important. (③) But be ⓔcare. (④) Also, you shouldn't go too fast when you're riding. (⑤)

26 위 글의 ①~⑤ 중 다음 주어진 문장이 들어갈 알맞은 곳은?

You should wear a helmet and gloves.

① ② ③ ④ ⑤

27 위 글의 밑줄 친 ⓐ에서 어법상 어색한 것을 고치시오.

_____ ➡ _____

28 위 글의 밑줄 친 ⓑ를 영어로 바꿔 쓸 때 알맞지 않은 것은? (2개)

① many   ② much
③ a few   ④ lots of
⑤ a lot of

29 위 글의 밑줄 친 ⓒ와 같은 뜻이 되도록 다음 문장의 빈칸에 알맞은 말을 쓰시오.

It's not easy, _____ it's very exciting.

30 위 글의 빈칸 ⓓ에 알맞은 것은?

① When   ② If
③ After   ④ Because
⑤ Though

31 위 글의 밑줄 친 ⓔ를 알맞은 어형으로 고치시오.

➡ _____

[01~03] 다음 대화를 읽고, 물음에 답하시오.

G: Dad, have you ever heard of Kim Soyun, the rock ___ⓐ___?
M: Yes, I've ⓑ<u>see</u> her on TV.
G: She's teaching rock climbing at a camp this Saturday. I want to join the camp.
M: Okay, Miso, but you shouldn't climb up too high.
G: All right. Thanks, Dad.

01 위 대화의 빈칸 ⓐ에 다음 정의에 해당하는 단어를 쓰시오.

someone who climbs rocks or mountains as a sport or a hobby

➡ _____

02 위 대화의 밑줄 친 ⓑ를 알맞은 형으로 고치시오.

➡ _____

03 What will Kim Soyun do this Saturday? Answer in English.

➡ _____

04 다음 대화의 순서를 바르게 배열하시오.

(A) Oh, okay.
(B) Wait, Jimin.
(C) Why?
(D) Look at that sign. You shouldn't take a photo here.

➡ _____

05 다음 〈보기〉와 같이 현재완료 시제를 이용해 두 문장을 한 문장으로 쓰시오.

┤ 보기 ├
Jane moved to Tokyo ten years ago. She still lives there.
➡ Jane has lived in Tokyo for ten years.

(1) Peter moved to Peking in 2010. He still lives in Peking.
➡ _____

(2) Tom went to hospital a week ago. He is still in hospital.
➡ _____

(3) My mother went shopping. She is not here.
➡ _____

06 다음 〈조건〉에 맞게 괄호 안의 단어를 이용하여 우리말을 영어로 옮기시오.

┤ 조건 ├
1. 필요시 관사를 붙이거나 단어를 추가하고 동사의 어형 변화를 할 것.
2. 대·소문자 및 구두점에 유의할 것.
3. (1), (2)는 접속사로 시작하는 부사절이 주절의 앞에 오고 (3)은 주절의 뒤에 올 것.

(1) 비록 바람이 불기는 했지만, 날씨가 별로 춥지 않았다. (though, it, windy, very, cold)
➡ _____

(2) Tim은 종종 Anne을 짜증스럽게 했지만, 그녀는 그를 좋아했다. (although, often, annoy, fond, of)
➡ _____
_____

(3) 너는 비록 그것이 마음에 들지 않는다고 해도 해야 한다. (though, must, do, it, like)
➡ _____

07 다음 문장에서 어법상 어색한 것을 찾아 바르게 고치시오.

(1) He has gone to Spain last year.

_____ ➡ _____

(2) When have you seen Kathy's little brother?

_____ ➡ _____

(3) I have often played the piano when I was a child.

_____ ➡ _____

[08~11] 다음 글을 읽고, 물음에 답하시오.

Have you ever ⓐhear of a "selfie"? ⓑWhen you take a photograph of you, it's a selfie. The students from Minji's photo club have searched ⓒ information about selfies ⓓ one month. Here are some of their presentations about selfies.

08 위 글의 밑줄 친 ⓐ를 알맞은 형으로 고치시오.

➡ _____

09 위 글의 밑줄 친 ⓑ에서 어법상 어색한 것을 고치시오.

_____ ➡ _____

10 위 글의 빈칸 ⓒ와 ⓓ에 공통으로 알맞은 전치사를 쓰시오.

➡ _____

11 What is a selfie? Answer in Korean.

➡ _____

[12~15] 다음 글을 읽고, 물음에 답하시오.

Selfies for a Better School Life - Soyun

I think we can use selfies ⓐ(making, to make) a better school life. We can do good things at school and ⓑ selfies. Then we can post the photos on our school website. I've watered the ⓒ and flowers at school for one month. I've also helped the teacher at the school library many times. Look at my selfies of those things. How about ⓓjoin me to create a better school life?

12 위 글의 괄호 ⓐ에서 알맞은 것을 고르시오.

➡ _____

13 위 글의 빈칸 ⓑ에 알맞은 단어를 쓰시오.

➡ _____

14 위 글의 빈칸 ⓒ에 다음 정의에 해당하는 단어를 쓰시오. 필요하면 어형 변화를 하시오.

a living thing that grows in the earth and has a stem, leaves, and roots, especially one that is smaller than a tree or bush

➡ _____

15 위 글의 밑줄 친 ⓓ를 알맞은 형으로 고치시오.

➡ _____

01 다음 주어진 말을 이용하여 현재완료형의 문장을 만드시오.

(1) I, just, send, e-mail

➡ _____

(2) Kate, just, clean, room

➡ _____

(3) Mike, already, finish, job

➡ _____

(4) you, take, medicine, yet

➡ _____

(5) Mary, sing, yet

➡ _____

(6) you, study, yet

➡ _____

(7) Tom, do, homework, yet

➡ _____

02 다음 괄호 안에 주어진 어구를 이용하여 자유롭게 문장을 만드시오. (A)는 접속사로 시작하는 부사절이 주절의 앞에 오고, (B)는 주절의 뒤에 올 것.

(1) (though)

➡ (A) _____

(B) _____

(2) (although)

➡ (A) _____

(B) _____

(3) (even though)

➡ (A) _____

(B) _____

단원별 모의고사

01 다음 중 우리말 뜻이 <u>잘못된</u> 것은?

① go up: 오르다
② for example: 예를 들면
③ over there: 저쪽에
④ be good for: ~을 잘하다
⑤ hang up: 전화를 끊다

02 다음 영영풀이에 해당하는 단어로 알맞은 것은?

better or more important than other people or things

① real
② special
③ popular
④ common
⑤ strange

03 다음 빈칸에 알맞은 것으로 짝지어진 것은?

• Will you call me _____ your lunch time?
• Ask somebody _____ to help you.

① for – else
② for – other
③ during – other
④ during – else
⑤ while – other

04 다음 짝지어진 두 단어의 관계가 같도록 빈칸에 알맞은 말을 쓰시오.

safe : dangerous = push : _____

05 다음 빈칸에 공통으로 들어갈 말을 쓰시오.

• We were very sorry to hear _____ your father's death.
• There are lots _____ nice parks in San Francisco.

06 다음 대화를 의미가 통하도록 알맞게 배열한 것은?

(A) No, I haven't. How was it?
(B) Have you ever ridden a horse?
(C) Yes, I have. How about you?
(D) It was fun, but it was a little scary, too.

① (A) – (D) – (B) – (C)
② (B) – (C) – (A) – (D)
③ (C) – (D) – (B) – (A)
④ (D) – (B) – (C) – (A)
⑤ (D) – (C) – (A) – (B)

07 다음 대화의 빈칸에 알맞은 것은?

A: Have you ever caught a big fish?
B: _____ I wish to catch one someday.

① Yes, I have.
② No, I haven't.
③ I caught a big fish.
④ Yes, my uncle caught a big fish.
⑤ I caught it and put it back.

08 다음 대화의 밑줄 친 부분과 바꾸어 쓸 수 있는 것은?

> A: Peter, you'd better not run when you cross the street.
> B: Okay, I will.

① you may run when you cross the street

② you must run when you cross the street

③ you need to run when you cross the street

④ you have to run when you cross the street

⑤ you shouldn't run when you cross the street

[09~13] 다음 대화를 읽고, 물음에 답하시오.

> B: Have you heard ___ⓐ___ bird watching?
> M: Sure. I tried it when I was a child.
> B: That's nice. Actually, I'm doing it ___ⓑ___ the first time this Saturday.
> M: Are you? You should bring warm clothes and something ⓒto eat.
> B: Okay. ⓓ(in / else / I / keep / what / mind / should)?
> M: You shouldn't make any noise ___ⓔ___ you watch the birds.
> B: I'll keep that in mind. Thanks, Dad.

09 위 대화의 빈칸 ⓐ와 ⓑ에 알맞은 것으로 짝지어진 것은?

① of – to   ② of – at

③ of – for   ④ at – for

⑤ from – at

10 위 대화의 밑줄 친 ⓒ와 용법이 같은 것은?

① We wished to reach the North Pole.

② Kathy was very sad to hear the song.

③ Please give me something to drink.

④ Do you want to go on a picnic now?

⑤ He must study hard to pass the math exam.

11 위 대화의 괄호 ⓓ를 알맞은 어순으로 배열하시오.

➡ _____

12 위 대화의 빈칸 ⓔ에 알맞은 것은?

① when   ② if

③ before   ④ after

⑤ although

13 위 대화의 내용으로 보아 알 수 없는 것은?

① The boy's father has tried bird watching.

② The boy is fond of bird watching.

③ The boy will do bird watching this Saturday.

④ The boy should bring warm clothes.

⑤ The boy will need food when he watches the birds.

14 다음 괄호 안에 주어진 단어를 어법상 바르게 쓴 것은?

> He left home at six and (not return) yet.

① doesn't return

② wasn't returned

③ didn't return

④ hasn't returned

⑤ hadn't returned

15 다음 두 문장의 뜻이 같도록 빈칸에 알맞은 것은?

> Even though we were hungry, we didn't eat the food.
> = _____ we were hungry, we didn't eat the food.

① Since
② Before
③ Though
④ Therefore
⑤ Because

16 다음 중 밑줄 친 부분의 쓰임이 바르지 <u>않은</u> 것은?

① I've <u>been</u> to Paris five years ago.
② Jack <u>has practiced</u> the piano since last year.
③ Ann <u>has been</u> sick in bed for two weeks.
④ I <u>have</u> never <u>seen</u> such a wonderful movie.
⑤ <u>Has</u> your teacher ever <u>been</u> to Europe?

17 다음 우리말과 같은 뜻이 되도록 빈칸에 알맞은 것은?

> 비록 어제 아팠지만, 나는 학교에 갔다.
> ➡ _____ I was sick yesterday, I went to school.

① If
② As
③ Besides
④ Though
⑤ While

18 다음 두 문장의 뜻이 같도록 빈칸에 알맞은 말을 쓰시오.

> I _____ _____ my car key.
> = I lost my car key. I don't have the key now.

19 다음 우리말을 영작한 것으로 <u>어색한</u> 것을 <u>모두</u> 고르면?

> 네가 비록 부자일지라도 내 마음을 살 수는 없다.

① Though you're rich, you can't buy my heart.
② Since if you're rich, you can't buy my heart.
③ Although you're rich, you can't buy my heart.
④ Unless you're rich, you can't buy my heart.
⑤ Even though you're rich, you can't buy my heart.

20 다음 문장의 빈칸에 알맞은 것은?

> Frank _____ never seen such a cute cat.

① be
② did
③ has
④ was
⑤ must

[21~23] 다음 글을 읽고, 물음에 답하시오.

> Have you heard ⓐ _____ the pyramids in Egypt? Though I ⓑ<u>have</u> never <u>been</u> to Egypt before, I'm standing in front ⓒ _____ a pyramid in this picture. I took it at the selfie museum.

21 위 글의 빈칸 ⓐ와 ⓒ에 공통으로 알맞은 것은?

① to
② at
③ of
④ on
⑤ about

22 위 글의 밑줄 친 ⓑ와 같은 용법으로 쓰인 것은?

① I <u>have been</u> in Japan since last month.
② I <u>have seen</u> a koala before.
③ My father <u>has</u> already <u>eaten</u> breakfast.
④ He <u>has wanted</u> to be a painter for a long time.
⑤ My grandmother <u>has lost</u> her smartphone somewhere.

23 Where did the writer take the picture? Answer in English.

➡ _____

[24~27] 다음 글을 읽고, 물음에 답하시오.

> **Selfie Safety – Jihun**
> These selfies look great, but were they a good idea? ⓐI don't think so. They don't look ____ⓑ____. You should take special care when you take selfies in the wild or at high places like these. A monkey could bite you at any time, ____ⓒ____ you could fall. Here are some safety tips:
> 1. Don't take selfies while you're walking.
> 2. Do not pose with or near wild animals.
> 3. Never take selfies in dangerous places.

24 위 글의 밑줄 친 ⓐ를 so의 의미가 구체적으로 드러나도록 우리말로 옮기시오.

➡ _____

25 위 글의 빈칸 ⓑ에 들어갈 알맞은 것은?

① safe   ② exciting
③ easy   ④ dangerous
⑤ difficult

26 위 글의 빈칸 ⓒ에 알맞은 것은?

① so   ② then
③ or   ④ but
⑤ for

27 위 글의 내용으로 보아 알 수 없는 것은?

① 이 글은 셀피를 찍을 때의 안전 수칙이다.
② 야생에서 사진을 찍을 때는 주의해야 한다.
③ 원숭이는 사람을 잘 따른다.
④ 걸을 때는 셀피를 찍으면 안 된다.
⑤ 야생 동물 근처에서 포즈를 취하면 위험하다.

[28~30] 다음 글을 읽고, 물음에 답하시오.

> Have you heard of fire safety ____ⓐ____? ____ⓑ____ there's a fire, you can be safe. You shouldn't take the elevator. You should follow the teacher's directions.

28 위 글의 빈칸 ⓐ에 다음 정의에 해당하는 단어를 쓰시오.

> instructions that tell you what you are allowed to do and what you are not allowed to do

➡ _____

29 위 글의 빈칸 ⓑ에 알맞은 것은?

① If   ② When
③ As   ④ Though
⑤ Because

30 위 글의 내용과 일치하도록 다음 문장의 빈칸에 알맞은 말을 쓰시오.

> When there is a _____, you shouldn't take the _____.

INSIGHT
on the textbook

교과서 파헤치기

※ 다음 영어를 우리말로 쓰시오.

01	post	
02	realize	
03	continue	
04	diary	
05	dish	
06	cover	
07	fan	
08	final	
09	floor	
10	really	
11	health	
12	solve	
13	trust	
14	ticket	
15	strict	
16	bell	
17	fresh	
18	delicious	
19	interesting	
20	corner	
21	judge	

22	kind	
23	activity	
24	note	
25	math	
26	right	
27	together	
28	word	
29	anyway	
30	shout	
31	pleased	
32	reply	
33	grow	
34	practice	
35	cut in	
36	think of	
37	bump into	
38	can't wait for	
39	find out	
40	be good for	
41	on one's way to	
42	pay someone back	
43	think to oneself	

※ 다음 우리말을 영어로 쓰시오.

01 지루한 _____

02 문제 _____

03 연습하다 _____

04 서둘러 가다, 서두르다 _____

05 데리고 가다 _____

06 흥분한, 신이 난 _____

07 마법, 마술 _____

08 구내식당 _____

09 바쁜 _____

10 외치다 _____

11 선물 _____

12 기억하다 _____

13 기르다, 재배하다 _____

14 항상 _____

15 진지한 _____

16 어쨌든 _____

17 열심히, 어려운 _____

18 멋진, 시원한 _____

19 담임선생님 _____

20 가입하다 _____

21 대답하다 _____

22 제공하다 _____

23 신나는, 흥미진진한 _____

24 수업 _____

25 기쁜 _____

26 의미하다 _____

27 속담 _____

28 마술 _____

29 건강 _____

30 바닥 _____

31 엄격한 _____

32 계속하다 _____

33 판단하다 _____

34 표지 _____

35 ~에 좋다 _____

36 ~에 부딪히다 _____

37 (말 · 대화에) 끼어들다 _____

38 방과 후에 _____

39 ~에 대해 생각하다 _____

40 ~을 알게 되다 _____

41 ~을 찾다 _____

42 낭장 _____

43 마음속으로 생각하다 _____

※ 다음 영영풀이에 알맞은 단어를 <보기>에서 골라 쓴 후, 우리말 뜻을 쓰시오.

1 _____ : to make plants grow: _____

2 _____ : to move, act, or go quickly: _____

3 _____ : the outer part of a book or magazine: _____

4 _____ : to say or write something as an answer to someone or something: _____

5 _____ : demanding that rules, especially rules about behavior, should be obeyed: _____

6 _____ : a shallow container that you cook or serve food in: _____

7 _____ : the last and most important game or race in a competition: _____

8 _____ : to understand or become aware of something: _____

9 _____ : to give food or drink to someone at a meal, in a restaurant, etc: _____

10 _____ : to form an opinion about something or someone after careful thought: _____

11 _____ : the art of doing tricks that seem impossible in order to entertain people: _____

12 _____ : to put up a sign, notice, etc. so that it can be seen by many people: _____

13 _____ : to believe that someone is honest or will not do anything bad or wrong: _____

14 _____ : an old and well-known phrase that expresses an idea that most people believe is true: _____

15 _____ : a restaurant where you choose and pay for your meal at a counter and carry it to a table: _____

16 _____ : a person who admires someone or something or enjoys watching or listening to someone or something very much: _____

보기

saying	judge	cover	strict
final	post	reply	cafeteria
hurry	trust	dish	grow
magic	realize	serve	fan

※ 다음 우리말과 일치하도록 빈칸에 알맞은 말을 쓰시오.

Get Ready - 2

1. **G:** Hey, _____ do you _____ _____ this notebook?

   B: It _____ great! Is it _____ science?

   G: Yes. _____ _____ I'm _____ _____ _____ science harder _____ this notebook.

2. **B:** _____ _____ the teachers. Who's _____ _____ be our new _____ _____?

   G: We'll _____ _____ in 10 minutes.

   B: I'm very _____. I _____ _____!

3. **M:** Hello, _____! My name is Yun Kihun. I'm _____ _____ _____.

   G&B: _____ _____ _____ you, Mr. Yun.

   M: _____ do you _____ _____ English?

   G: It's _____. I like English _____ _____.

Start Off - Listen & Talk A

1. **B:** This club _____ _____ you. _____ do you _____ _____ _____?

   G: The health club? I _____ it's _____.

   B: Then _____ _____ do you want _____ _____?

   G: I'll _____ _____ club. I like _____ soccer.

2. **G:** What do you _____ _____ the magic club?

   B: I _____ it's the _____ club for me. I want _____ _____ _____ _____ _____.

   G: I'll join it, _____. When is the _____ _____?

   B: Next Wednesday. I _____ _____ _____ the first meeting!

Start Off - Listen & Talk B

B: _____ join the Green Garden club together. _____ _____ _____ _____ _____ it?

G: Okay. I like _____ _____.

B: You know _____? I like _____ vegetables.

G: _____ _____ the club _____ _____. We can have a party _____ fresh vegetables _____ _____.

B: Great. The first party is _____ _____ _____.

G: I _____ _____ _____ _____ the party.

해석

1. G: 이 봐, 이 공책 어떻게 생각하니?
   B: 멋져 보여! 과학용이니?
   G: 응. 올해에는 이 공책을 가지고 과학을 더 열심히 공부할 거야.

2. B: 선생님들을 좀 봐. 누가 우리 새 담임선생님이 될까?
   G: 우리는 10분 후에 알게 될 거야.
   B: 너무 흥분돼. 너무 기대돼!

3. M: 안녕하세요, 여러분! 제 이름은 윤기훈입니다. 저는 여러분의 영어 선생님입니다.
   G&B: 만나서 반갑습니다, 윤 선생님.
   M: 여러분은 영어에 대해 어떻게 생각하세요?
   G: 재미있어요. 저는 영어를 매우 좋아해요.

1. B: 이 동아리는 너에게 맞는 것 같아. 그것에 대해 어떻게 생각하니?
   G: 헬스 동아리? 지루하다고 생각해.
   B: 그럼 넌 어떤 동아리에 가입하고 싶니?
   G: 난 축구 동아리에 가입할 거야. 나는 축구를 좋아해.

2. G: 마술 동아리에 대해 어떻게 생각하니?
   B: 나한테 맞는 동아리인 것 같아. 나는 재미있는 마술을 많이 배우고 싶어.
   G: 나도 가입할게. 첫 모임은 언제니?
   B: 다음 주 수요일이야. 나는 첫 모임이 너무 기다려져!

B: 초록 정원 동아리에 함께 가입하자. 그것에 대해 어떻게 생각하니?
G: 좋아, 나는 채소를 기르는 것을 좋아해.
B: 그거 알아?(있잖아.) 나는 채소를 먹는 것을 좋아해.
G: 지금 당장 그 동아리에 가입하자. 매달 신선한 채소가 있는 파티를 열 수 있어.
B: 좋아. 첫 번째 파티는 4월 30일이야.
G: 나는 파티가 너무 기다려져.

Step Up - Real-life Scene

I Can't Wait for His Class

Seho: Miso, _____ do you _____ _____ Mr. Park?

Miso: The new math teacher? He _____ very _____ and _____.

Seho: _____ _____ a book _____ its cover.

Miso: _____ do you _____, Seho?

Seho: My first class _____ Mr. Park _____ _____. He was very kind, and his class was so _____.

Miso: Really?

Seho: Yes. _____ the first _____, we did interesting _____ _____ _____ our cell phones.

Miso: Wow! I _____ _____ _____ his class tomorrow. It's my first math class _____ _____.

Express Yourself A

1. **B:** _____ _____ _____ _____ of today's lunch?

   G: _____ it's okay. What's _____ tomorrow's menu?

   B: Wow! We _____ _____ spaghetti tomorrow.

   G: I _____ _____ _____ _____ tomorrow.

2. **G:** Look! Two _____ of vegetables! What do you _____ _____ today's menu?

   B: It's _____ _____. I like _____.

   G: I _____ _____ vegetables.

   B: _____ some. They are _____ _____ _____ _____.

Check Yourself - Listen & Speak

B: _____ _____ the School Band club together. _____ do you think _____ it?

G: Okay. I like _____ _____ _____.

B: I _____ _____ the ukulele.

G: Let's join the club _____ _____. They practice _____ _____ every _____ and _____.

B: They're _____ _____ _____ the first concert _____ July 15.

G: Great. I hope _____ _____ in the concert.

B: Me, _____. I _____ _____ _____ the concert.

나는 그의 수업이 너무 기다려져.

세호: 미소야, 박 선생님에 대해 어떻게 생각하니?

미소: 새로 오신 수학 선생님? 그는 매우 엄격하고 진지해 보이셔.

세호: 겉모습만으로 판단하지 마.

미소: 무슨 뜻이야, 세호?

세호: 박 선생님과의 첫 수업은 훌륭했어. 그는 매우 친절하셨고, 그의 수업은 매우 흥미로웠어.

미소: 정말?

세호: 응. 첫 수업 동안, 우리는 휴대 전화로 흥미로운 수학 활동을 했어.

미소: 와! 내일 수업이 너무 기다려진다. 올해 첫 번째 수학 수업이야.

1. B: 오늘 점심에 대해 어떻게 생각하니?
   G: 괜찮은 것 같아. 내일 메뉴는 뭐니?
   B: 와! 내일 우리는 스파게티를 먹을 수 있어.
   G: 내일 점심시간이 몹시 기다려진다.

2. G: 봐! 야채 두 접시! 오늘 메뉴 어때?
   B: 나쁘지 않아. 나는 야채를 좋아해.
   G: 나는 야채를 안 먹어.
   B: 조금 먹어 봐. 그것들은 우리 건강에 좋아.

B: 우리 학교 밴드 동아리에 같이 가입하자. 그것에 대해서 어떻게 생각하니?

G: 좋아. 나는 플루트 연주하는 것을 좋아해.

B: 난 우쿨렐레 연주하는 걸 좋아해.

G: 지금 당장 그 동아리에 가입하자. 그들은 매주 화요일과 목요일 방과 후에 연습을 해.

B: 그들은 7월 15일에 첫 번째 음악회를 열 거야.

G: 좋아. 나는 음악회에서 연주를 하고 싶어.

B: 나도. 나는 음악회가 너무 기다려져.

※ 다음 우리말에 맞도록 대화를 영어로 쓰시오.

Get Ready - 2

1. G: _____
   B: _____
   G: _____

2. B: _____
   G: _____
   B: _____

3. M: _____
   G&B: _____
   M: _____
   G: _____

Start Off - Listen & Talk A

1. B: _____
   G: _____
   B: _____
   G: _____

2. G: _____
   B: _____
   G: _____
   B: _____

Start Off - Listen & Talk B

B: _____
G: _____
B: _____
G: _____
   _____
B: _____
G: _____

1. G: 이 봐, 이 공책 어떻게 생각하니?
   B: 멋져 보여! 과학용이니?
   G: 응. 올해에는 이 공책을 가지고 과학을 더 열심히 공부할 거야.

2. B: 선생님들을 좀 봐. 누가 우리 새 담임선생님이 될까?
   G: 우리는 10분 후에 알게 될 거야.
   B: 너무 흥분돼. 너무 기대돼!

3. M: 안녕하세요, 여러분! 제 이름은 윤기훈입니다. 저는 여러분의 영어 선생님입니다.
   G&B: 만나서 반갑습니다, 윤 선생님.
   M: 여러분은 영어에 대해 어떻게 생각하세요?
   G: 재미있어요. 저는 영어를 매우 좋아해요.

1. B: 이 동아리는 너에게 맞는 것 같아. 그것에 대해 어떻게 생각하니?
   G: 헬스 동아리? 지루하다고 생각해.
   B: 그럼 넌 어떤 동아리에 가입하고 싶니?
   G: 난 축구 동아리에 가입할 거야. 나는 축구를 좋아해.

2. G: 마술 동아리에 대해 어떻게 생각하니?
   B: 나한테 맞는 동아리인 것 같아. 나는 재미있는 마술을 많이 배우고 싶어.
   G: 나도 가입할게. 첫 모임은 언제니?
   B: 다음 주 수요일이야. 나는 첫 모임이 너무 기다려져!

B: 초록 정원 동아리에 함께 가입하자. 그것에 대해 어떻게 생각하니?
G: 좋아. 나는 채소를 기르는 것을 좋아해.
B: 그거 알아?(있잖아.) 나는 채소를 먹는 것을 좋아해.
G: 지금 당장 그 동아리에 가입하자. 매달 신선한 채소가 있는 파티를 열 수 있어.
B: 좋아. 첫 번째 파티는 4월 30일이야.
G: 나는 파티가 너무 기다려져.

Step Up - Real-life Scene

I Can't Wait for His Class

Seho: _____

Miso: _____

Seho: _____

Miso: _____

Seho: _____
_____

Miso: _____

Seho: _____
_____

Miso: _____

Express Yourself A

1. B: _____

   G: _____

   B: _____

   G: _____

2. G: _____

   B: _____

   G: _____

   B: _____

Check Yourself - Listen & Speak

B: _____

G: _____

B: _____

G: _____

B: _____

G: _____

B: _____

나는 그의 수업이 너무 기다려져.

세호: 미소야, 박 선생님에 대해 어떻게 생각하니?

미소: 새로 오신 수학 선생님? 그는 매우 엄격하고 진지해 보이셔.

세호: 겉모습만으로 판단하지 마.

미소: 무슨 뜻이야, 세호?

세호: 박 선생님과의 첫 수업은 훌륭했어. 그는 매우 친절하셨고, 그의 수업은 매우 흥미로웠어.

미소: 정말?

세호: 응. 첫 수업 동안, 우리는 휴대 전화로 흥미로운 수학 활동을 했어.

미소: 와! 내일 수업이 너무 기다려진다. 올해 첫 번째 수학 수업이야.

1. B: 오늘 점심에 대해 어떻게 생각하니?

   G: 괜찮은 것 같아. 내일 메뉴는 뭐니?

   B: 와! 내일 우리는 스파게티를 먹을 수 있어.

   G: 내일 점심시간이 몹시 기다려진다.

2. G: 봐! 야채 두 접시! 오늘 메뉴 어때?

   B: 나쁘지 않아. 나는 야채를 좋아해.

   G: 나는 야채를 안 먹어.

   B: 조금 먹어 봐. 그것들은 우리 건강에 좋아.

B: 우리 학교 밴드 동아리에 같이 가입하자. 그것에 대해서 어떻게 생각하니?

G: 좋아. 나는 플루트 연주하는 것을 좋아해.

B: 난 우쿨렐레 연주하는 걸 좋아해.

G: 지금 당장 그 동아리에 가입하자. 그들은 매주 화요일과 목요일 방과 후에 연습을 해.

B: 그들은 7월 15일에 첫 번째 음악회를 열 거야.

G: 좋아. 나는 음악회에서 연주를 하고 싶어.

B: 나도. 나는 음악회가 너무 기다려져.

※ 다음 우리말과 일치하도록 빈칸에 알맞은 것을 골라 쓰시오.

1 Seho and Jihun were _____ in the hallway _____ Dami _____ over.

A. came   B. when   C. talking

2 "_____ birthday!" she _____ _____ Seho.

A. to   B. said   C. happy

3 "Here. They're _____ _____ dad."

A. my   B. from

4 "Wow, _____ KBL _____! Thanks!"

A. tickets   B. two

5 "Who are you _____ to _____ with you?" Dami _____.

A. asked   B. take   C. going

6 "Minjun. He _____ me _____ a soccer game _____.

A. before   B. to   C. took

7 So, it's _____ to pay him _____."

A. back   B. time

8 "You know _____?" Jihun _____ in.

A. cut   B. what

9 "Minjun _____ a _____ of basketball. But I _____!"

A. am   B. fan   C. isn't

10 "Well, I'll _____ him first _____," _____ Seho.

A. replied   B. anyway   C. ask

11 "He _____ go _____ you. _____ me," said Jihun.

A. with   B. won't   C. trust

12 "Who is this guy?" Dami _____ to _____, "He _____ Minjun's ticket."

A. wants   B. herself   C. thought

13 "Oh! There's the _____. _____ you _____," said Dami.

A. later   B. see   C. bell

14 She _____ to _____.

A. class   B. hurried

15 "Come _____, Jihun," said Seho, and he _____ _____ run.

A. to   B. started   C. on

16 _____ the corner, Seho _____ _____ someone.

A. into   B. bumped   C. at

17 "Sorry!" he _____ and _____ _____ run.

A. to   B. continued   C. said

18 Just _____, Jihun _____ something _____ the floor.

A. saw   B. then   C. on

---

1 세호와 지훈이는 다미가 왔을 때 복도에서 이야기를 나누고 있었다.

2 "생일 축하해!" 다미가 세호에게 말했다.

3 "이거 받아. 우리 아빠가 주신 거야."

4 "와, KBL 입장권 두 장! 고마워!"

5 "넌 누구를 데려 갈 거니?" 다미가 물었다.

6 "민준이. 그가 전에 나를 축구 경기에 데려갔어.

7 그래서 그에게 신세를 갚아야 할 때야."

8 "그거 알아?" 지훈이가 끼어들었다.

9 "민준이는 농구 팬이 아니야. 하지만 난 농구 팬이야!"

10 "음, 어쨌든 먼저 민준이에게 물어볼 거야." 세호가 대답했다.

11 "그는 너와 함께 가지 않을 거야. 날 믿어." 지훈이가 말했다.

12 "이 녀석은 누구지?" 다미는 "그는 민준이의 입장권을 원하는구나." 라고 마음속으로 생각했다.

13 "아, 종이 울린다. 나중에 보자." 다미가 말했다.

14 그녀는 서둘러 수업에 들어갔다.

15 "어서, 지훈아." 세호는 말하고 달리기 시작했다.

16 모퉁이에서, 세호는 누군가와 부딪혔다.

17 그는 "미안해!"라고 말하고는 계속 달렸다.

18 바로 그때, 지훈이가 바닥에 있는 무언가를 보았다.

19 "_____, Seho!" he said, _____ Seho was _____ there.
A. not   B. but   C. wait

20 _____ class, Seho _____ to Dami and said, "I _____ _____ one of my tickets.
A. find   B. went   C. after   D. can't

21 Did you _____ to _____ it?"
A. see   B. happen

22 "No," _____ _____.
A. answered   B. she

23 "_____ it in _____ bag?"
A. your   B. isn't

24 "No, it's _____ there. I _____ I _____ it," said Seho.
A. lost   B. think   C. not

25 _____ her _____ home, Dami _____ Jihun.
A. saw   B. way   C. on

26 He _____ the ticket _____ his hand.
A. in   B. had

27 Dami _____ _____ and said, "Hey! _____ do you ...?"
A. why   B. angry   C. got

28 Just then, Jihun _____ Seho and _____, "Seho! I _____ a ticket in the hallway.
A. found   B. shouted   C. saw

29 I _____ it's _____."
A. yours   B. think

30 "Thanks! I was _____ _____ that!" _____ Seho.
A. said   B. for   C. looking

31 "He's _____ so bad," Dami _____.
A. thought   B. not

32 "So, what _____ you _____?
A. saying   B. were

33 Do you have _____ to _____, Dami?" _____ Jihun.
A. asked   B. say   C. something

34 "Um, how _____ _____ _____ the school basketball game with me this Friday?
A. to   B. about   C. going

35 _____ the _____."
A. finals   B. it's

36 Jihun _____ really _____. "I'd love _____!"
A. to   B. pleased   C. looked

---

19 "기다려, 세호야!"라고 그가 말했지만 세호는 거기에 없었다.

20 수업이 끝난 후, 세호는 다미에게 가서 말했다. "내 입장권 한 장을 찾을 수 없어.

21 너 혹시 입장권을 봤니?"

22 "아니." 그녀가 대답했다.

23 "네 가방 안에 있지 않니?"

24 "아니, 거기에 없어. 내 생각에 그것을 잃어버린 것 같아," 세호가 말했다.

25 집으로 돌아오는 길에 다미는 지훈을 보았다.

26 그는 손에 입장권을 가지고 있었다.

27 다미는 화가 나서 "이봐! 너가 왜 ...?"라고 말했다

28 바로 그때, 지훈이는 세호를 보고 소리쳤다. "세호야! 내가 복도에서 입장권을 찾았어.

29 네 것 같아."

30 "고마워! 나는 그것을 찾고 있었어!" 세호가 말했다.

31 "그는 그렇게 나쁘진 않아."라고 다미는 생각했다.

32 "그래서, 무슨 말을 하고 있었던 거야?

33 너 할 말이 있니, 다미야?" 지훈이가 물었다.

34 "음, 이번 금요일에 나랑 학교 농구 경기에 같이 가는 게 어때?

35 그것은 결승전이야."

36 지훈은 정말 기뻐 보였다. "가고 싶어!"

※ 다음 우리말과 일치하도록 빈칸에 알맞은 말을 쓰시오.

1 Seho and Jihun _____ _____ in the hallway _____ Dami _____ _____.

2 "_____ _____!" she _____ _____ Seho.

3 "Here. They're _____ _____ _____."

4 "Wow, _____ _____ _____! Thanks!"

5 "Who are you _____ _____ _____ with you?" Dami asked.

6 "Minjun. He _____ _____ _____ a soccer game before.

7 So, it's _____ _____ _____ _____ _____."

8 "You _____ _____?" Jihun _____ _____.

9 "Minjun _____ a _____ of basketball. _____ I am!"

10 "Well, I'll _____ him first _____," _____ Seho.

11 "He _____ _____ you. _____ me," said Jihun.

12 "Who is this guy?" Dami _____ _____ _____, "He _____ Minjun's _____."

13 "Oh! _____ the bell. _____ _____ _____," said Dami.

14 She _____ _____ _____.

15 "Come _____, Jihun," said Seho, and he _____ _____ _____.

16 _____ the corner, Seho _____ _____ _____.

17 "Sorry!" he said and _____ _____ _____.

18 _____, Jihun saw something _____ the floor.

---

1 세호와 지훈이는 다미가 왔을 때 복도에서 이야기를 나누고 있었다.

2 "생일 축하해!" 다미가 세호에게 말했다.

3 "이거 받아. 우리 아빠가 주신 거야."

4 "와, KBL 입장권 두 장! 고마워!"

5 "넌 누구를 데려 갈 거니?" 다미가 물었다.

6 "민준이. 그가 전에 나를 축구 경기에 데려갔어.

7 그래서 그에게 신세를 갚아야 할 때야."

8 "그거 알아?" 지훈이가 끼어들었다.

9 "민준이는 농구 팬이 아니야. 하지만 난 농구 팬이야!"

10 "음, 어쨌든 먼저 민준이에게 물어볼 거야." 세호가 대답했다.

11 "그는 너와 함께 가지 않을 거야. 날 믿어." 지훈이가 말했다.

12 "이 녀석은 누구지?" 다미는 "그는 민준이의 입장권을 원하는구나." 라고 마음속으로 생각했다.

13 "아, 종이 울린다. 나중에 보자." 다미가 말했다.

14 그녀는 서둘러 수업에 들어갔다.

15 "어서, 지훈아." 세호는 말하고 달리기 시작했다.

16 모퉁이에서, 세호는 누군가와 부딪혔다.

17 그는 "미안해!"라고 말하고는 계속 달렸다.

18 바로 그때, 지훈이가 바닥에 있는 무언가를 보았다.

19 "Wait, Seho!" he said, _____ Seho _____ _____ there.

20 _____ _____, Seho _____ _____ Dami and said, "I can't find _____ _____ _____ _____.

21 Did you _____ _____ see it?"

22 "No," she _____.

23 "_____ it _____ _____ _____?"

24 "No, it's _____ there. I _____ I _____ it," said Seho.

25 _____ _____ _____ _____ _____, Dami saw Jihun.

26 He _____ the ticket _____ _____ _____.

27 Dami _____ _____ and said, "Hey! _____ do you ...?"

28 _____ _____, Jihun saw Seho and _____, "Seho! I _____ _____ _____ _____ the hallway.

29 I _____ it's _____."

30 "Thanks! I _____ _____ _____ that!" said Seho.

31 "He's _____ _____ _____," Dami _____.

32 "So, what _____ you _____?

33 Do you _____ something _____ _____, Dami?" _____ Jihun.

34 "Um, how _____ _____ _____ the school basketball game _____ _____ this Friday?

35 It's the _____."

36 Jihun _____ really _____. "I'd _____ _____!"

19 "기다려, 세호야!"라고 그가 말했지만 세호는 거기에 없었다.

20 수업이 끝난 후, 세호는 다미에게 가서 말했다. "내 입장권 한 장을 찾을 수 없어.

21 너 혹시 입장권을 봤니?"

22 "아니." 그녀가 대답했다.

23 "네 가방 안에 있지 않니?"

24 "아니, 거기에 없어. 내 생각에 그것을 잃어버린 것 같아." 세호가 말했다.

25 집으로 돌아오는 길에 다미는 지훈을 보았다.

26 그는 손에 입장권을 가지고 있었다.

27 다미는 화가 나서 "이봐! 너가 왜 ...?"라고 말했다

28 바로 그때, 지훈이는 세호를 보고 소리쳤다. "세호야! 내가 복도에서 입장권을 찾았어.

29 네 것 같아."

30 "고마워! 나는 그것을 찾고 있었어!" 세호가 말했다.

31 "그는 그렇게 나쁘진 않아."라고 다미는 생각했다.

32 "그래서, 무슨 말을 하고 있었던 거야?

33 너 할 말이 있니, 다미야?" 지훈이가 물었다.

34 "음, 이번 금요일에 나랑 학교 농구 경기에 같이 가는 게 어때?

35 그것은 결승전이야."

36 지훈은 정말 기뻐 보였다. "가고 싶어!"

※ 다음 문장을 우리말로 쓰시오.

1 Seho and Jihun were talking in the hallway when Dami came over.
➡ _____

2 "Happy birthday!" she said to Seho.
➡ _____

3 "Here. They're from my dad."
➡ _____

4 "Wow, two KBL tickets! Thanks!"
➡ _____

5 "Who are you going to take with you?" Dami asked.
➡ _____

6 "Minjun. He took me to a soccer game before.
➡ _____

7 So, it's time to pay him back."
➡ _____

8 "You know what?" Jihun cut in.
➡ _____

9 "Minjun isn't a fan of basketball. But I am!"
➡ _____

10 "Well, I'll ask him first anyway," replied Seho.
➡ _____

11 "He won't go with you. Trust me," said Jihun.
➡ _____

12 "Who is this guy?" Dami thought to herself, "He wants Minjun's ticket."
➡ _____

13 "Oh! There's the bell. See you later," said Dami.
➡ _____

14 She hurried to class.
➡ _____

15 "Come on, Jihun," said Seho, and he started to run.
➡ _____

16 At the corner, Seho bumped into someone.
➡ _____

17 "Sorry!" he said and continued to run.
➡ _____

18 Just then, Jihun saw something on the floor.
➡ _____

19 "Wait, Seho!" he said, but Seho was not there.

➡ _____

20 After class, Seho went to Dami and said, "I can't find one of my tickets.

➡ _____

21 Did you happen to see it?"

➡ _____

22 "No," she answered.

➡ _____

23 "Isn't it in your bag?"

➡ _____

24 "No, it's not there. I think I lost it," said Seho.

➡ _____

25 On her way home, Dami saw Jihun.

➡ _____

26 He had the ticket in his hand.

➡ _____

27 Dami got angry and said, "Hey! Why do you ...?"

➡ _____

28 Just then, Jihun saw Seho and shouted, "Seho! I found a ticket in the hallway.

➡ _____

29 I think it's yours."

➡ _____

30 "Thanks! I was looking for that!" said Seho.

➡ _____

31 "He's not so bad," Dami thought.

➡ _____

32 "So, what were you saying?

➡ _____

33 Do you have something to say, Dami?" asked Jihun.

➡ _____

34 "Um, how about going to the school basketball game with me this Friday?

➡ _____

35 It's the finals."

➡ _____

36 Jihun looked really pleased. "I'd love to!"

➡ _____

※ 다음 괄호 안의 단어들을 우리말에 맞도록 바르게 배열하시오.

1 (Jihun / and / Seho / talking / were / the / in / hallway / Dami / when / over. / came)
➡ _____

2 (birthday!" / "happy / to / she / Seho. / said)
➡ _____

3 ("here. // from / they're / dad." / my)
➡ _____

4 ("wow, / KBL / tickets! / two / thanks!")
➡ _____

5 (are / who / going / you / take / to / you?" / with / asked. / Dami)
➡ _____

6 ("Minjun. // took / he / to / me / game / a / before. / soccer)
➡ _____

7 (so, / time / it's / him / to / back." / pay)
➡ _____

8 (what?" / know / "you / in. / Jihun / cut)
➡ _____

9 (isn't / "Minjun / of / fan / a / basketball. // am!" / I / but)
➡ _____

10 ("well, / ask / I'll / him / anyway," / first / Seho. / replied)
➡ _____

11 (won't / "he / with / go / you. / me," / trust / Jihun. / said)
➡ _____

12 (this / is / guy?" / "who / Dami / herself, / to / thought / "he / Minjun's / ticket." / wants)
➡ _____

13 (oh! / the / there's / bell. / you / see / later," / Dami. / said)
➡ _____

14 (hurried / she / class. / to)
➡ _____

15 (on, / "come / Jihun," / Seho, / said / and / started / he / run. / to)
➡ _____

16 (corner, / the / at / Seho / into / someone. / bumped)
➡ _____

17 (he / said / "sorry!" / and / run. / to / continued)
➡ _____

18 (then, / just / Jihun / something / saw / floor. / on / the)
➡ _____

19 (Seho!" / "wait, / said, / he / but / was / Seho / there. / not)
➡ _____

1 세호와 지훈이는 다미가 왔을 때 복도에서 이야기를 나누고 있었다.

2 "생일 축하해!" 다미가 세호에게 말했다.

3 "이거 받아. 우리 아빠가 주신 거야."

4 "와, KBL 입장권 두 장! 고마워!"

5 "넌 누구를 데려 갈 거니?" 다미가 물었다.

6 "민준이. 그가 전에 나를 축구 경기에 데려갔어.

7 그래서 그에게 신세를 갚아야 할 때야."

8 "그거 알아?" 지훈이가 끼어들었다.

9 "민준이는 농구 팬이 아니야. 하지만 난 농구 팬이야!"

10 "음, 어쨌든 먼저 민준이에게 물어볼 거야." 세호가 대답했다.

11 "그는 너와 함께 가지 않을 거야. 날 믿어." 지훈이가 말했다.

12 "이 녀석은 누구지?" 다미는 "그는 민준이의 입장권을 원하는구나." 라고 마음속으로 생각했다.

13 "아, 종이 울린다. 나중에 보자," 다미가 말했다.

14 그녀는 서둘러 수업에 들어갔다.

15 "어서, 지훈아." 세호는 말하고 달리기 시작했다.

16 모퉁이에서, 세호는 누군가와 부딪혔다.

17 그는 "미안해!"라고 말하고는 계속 달렸다.

18 바로 그때, 지훈이가 바닥에 있는 무언가를 보았다.

19 "기다려, 세호야!"라고 그가 말했지만 세호는 거기에 없었다.

20 (class, / after / went / Seho / Dami / to / said, / and / "I / find / can't / of / my / tickets. / one)

➡ _____

21 (you / did / happen / see / it?" / to)

➡ _____

22 (she / answered. / "no,")

➡ _____

23 (it / isn't / your / bag?" / in)

➡ _____

24 ("no, / there. / not / it's / I / lost / I / think / it," / Seho. / said)

➡ _____

25 (her / on / home, / way / Jihun. / saw / Dami)

➡ _____

26 (had / he / ticket / the / hand. / in / his)

➡ _____

27 (got / Dami / said, / and / angry / "hey! / you / do / ...?" / why)

➡ _____

28 (then, / just / saw / Jihun / and / Seho / shouted, / "Seho! / found / I / a / ticket / hallway. / the / in)

➡ _____

29 (it's / yours." / think / I)

➡ _____

30 ("thanks! / was / I / looking / that!" / for / Seho. / said)

➡ _____

31 (not / bad," / so / "he's / thought. / Dami)

➡ _____

32 (what / "so, / you / saying? / were)

➡ _____

33 (you / do / something / have / to / say, / Dami?" / Jihun. / asked)

➡ _____

34 ("um, / about / how / going / the / to / basketball / school / game / me / with / Friday? / this)

➡ _____

35 (the / finals." / it's)

➡ _____

36 (looked / Jihun / pleased. // really / "I'd / to!" / love)

➡ _____

20 수업이 끝난 후, 세호는 다미에게 가서 말했다. "내 입장권 한 장을 찾을 수 없어.

21 너 혹시 입장권을 봤니?"

22 "아니." 그녀가 대답했다.

23 "네 가방 안에 있지 않니?"

24 "아니, 거기에 없어. 내 생각에 그것을 잃어버린 것 같아." 세호가 말했다.

25 집으로 돌아오는 길에 다미는 지훈을 보았다.

26 그는 손에 입장권을 가지고 있었다.

27 다미는 화가 나서 "이봐! 너가 왜 ...?"라고 말했다

28 바로 그때, 지훈이는 세호를 보고 소리쳤다. "세호야! 내가 복도에서 입장권을 찾았어.

29 네 것 같아."

30 "고마워! 나는 그것을 찾고 있었어!" 세호가 말했다.

31 "그는 그렇게 나쁘진 않아."라고 다미는 생각했다.

32 "그래서, 무슨 말을 하고 있었던 거야?

33 너 할 말이 있니, 다미야?" 지훈이가 물었다.

34 "음, 이번 금요일에 나랑 학교 농구 경기에 같이 가는 게 어때?

35 그것은 결승전이야."

36 지훈은 정말 기뻐 보였다. "가고 싶어!"

※ 다음 우리말을 영어로 쓰시오.

1 세호와 지훈이는 다미가 왔을 때 복도에서 이야기를 나누고 있었다.
➡ _____

2 "생일 축하해!" 다미가 세호에게 말했다.
➡ _____

3 "이거 받아. 우리 아빠가 주신 거야."
➡ _____

4 "와, KBL 입장권 두 장! 고마워!"
➡ _____

5 "넌 누구를 데려 갈 거니?" 다미가 물었다.
➡ _____

6 "민준이. 그가 전에 나를 축구 경기에 데려갔어.
➡ _____

7 그래서 그에게 신세를 갚아야 할 때야."
➡ _____

8 "그거 알아?" 지훈이가 끼어들었다.
➡ _____

9 "민준이는 농구 팬이 아니야. 하지만 난 농구 팬이야!"
➡ _____

10 "음, 어쨌든 먼저 민준이에게 물어볼 거야." 세호가 대답했다.
➡ _____

11 "그는 너와 함께 가지 않을 거야. 날 믿어." 지훈이가 말했다.
➡ _____

12 "이 녀석은 누구지?" 다미는 "그는 민준이의 입장권을 원하는구나."라고 마음속으로 생각했다.
➡ _____

13 "아, 종이 울린다. 나중에 보자,"라고 다미가 말했다.
➡ _____

14 그녀는 서둘러 수업에 들어갔다.
➡ _____

15 "어서, 지훈아." 세호는 말하고 달리기 시작했다.
➡ _____

16 모퉁이에서, 세호는 누군가와 부딪혔다.
➡ _____

17 그는 "미안해!"라고 말하고는 계속 달렸다.
➡ _____

18 바로 그때, 지훈이가 바닥에 있는 무언가를 보았다.
➡ _____

19 "기다려, 세호야!" 그가 말했지만 세호는 거기에 없었다.

➡ _____

20 수업이 끝난 후, 세호는 다미에게 가서 말했다, "내 입장권 한 장을 찾을 수 없어.

➡ _____

21 너 혹시 입장권을 봤니?"

➡ _____

22 "아니," 그녀가 대답했다.

➡ _____

23 "네 가방 안에 있지 않니?"

➡ _____

24 "아니, 거기에 없어. 내 생각에 그것을 잃어버린 것 같아." 세호가 말했다.

➡ _____

25 집으로 돌아오는 길에 다미는 지훈을 보았다.

➡ _____

26 그는 손에 입장권을 가지고 있었다.

➡ _____

27 다미는 화가 나서 "이봐! 너가 왜 ...?"라고 말했다.

➡ _____

28 바로 그때, 지훈이는 세호를 보고 소리쳤다, "세호야! 내가 복도에서 입장권을 찾았어.

➡ _____

29 네 것 같아."

➡ _____

30 "고마워! 나는 그것을 찾고 있었어!" 세호가 말했다.

➡ _____

31 "그는 그렇게 나쁘진 않아." 다미는 생각했다.

➡ _____

32 "그래서, 무슨 말을 하고 있었던 거야?

➡ _____

33 너 할 말이 있니, 다미야?" 지훈이가 물었다.

➡ _____

34 "음, 이번 금요일에 나랑 학교 농구 경기에 같이 가는 게 어때?

➡ _____

35 그것은 결승전이야."

➡ _____

36 지훈은 정말 기뻐 보였다. "가고 싶어!"

➡ _____

※ 다음 우리말과 일치하도록 빈칸에 알맞은 말을 쓰시오.

Project - Link to the World

가는 말이 고와야 오는 말이 곱다

1. This saying _____ "Nice _____ for nice words" _____ English.

2. I _____ _____ nice words to _____ first.

3. Then they will say _____ _____ to me, _____.

4. I _____ that I can _____ lots of good _____ this way.

5. This year, I will _____ _____ _____ remember this _____ and say nice words to _____.

가는 말이 고와야 오는 말이 곱다
1. 이 속담은 영어로 '좋은 말에는 좋은 말로'를 뜻한다.
2. 나는 먼저 다른 사람들에게 좋은 말을 할 것이다.
3. 그러면 그들도 나에게 좋은 말을 할 것이다.
4. 나는 이런 식으로 좋은 친구들을 많이 사귈 수 있다고 믿어.
5. 올해, 나는 항상 이 속담을 기억하고 다른 사람들에게 좋은 말을 하려고 노력할 것이다.

Check Yourself - Read & Write

1. Dami gave _____ _____ _____ _____.

2. Jihun _____ _____ _____ to the basketball game _____ Seho.

3. Seho _____ one of the tickets _____ _____ _____ go class.

4. Jihun _____ Seho's ticket in the _____.

5. Dami _____ Seho's ticket in Jihun's hand, and she _____, "He's a bad boy."

6. Jihun _____ the ticket _____ _____ Seho, and Dami _____ that she _____ _____.

7. Dami _____ _____ _____ _____ the school basketball game with Jihun.

8. Jihun was really _____.

1. 다미가 세호에게 농구 입장권 두 장을 주었다.
2. 지훈이는 세호와 농구 경기에 가고 싶어했다.
3. 세호는 수업에 가는 길에 입장권 하나를 떨어뜨렸다.
4. 지훈이는 복도에서 세호의 입장권을 발견했다.
5. 다미는 지훈이의 손에 있는 세호의 입장권을 보았고 그녀는 "그는 나쁜 소년이야."라고 생각했다.
6. 지훈이는 세호에게 입장권을 돌려주었고 다미는 그녀가 틀렸다는 것을 깨달았다.
7. 다미는 지훈이와 함께 학교 농구 경기에 가고 싶었다.
8. 지훈이는 정말 기뻐했다.

※ 다음 우리말을 영어로 쓰시오.

Project - Link to the World

가는 말이 고와야 오는 말이 곱다

1. 이 속담은 영어로 '좋은 말에는 좋은 말로'를 뜻한다.

   ➡ _____

2. 나는 먼저 다른 사람들에게 좋은 말을 할 것이다.

   ➡ _____

3. 그러면 그들도 나에게 좋은 말을 할 것이다.

   ➡ _____

4. 나는 이런 식으로 좋은 친구들을 많이 사귈 수 있다고 믿어.

   ➡ _____

5. 올해, 나는 항상 이 속담을 기억하고 다른 사람들에게 좋은 말을 하려고 노력할 것이다.

   ➡ _____

Check Yourself - Read & Write

1. 다미가 세호에게 농구 입장권 두 장을 주었다.

   ➡ _____

2. 지훈이는 세호와 농구 경기에 가고 싶어했다.

   ➡ _____

3. 세호는 수업에 가는 길에 입장권 하나를 떨어뜨렸다.

   ➡ _____

4. 지훈이는 복도에서 세호의 입장권을 발견했다.

   ➡ _____

5. 다미는 지훈이의 손에 있는 세호의 입장권을 보았고 그녀는 "그는 나쁜 소년이야."라고 생각했다.

   ➡ _____

6. 지훈이는 세호에게 입장권을 돌려주었고 다미는 그녀가 틀렸다는 것을 깨달았다.

   ➡ _____

7. 다미는 지훈이와 함께 학교 농구 경기에 가고 싶었다.

   ➡ _____

8. 지훈이는 정말 기뻤다.

   ➡ _____

※ 다음 영어를 우리말로 쓰시오.

01	elderly
02	closely
03	block
04	neighbor
05	butterfly
06	address
07	cute
08	director
09	doorbell
10	feed
11	free
12	check
13	gate
14	green
15	hurry
16	leave
17	cut
18	lost
19	build
20	chat
21	volunteer

22	hope
23	brown
24	rest
25	cry
26	strange
27	wash
28	borrow
29	clothes
30	lonely
31	perfect
32	nervous
33	exactly
34	outside
35	run after
36	take a break
37	look around
38	get better
39	take A to B
40	get enough rest
41	put up
42	be good at
43	take care of

Step2

※ 다음 우리말을 영어로 쓰시오.

01 ~ 주위에	
02 (고개를) 끄덕이다	
03 모양	
04 완벽한	
05 돌봄, 보살핌	
06 옷, 의복	
07 연습하다	
08 특별한	
09 충분한	
10 따라가다	
11 점, 반점	
12 무대	
13 꼭, 정확히	
14 열심히	
15 안에	
16 돌아오다[가다]	
17 외로운	
18 놓치다, 그리워하다	
19 여전히	
20 이사하다, 옮기다	
21 긴장되는	

22 밖에, 밖에서	
23 지나가다, 통과하다	
24 팔다	
25 알아맞히다	
26 중고의	
27 빌리다	
28 이상한	
29 수다를 떨다	
30 이웃	
31 먹이를 주다	
32 연세가 드신	
33 주소	
34 초인종	
35 ~에 늦다	
36 ~을 준비하다	
37 A를 B로 데려가다	
38 ~의 앞쪽에[앞에]	
39 둘러보다	
40 휴식을 취하다	
41 ~을 붙이다	
42 청소하다	
43 ~ 덕분에	

※ 다음 영영풀이에 알맞은 단어를 <보기>에서 골라 쓴 후, 우리말 뜻을 쓰시오.

1 _____ : complete and without faults or weaknesses: _____

2 _____ : to make something by putting together parts or materials: _____

3 _____ : to give food to a person or an animal: _____

4 _____ : unhappy because you have no friends or people to talk to: _____

5 _____ : to come or go to a place again: _____

6 _____ : a person who does a job without being paid for it: _____

7 _____ : details of where someone lives or works and where letters, etc. can be
sent: _____

8 _____ : a group of buildings with streets on all sides: _____

9 _____ : someone who lives next to you or near you: _____

10 _____ : a flying insect with a long thin body and four large, usually brightly
colored, wings: _____

11 _____ : a wound on a person's body that is made by something sharp:
_____

12 _____ : to move your head up and down, especially in order to show agreement
or understanding: _____

13 _____ : a period of time in which you relax, sleep, or do nothing after you have
been active or doing work: _____

14 _____ : a small round area that has a different color or feels different from the
surface it is on: _____

15 _____ : to take and use something that belongs to someone else, and return it to
them at a later time: _____

16 _____ : a bell on the outside of a house which you can ring so that the people
inside know that you want to see them: _____

spot	feed	volunteer	block
cut	address	borrow	return
butterfly	lonely	perfect	build
doorbell	rest	neighbor	nod

※ 다음 우리말과 일치하도록 빈칸에 알맞은 말을 쓰시오.

 해석

Get Ready - 2

1. B: I'm _____ _____ _____ some pictures _____ _____
   _____ the flower gate.
   G: _____ good. It's _____ _____.

2. B: Hello. _____ me, Jamie. I _____ I'll _____ there in 20
   minutes.
   G: Okay. _____ _____ _____ 2 p.m. _____ _____
   _____ the clock tower.

3. B: I'm _____ to buy some clothes _____ a school picnic.
   G: Look. They're _____ old books and clothes _____ _____.
   B: Great. _____ _____ and _____ _____.

1. B: 꽃문 앞에서 사진 몇 장을 찍을 거야.
   G: 좋은 생각이야. 그것은 저쪽에 있어.
2. B: 여보세요. 나야, Jamie. 20분 후에 도착할 것 같아.
   G: 알았어. 오후 2시에 시계탑 앞에서 만나자.
3. B: 학교 소풍을 위해 옷을 살 계획이야.
   G: 봐. 저기서 헌 책과 옷을 팔고 있어.
   B: 잘됐다. 가서 둘러보자.

Start Off - Listen & Talk A

1. G: Do you have _____ _____ _____ the weekend?
   B: Yes. I'm _____ _____ practice _____ at the youth center.
   G: _____ great. _____ I _____ you?
   B: Why _____?

2. G: I'm _____ _____ _____ to the library _____ _____
   _____ the exam.
   B: You _____ City Library? I want _____ _____ with you.
   G: Great. Can you _____ _____ _____ 3 p.m. tomorrow?
   B: Sure. _____ _____ _____.

1. G: 주말에 무슨 계획 있니?
   B: 응. 청소년 센터에서 춤을 연습하려고 해.
   G: 정말 잘 됐다. 같이 가도 될까?
   B: 물론이지.
2. G: 나는 시험을 준비하기 위해 도서관에 갈 계획이야.
   B: 시립 도서관 말하는 거니? 나는 너와 함께 공부하고 싶어.
   G: 좋아. 내일 오후 3시에 만날 수 있니?
   B: 물론. 그럼 그때 봐.

Start Off - Listen & Talk B

B: What _____ you _____ _____ _____ _____ this Saturday?
G: I'm planning _____ _____ _____ the park _____ my dad.
B: Sounds _____ a wonderful plan. _____ I _____ you?
G: Sure. Can you _____ _____ at the bus stop _____ 1 p.m.?
B: I'm _____ _____. _____ _____ 2?
G: _____ _____ me. Please _____ _____ _____
   _____ gloves and a big plastic bag.
B: Okay. _____ you _____ _____.

B: 이번 토요일에 뭐 할 거니?
G: 아빠와 함께 공원을 청소할 계획이야.
B: 멋진 계획인 것 같구나. 같이 가도 될까?
G: 물론이지. 버스 정류장에서 오후 1시에 만날 수 있니?
B: 안 될 것 같아. 2시는 어때?
G: 난 괜찮아. 장갑 한 켤레와 커다란 비닐봉지를 가져와.
B: 알았어. 토요일에 보자.

Start Off - Speak Up - Look and talk.

A: I'm _____ _____ _____ at the library this Tuseday.
B: Great. _____ I _____ _____ _____?
A: _____ _____? _____ you _____ at 3 p.m.?
B: Sure. _____ _____ _____ _____ _____ the library.

A: 이번 화요일에 도서관에서 자원봉사를 할 계획이야.
B: 멋지다. 같이 가도 될까?
A: 왜 안 되겠니? 오후 3시에 만날 수 있을까?
B: 물론이지. 도서관 앞에서 만나자.

Step Up - Real-life Scene

Let's Volunteer for a Better Town!

Jina: I'm _____ _____ _____ at the _____ _____ _____ this Sunday morning.

Alex: You _____ the one _____ Grand Park, Jina?

Jina: Right. _____ you _____ _____ me, Alex? They need _____ _____ _____ _____ _____ _____ the animals.

Alex: I'd _____ _____ join. I like _____ and _____ animals. I'm also _____ _____ _____ them.

Jina: Great. You can _____ other friends _____ you, _____.

Alex: Okay. I'll _____ _____ _____ Nancy. She loves animals, _____. What time _____ we _____?

Jina: Can you _____ it _____ 8 a.m. _____ the Grand Park bus stop?

Alex: Sure. I'll _____ you _____ _____.

Express Yourself A

1. **M:** _____ _____ _____ _____ _____ the town festival _____ _____ a dance show.

   W: Sounds _____. Can I _____ _____ you?

   M: _____ _____. _____ _____ _____ _____ at the school gate _____ 6 p.m.?

   W: _____ problem. _____ _____ _____.

2. **W:** I'm _____ _____ _____ a singing contest in my town, but I'm _____.

   M: _____ _____. _____ you _____ hard, you _____ _____ the contest.

   W: _____ you.

Learning Diary - Listen & Speak

B: What _____ _____ _____ _____ do this Friday, Aria?

G: I'm _____ _____ _____ at the post office.

B: Sounds _____!

G: _____ you _____ _____ me, Eric?

B: Sure. _____ _____ we _____?

G: _____ _____ _____ at 3 p.m.?

B: I'm _____ _____. _____ 4 p.m.?

G: Good. _____ _____ _____.

더 나은 마을을 위해 자원 봉사합시다!

지나: 이번 일요일 아침에 동물 보호 센터에서 자원봉사를 할 계획이야.

Alex: Grand Park 근처에 있는 거 말하는 거니, 지나야?

지나: 맞아. 나랑 같이 갈래, Alex? 그들은 동물들을 돌볼 자원 봉사자들이 필요해.

Alex: 나도 함께하고 싶어. 나는 동물들에게 먹이를 주고 산책시키는 것을 좋아해. 그리고 그들을 씻기는 것도 잘해.

지나: 좋아. 다른 친구들도 데려와도 돼.

Alex: 알았어. 내 이웃인 Nancy에게 물어볼게. 그녀도 동물들을 아주 좋아해. 몇 시에 만날까?

지나: Grand Park 버스 정류장에서 오전 8시에 만날까?

Alex: 물론. 일요일에 보자.

1. M: 나는 춤 공연을 보기 위해 마을 축제에 갈 계획이야.
   W: 재미있겠다. 같이 가도 될까?
   M: 물론이지. 오후 6시에 학교 정문에서 만날까?
   W: 그래. 그럼 그때 보자.

2. W: 나는 우리 동네 노래 경연 대회에 나갈 계획인데, 긴장돼.
   M: 걱정하지 마. 열심히 연습하면 너는 대회에서 우승할 수 있어.
   W: 고마워.

B: 이번 금요일에 뭐 할 거니, Aria?
G: 우체국에서 자원봉사를 할 계획이야.
B: 멋지다!
G: 나랑 같이 갈래, Eric?
B: 물론이지. 우리 언제 만날까?
G: 오후 3시에 만날 수 있을까?
B: 안 될 것 같아. 오후 4시는 어때?
G: 좋아. 그때 보자.

※ 다음 우리말에 맞도록 대화를 영어로 쓰시오.

Get Ready - 2

1. B: _____
   G: _____

2. B: _____
   G: _____

3. B: _____
   G: _____
   B: _____

1. B: 꽃문 앞에서 사진 몇 장을 찍을 거야.
   G: 좋은 생각이야. 그것은 저쪽에 있어.
2. B: 여보세요. 나야, Jamie. 20분 후에 도착할 것 같아.
   G: 알았어. 오후 2시에 시계탑 앞에서 만나자.
3. B: 학교 소풍을 위해 옷을 살 계획이야.
   G: 봐. 저기서 헌 책과 옷을 팔고 있어.
   B: 잘됐다. 가서 둘러보자.

Start Off - Listen & Talk A

1. G: _____
   B: _____
   G: _____
   B: _____

2. G: _____
   B: _____
   G: _____
   B: _____

1. G: 주말에 무슨 계획 있니?
   B: 응. 청소년 센터에서 춤을 연습하려고 해.
   G: 정말 잘 됐다. 같이 가도 될까?
   B: 물론이지.
2. G: 나는 시험을 준비하기 위해 도서관에 갈 계획이야.
   B: 시립 도서관 말하는 거니? 나는 너와 함께 공부하고 싶어.
   G: 좋아. 내일 오후 3시에 만날 수 있니?
   B: 물론. 그럼 그때 봐.

Start Off - Listen & Talk B

B: _____
G: _____
B: _____
G: _____
B: _____
G: _____
B: _____

B: 이번 토요일에 뭐 할 거니?
G: 아빠와 함께 공원을 청소할 계획이야.
B: 멋진 계획인 것 같구나. 같이 가도 될까?
G: 물론이지. 버스 정류장에서 오후 1시에 만날 수 있니?
B: 안 될 것 같아. 2시는 어때?
G: 난 괜찮아. 장갑 한 켤레와 커다란 비닐봉지를 가져와.
B: 알았어. 토요일에 보자.

Start Off - Speak Up - Look and talk.

A: _____
B: _____
A: _____
B: _____

A: 이번 화요일에 도서관에서 자원봉사를 할 계획이야.
B: 멋지다. 같이 가도 될까?
A: 왜 안 되겠니? 오후 3시에 만날 수 있을까?
B: 물론이지. 도서관 앞에서 만나자.

Step Up - Real-life Scene

Let's Volunteer for a Better Town!

Jina: _____

Alex: _____

Jina: _____

_____

Alex: _____

_____

Jina: _____

Alex: _____

_____

Jina: _____

Alex: _____

Express Yourself A

1. M: _____

W: _____

M: _____

W: _____

2. W: _____

M: _____

W: _____

Learning Diary - Listen & Speak

B: _____

G: _____

B: _____

G: _____

B: _____

G: _____

B: _____

G: _____

더 나은 마을을 위해 자원 봉사합시다!

지나: 이번 일요일 아침에 동물 보호 센터에서 자원봉사를 할 계획이야.

Alex: Grand Park 근처에 있는 거 말하는 거니, 지나야?

지나: 맞아. 나랑 같이 갈래, Alex? 그들은 동물들을 돌볼 자원 봉사자들이 필요해.

Alex: 나도 함께하고 싶어. 나는 동물들에게 먹이를 주고 산책시키는 것을 좋아해. 그리고 그들을 씻기는 것도 잘해.

지나: 좋아. 다른 친구들도 데려와도 돼.

Alex: 알았어. 내 이웃인 Nancy에게 물어볼게. 그녀도 동물들을 아주 좋아해. 몇 시에 만날까?

지나: Grand Park 버스 정류장에서 오전 8시에 만날까?

Alex: 물론. 일요일에 보자.

1. M: 나는 춤 공연을 보기 위해 마을 축제에 갈 계획이야.

W: 재미있겠다. 같이 가도 될까?

M: 물론이지. 오후 6시에 학교 정문에서 만날까?

W: 그래. 그럼 그때 보자.

2. W: 나는 우리 동네 노래 경연 대회에 나갈 계획인데, 긴장돼.

M: 걱정하지 마. 열심히 연습하면 너는 대회에서 우승할 수 있어.

W: 고마워.

B: 이번 금요일에 뭐 할 거니, Aria?

G: 우체국에서 자원봉사를 할 계획이야.

B: 멋지다!

G: 나랑 같이 갈래, Eric?

B: 물론이지. 우리 언제 만날까?

G: 오후 3시에 만날 수 있을까?

B: 안 될 것 같아. 오후 4시는 어때?

G: 좋아. 그때 보자.

※ 다음 우리말과 일치하도록 빈칸에 알맞은 것을 골라 쓰시오.

1 Bear was a _____ and _____ cat _____ green eyes.
A. with　　　　B. brown　　　　C. black

2 He _____ _____ a boy, Ryan.
A. with　　　　B. lived

3 Ryan always thought that "Bear" was a _____ name for the cat _____ he had a black _____ in the _____ of a bear.
A. shape　　　B. spot　　　C. because　　　D. perfect

4 Bear liked to go _____ every morning and _____ _____ butterflies.
A. after　　　　B. run　　　　C. outside

5 He _____ _____ home just _____ time for dinner.
A. in　　　　B. came　　　　C. always

6 Five blocks _____, Max the cat _____ _____ a girl, Sheila.
A. with　　　　B. lived　　　　C. away

7 When Sheila _____ to this town _____ month, she was _____.
A. lonely　　　　B. last　　　　C. moved

8 She _____ _____ friends there.
A. no　　　　B. had

9 But, _____ Max _____ her home, he _____ a good friend to her.
A. became　　　B. followed　　　C. after

10 _____ day, Sheila _____ Max sitting _____ the desk.
A. under　　　　B. saw　　　　C. one

11 He was _____ a strange _____.
A. sound　　　　B. making

12 "What's _____?" _____ Sheila.
A. asked　　　　B. wrong

13 She looked _____ him and _____ a bad _____ on his leg.
A. cut　　　B. closely　　　C. found　　　D. at

14 She _____ him _____ the animal _____.
A. hospital　　　B. to　　　C. took

15 The doctor said, "He will get _____ if he _____ enough _____. _____ him inside for a week."
A. keep　　　B. rest　　　C. gets　　　D. better

16 That night, _____ Ryan's house, there _____ _____ Bear.
A. no　　　　B. was　　　　C. at

17 Ryan checked _____, but he _____ _____ him.
A. outside　　　B. find　　　C. couldn't

18 He _____ posters and _____ them _____ around town.
A. up　　　　B. put　　　　C. made

19 A _____ night _____. Still _____ Bear.
A. no　　　　B. passed　　　　C. third

20 When Sheila was _____ _____ her house, she _____ a poster about the _____ cat.
A. lost　　　B. near　　　C. saw　　　D. walking

1 Bear는 초록색 눈을 가진 검은 색과 갈색의 고양이였다.

2 그는 소년 Ryan과 함께 살았다.

3 Ryan은 항상 "Bear"가 곰 모양의 검은 반점이 있기 때문에 그 고양이에게 딱 맞는 이름이라고 생각했다.

4 Bear는 매일 아침 밖으로 나가 나비를 쫓아다니는 것을 좋아했다.

5 그는 항상 저녁 식사 시간에 맞춰 집에 왔다.

6 다섯 블록 떨어진 곳에, 고양이 Max는 Sheila라는 소녀와 함께 살았다.

7 지난달에 Sheila가 이 마을로 이사 왔을 때, 그녀는 외로웠다.

8 그녀는 그곳에 친구가 없었다.

9 하지만 Max가 그녀를 따라 집으로 온 후, 그는 그녀에게 좋은 친구가 되었다.

10 어느 날, Sheila는 책상 밑에 앉아 있는 Max를 보았다.

11 그는 이상한 소리를 내고 있었다.

12 "무슨 일 있니?" Sheila가 물었다.

13 그녀는 그를 자세히 살펴보고 그의 다리에 심한 상처가 난 것을 발견했다.

14 그녀는 그를 동물 병원으로 데려갔다.

15 의사는 "충분한 휴식을 취하면 좋아질 거야. 그를 일주일 동안 안에 있도록 해라."라고 말했다.

16 그날 밤, Ryan의 집에는 Bear가 없었다.

17 Ryan은 바깥을 살폈지만 그는 그를 찾을 수 없었다.

18 그는 포스터를 만들어서 마을을 다니며 그것을 붙였다.

19 세 번째 밤이 지났다. 여전히 Bear는 나타나지 않았다.

20 Sheila가 그녀의 집 근처를 걷고 있었을 때, 그녀는 잃어버린 고양이에 대한 포스터를 보았다.

21 She _____ it _____, and her eyes _____ big.
A. got   B. closely   C. read

22 "This cat _____ exactly _____ Max. It's so _____."
A. strange   B. like   C. looks

23 She _____ _____.
A. home   B. hurried

24 "Come _____, Max! _____ go!"
A. let's   B. on

25 She _____ him _____ the address _____ the poster.
A. on   B. to   C. took

26 "Ding-Dong." When Ryan _____ the doorbell _____, he _____ to the door and _____ it.
A. opened   B. ran   C. ring   D. heard

27 "Bear, you're _____!" Ryan _____.
A. cried   B. back

28 Max _____ up _____ Ryan's _____.
A. arms   B. into   C. jumped

29 "_____ me _____," said Sheila.
A. guess   B. let

30 "Your cat _____ home _____ in the evenings, _____ he?"
A. doesn't   B. only   C. comes

31 _____ _____.
A. nodded   B. Ryan

32 "And you _____ him _____ Friday, _____ you?" Sheila said.
A. didn't   B. last   C. lost

33 "Yes! _____ did you _____?" said Ryan.
A. know   B. how

34 "_____ this is my cat, _____, and he usually comes to my home _____ _____ the day."
A. during   B. too   C. only   D. because

35 "_____ cat _____ two families!" _____ Ryan.
A. said   B. has   C. our

36 "Hey, _____ you have time, please come _____ and _____ some cookies."
A. have   B. in   C. if

37 "_____," _____ Sheila.
A. said   B. sure

38 "_____ you, Max," she _____.
A. thought   B. thank

39 "I _____ a good neighbor _____ _____ you!"
A. thanks   B. to   C. met

21 그녀는 그것을 자세히 읽고, 그녀의 눈은 커졌다.

22 "이 고양이는 꼭 Max 같아 보여. 너무 이상해."

23 그녀는 서둘러 집으로 돌아갔다.

24 "자, Max! 가자!"

25 그녀는 그를 포스터에 적힌 주소로 데려갔다.

26 "딩동." Ryan은 초인종이 울리는 소리를 듣고 문으로 달려가 문을 열었다.

27 "Bear야, 돌아왔구나!" Ryan이 외쳤다.

28 Max가 Ryan의 팔 안으로 뛰어올랐다.

29 "내가 맞춰 볼게," Sheila가 말했다.

30 "너의 고양이는 저녁에만 집에 오지, 그렇지?"

31 Ryan은 고개를 끄덕였다.

32 "그리고 너는 지난 금요일에 그를 잃어버렸지, 그렇지 않니?" Sheila가 말했다.

33 "응! "어떻게 알았니?"라고 Ryan은 말했다.

34 "이것은 또한 내 고양이이기 때문이야, 보통 낮에만 우리 집에 오거든."

35 "우리 고양이는 가족이 둘이야!" Ryan이 말했다.

36 이봐, 시간이 있으면 들어와서 쿠키 좀 먹어."

37 "그래." Sheila가 말했다.

38 "고마워, Max." 그녀는 생각했다.

39 "나는 네 덕분에 좋은 이웃을 만났어!"

※ 다음 우리말과 일치하도록 빈칸에 알맞은 말을 쓰시오.

1 Bear was a black and brown cat _____ _____ _____.

2 He _____ _____ a boy, Ryan.

3 Ryan _____ _____ that "Bear" was a _____ name for the cat _____ he had a black _____ in the _____ of a bear.

4 Bear _____ _____ _____ _____ every morning and _____ _____ butterflies.

5 He _____ came home just _____ time _____ dinner.

6 Five blocks _____, Max the cat _____ _____ a girl, Sheila.

7 _____ Sheila _____ _____ this town _____ _____, she was _____.

8 She _____ _____ _____ there.

9 But, _____ Max _____ _____ _____, he _____ a good friend to her.

10 _____ _____, Sheila _____ Max _____ under the desk.

11 He _____ _____ _____ _____ _____ _____.

12 "What's _____?" _____ Sheila.

13 She _____ _____ him _____ and _____ _____ _____ on his leg.

14 She _____ him _____ the _____ _____.

15 The doctor said, "He will _____ _____ if he _____ _____ _____. _____ _____ _____ for a week."

16 That night, _____ Ryan's house, there _____ _____ Bear.

17 Ryan _____ _____, but he _____ _____ him.

18 He _____ posters and _____ them _____ around town.

19 A _____ _____ _____. _____ no Bear.

20 _____ Sheila _____ _____ _____ her house, she _____ a poster about _____ _____ _____.

---

1 Bear는 초록색 눈을 가진 검은 색과 갈색의 고양이였다.

2 그는 소년 Ryan과 함께 살았다.

3 Ryan은 항상 "Bear"가 곰 모양의 검은 반점이 있기 때문에 그 고양이에게 딱 맞는 이름이라고 생각했다.

4 Bear는 매일 아침 밖으로 나가 나비를 쫓아다니는 것을 좋아했다.

5 그는 항상 저녁 식사 시간에 맞춰 집에 왔다.

6 다섯 블록 떨어진 곳에, 고양이 Max는 Sheila라는 소녀와 함께 살았다.

7 지난달에 Sheila가 이 마을로 이사 왔을 때, 그녀는 외로웠다.

8 그녀는 그곳에 친구가 없었다.

9 하지만 Max가 그녀를 따라 집으로 온 후, 그는 그녀에게 좋은 친구가 되었다.

10 어느 날, Sheila는 책상 밑에 앉아 있는 Max를 보았다.

11 그는 이상한 소리를 내고 있었다.

12 "무슨 일이니?" Sheila가 물었다.

13 그녀는 그를 자세히 살펴보고 그의 다리에 심한 상처가 난 것을 발견했다.

14 그녀는 그를 동물 병원으로 데려갔다.

15 의사는 "충분한 휴식을 취하면 좋아질 거야. 그를 일주일 동안 안에 있도록 해라."라고 말했다.

16 그날 밤, Ryan의 집에는 Bear가 없었다.

17 Ryan은 바깥을 살폈지만 그를 찾을 수 없었다.

18 그는 포스터를 만들어서 마을을 다니며 그것을 붙였다.

19 세 번째 밤이 지났다. 여전히 Bear는 나타나지 않았다.

20 Sheila가 그녀의 집 근처를 걷고 있었을 때, 그녀는 잃어버린 고양이에 대한 포스터를 보았다.

21 She _____ it _____, and her eyes _____ _____.

22 "This cat _____ exactly _____ Max. It's so _____."

23 She _____ _____.

24 "Come _____, Max! _____ _____!"

25 She _____ him _____ the address on the poster.

26 "Ding-Dong." _____ Ryan _____ the doorbell _____, he _____ _____ the door and _____ it.

27 "Bear, you're _____!" Ryan _____.

28 Max _____ _____ _____ Ryan's arms.

29 "_____ _____ _____," said Sheila.

30 "Your cat _____ _____ only _____ the evenings, _____ he?"

31 Ryan _____.

32 "And you _____ him _____ Friday, _____ _____?" Sheila said.

33 "Yes! _____ _____ you _____?" said Ryan.

34 "_____ this is my cat, _____, and he _____ _____ to my home only _____ _____ _____."

35 "Our cat _____ _____ _____!" said Ryan.

36 "Hey, _____ _____ _____ _____, please _____ _____ and _____ some cookies."

37 "_____," said Sheila.

38 "_____ you, Max," she _____.

39 "I _____ a good neighbor _____ _____ _____!"

21 그녀는 그것을 자세히 읽고, 그녀의 눈은 커졌다.

22 "이 고양이는 꼭 Max 같아 보여. 너무 이상해."

23 그녀는 서둘러 집으로 돌아갔다.

24 "자, Max! 가자!"

25 그녀는 그를 포스터에 적힌 주소로 데려갔다.

26 "딩동." Ryan은 초인종이 울리는 소리를 듣고 문으로 달려가 문을 열었다.

27 "Bear야, 돌아왔구나!" Ryan이 외쳤다.

28 Max가 Ryan의 팔 안으로 뛰어올랐다.

29 "내가 맞춰 볼게," Sheila가 말했다.

30 "너의 고양이는 저녁에만 집에 오지, 그렇지?"

31 Ryan은 고개를 끄덕였다.

32 "그리고 너는 지난 금요일에 그를 잃어버렸지, 그렇지 않니?" Sheila가 말했다.

33 "응! "어떻게 알았니?"라고 Ryan은 말했다.

34 "이것은 또한 내 고양이이기 때문이야, 보통 낮에만 우리 집에 오거든."

35 "우리 고양이는 가족이 둘이야!" Ryan이 말했다.

36 이봐, 시간이 있으면 들어와서 쿠키 좀 먹어."

37 "그래," Sheila가 말했다.

38 "고마워, Max." 그녀는 생각했다.

39 "나는 네 덕분에 좋은 이웃을 만났어!"

※ 다음 문장을 우리말로 쓰시오.

1 Bear was a black and brown cat with green eyes.
➡ _____

2 He lived with a boy, Ryan.
➡ _____

3 Ryan always thought that "Bear" was a perfect name for the cat because he had a black spot in the shape of a bear.
➡ _____

4 Bear liked to go outside every morning and run after butterflies.
➡ _____

5 He always came home just in time for dinner.
➡ _____

6 Five blocks away, Max the cat lived with a girl, Sheila.
➡ _____

7 When Sheila moved to this town last month, she was lonely.
➡ _____

8 She had no friends there.
➡ _____

9 But, after Max followed her home, he became a good friend to her.
➡ _____

10 One day, Sheila saw Max sitting under the desk.
➡ _____

11 He was making a strange sound.
➡ _____

12 "What's wrong?" asked Sheila.
➡ _____

13 She looked at him closely and found a bad cut on his leg.
➡ _____

14 She took him to the animal hospital.
➡ _____

15 The doctor said, "He will get better if he gets enough rest. Keep him inside for a week."
➡ _____

16 That night, at Ryan's house, there was no Bear.
➡ _____

17 Ryan checked outside, but he couldn't find him.
➡ _____

18 He made posters and put them up around town.
➡ _____

19 A third night passed. Still no Bear.
➡ _____

20 When Sheila was walking near her house, she saw a poster about the lost cat.
➡ _____

21 She read it closely, and her eyes got big.

➡ _____

22 "This cat looks exactly like Max. It's so strange."

➡ _____

23 She hurried home.

➡ _____

24 "Come on, Max! Let's go!"

➡ _____

25 She took him to the address on the poster.

➡ _____

26 "Ding-Dong." When Ryan heard the doorbell ring, he ran to the door and opened it.

➡ _____

27 "Bear, you're back!" Ryan cried.

➡ _____

28 Max jumped up into Ryan's arms.

➡ _____

29 "Let me guess," said Sheila.

➡ _____

30 "Your cat comes home only in the evenings, doesn't he?"

➡ _____

31 Ryan nodded.

➡ _____

32 "And you lost him last Friday, didn't you?" Sheila said.

➡ _____

33 "Yes! How did you know?" said Ryan.

➡ _____

34 "Because this is my cat, too, and he usually comes to my home only during the day."

➡ _____

35 "Our cat has two families!" said Ryan.

➡ _____

36 "Hey, if you have time, please come in and have some cookies."

➡ _____

37 "Sure," said Sheila.

➡ _____

38 "Thank you, Max," she thought.

➡ _____

39 "I met a good neighbor thanks to you!"

➡ _____

※ 다음 괄호 안의 단어들을 우리말에 맞도록 바르게 배열하시오.

1 (was / Bear / black / and / a / brown / with / cat / eyes. / green)
➡ _____

2 (lived / he / a / with / Ryan. / boy,)
➡ _____

3 (always / Ryan / thought / that / was / "Bear" / perfect / a / name / for / cat / the / because / had / he / a / spot / black / in / the / bear. / of / a / shape)
➡ _____

4 (liked / Bear / go / to / outside / morning / every / and / run / butterflies. / after)
➡ _____

5 (always / he / came / just / home / in / dinner. / for / time)
➡ _____

6 (away, / blocks / five / the / Max / cat / with / lived / Sheila. / girl, / a)
➡ _____

7 (Sheila / moved / when / this / to / town / month, / last / lonely. / was / she)
➡ _____

8 (had / no / she / there. / friends)
➡ _____

9 (but, / Max / followed / after / her / home, / he / became / her. / to / a / friend / good)
➡ _____

10 (day, / one / Max / saw / Sheila / under / desk. / the / sitting)
➡ _____

11 (he / making / was / sound. / strange / a)
➡ _____

12 (wrong?" / "what's / Sheila. / asked)
➡ _____

13 (she / at / looked / him / closely / and / found / a / cut / leg. / bad / his / on)
➡ _____

14 (she / him / to / took / the / hospital. / animal)
➡ _____

15 (the / said, / doctor / "he / get / will / better / if / gets / he / rest. / enough // him / keep / for / inside / week." / a)
➡ _____

16 (night, / that / Ryan's / at / house, / was / there / Bear. / no)
➡ _____

17 (Ryan / outside, / checked / but / couldn't / he / him. / find)
➡ _____

18 (he / posters / made / and / them / put / town. / up / around)
➡ _____

19 (a / night / passed. / third / Bear. / no / still)
➡ _____

20 (Sheila / when / walking / was / her / near / house, / she / a / saw / poster / the / cat. / about / lost)
➡ _____

1 Bear는 초록색 눈을 가진 검은색과 갈색의 고양이였다.

2 그는 소년 Ryan과 함께 살았다.

3 Ryan은 항상 "Bear"가 곰 모양의 검은 반점이 있기 때문에 그 고양이에게 딱 맞는 이름이라고 생각했다.

4 Bear는 매일 아침 밖으로 나가 나비를 쫓아다니는 것을 좋아했다.

5 그는 항상 저녁 식사 시간에 맞춰 집에 왔다.

6 다섯 블록 떨어진 곳에, 고양이 Max는 Sheila라는 소녀와 함께 살았다.

7 지난달에 Sheila가 이 마을로 이사 왔을 때, 그녀는 외로웠다.

8 그녀는 그곳에 친구가 없었다.

9 하지만 Max가 그녀를 따라 집으로 온 후, 그는 그녀에게 좋은 친구가 되었다.

10 어느 날, Sheila는 책상 밑에 앉아 있는 Max를 보았다.

11 그는 이상한 소리를 내고 있었다.

12 "무슨 일 있니?" Sheila가 물었다.

13 그녀는 그를 자세히 살펴보고 그의 다리에 심한 상처가 난 것을 발견했다.

14 그녀는 그를 동물 병원으로 데려갔다.

15 의사는 "충분한 휴식을 취하면 좋아질 거야. 그를 일주일 동안 안에 있도록 해라."라고 말했다.

16 그날 밤, Ryan의 집에는 Bear가 없었다.

17 Ryan은 바깥을 살폈지만 그는 그를 찾을 수 없었다.

18 그는 포스터를 만들어서 마을을 다니며 그것을 붙였다.

19 세 번째 밤이 지났다. 여전히 Bear는 나타나지 않았다.

20 Sheila가 그녀의 집 근처를 걷고 있었을 때, 그녀는 잃어버린 고양이에 대한 포스터를 보았다.

21 (it / read / she / closely, / and / eyes / her / big. / got)
➡ _____

22 (cat / like / looks / this / exactly / Max. / so / strange." / it's)
➡ _____

23 (home. / hurried / she)
➡ _____

24 (on, / Max! / "come / go!" / let's)
➡ _____

25 (took / she / to / him / address / the / on / poster. / the)
➡ _____.

26 ("Dong-Dong." / Ryan / when / the / ring, / doorbell / heard / he / to / ran / door / the / it. / opened / and)
➡ _____

27 (you're / "Bear, / back!" / cried. / Ryan)
➡ _____

28 (jumped / Max / up / arms. / Ryan's / into)
➡ _____

29 (me / "let / guess," / Sheila. / said)
➡ _____

30 ("your / comes / cat / home / only / the / evenings, / in / he?" / doesn't)
➡ _____

31 (nodded. / Ryan)
➡ _____

32 ("and / him / lost / you / Firday, / last / you?" / didn't / said. / Sheila)
➡ _____

33 ("yes! / you / did / know?" / how / Ryan. / said)
➡ _____

34 (this / "because / is / cat, / my / too, / and / he / usually / to / comes / home / my / during / day." / the / only)
➡ _____

35 (cat / "our / two / families!" / has / Ryan. / said)
➡ _____

36 ("hey, / you / if / time, / have / please / in / come / and / cookies." / some / have)
➡ _____

37 ("sure,' / Sheila. / said)
➡ _____

38 (you, / "thank / Max," / thought. / she)
➡ _____

39 ("I / a / met / neighbor / good / to / you!" / thanks)
➡ _____

21 그녀는 그것을 자세히 읽고, 그녀의 눈은 커졌다.

22 "이 고양이는 꼭 Max 같아 보여. 너무 이상해."

23 그녀는 서둘러 집으로 돌아갔다.

24 "자, Max! 가자!"

25 그녀는 그를 포스터에 적힌 주소로 데려갔다.

26 "딩동." Ryan은 초인종이 울리는 소리를 듣고 문으로 달려가 문을 열었다.

27 "Bear야, 돌아왔구나!" Ryan이 외쳤다.

28 Max가 Ryan의 팔 안으로 뛰어올랐다.

29 "내가 맞춰 볼게." Sheila가 말했다.

30 "너의 고양이는 저녁에만 집에 오지, 그렇지?"

31 Ryan은 고개를 끄덕였다.

32 "그리고 너는 지난 금요일에 그를 잃어버렸지, 그렇지 않니?" Sheila가 말했다.

33 "응! "어떻게 알았니?"라고 Ryan은 말했다.

34 "이것은 또한 내 고양이이기 때문이야, 보통 낮에만 우리 집에 오거든."

35 "우리 고양이는 가족이 둘이야!" Ryan이 말했다.

36 이봐, 시간이 있으면 들어와서 쿠키 좀 먹어."

37 "그래." Sheila가 말했다.

38 "고마워, Max." 그녀는 생각했다.

39 "나는 네 덕분에 좋은 이웃을 만났어!"

※ 다음 우리말을 영어로 쓰시오.

1 Bear는 초록색 눈을 가진 검은색과 갈색의 고양이였다.
➡ _____

2 그는 소년 Ryan과 함께 살았다.
➡ _____

3 Ryan은 항상 "Bear"가 곰 모양의 검은 반점이 있기 때문에 그 고양이에게 딱 맞는 이름이라고 생각했다.
➡ _____
_____

4 Bear는 매일 아침 밖으로 나가 나비를 쫓아다니는 것을 좋아했다.
➡ _____

5 그는 항상 저녁 식사 시간에 맞춰 집에 왔다.
➡ _____

6 다섯 블록 떨어진 곳에, 고양이 Max는 Sheila라는 소녀와 함께 살았다.
➡ _____

7 지난달에 Sheila가 이 마을로 이사 왔을 때, 그녀는 외로웠다.
➡ _____

8 그녀는 그곳에 친구가 없었다.
➡ _____

9 하지만 Max가 그녀를 따라 집으로 온 후, 그는 그녀에게 좋은 친구가 되었다.
➡ _____

10 어느 날, Sheila는 책상 밑에 앉아 있는 Max를 보았다.
➡ _____

11 그는 이상한 소리를 내고 있었다.
➡ _____

12 "무슨 일 있니?" Sheila가 물었다.
➡ _____

13 그녀는 그를 자세히 살펴보고 그의 다리에 심한 상처가 난 것을 발견했다.
➡ _____

14 그녀는 그를 동물 병원으로 데려갔다.
➡ _____

15 의사는 "충분한 휴식을 취하면 좋아질 거야. 그를 일주일 동안 안에 있도록 해라."라고 말했다.
➡ _____

16 그날 밤, Ryan의 집에는 Bear가 없었다.
➡ _____

17 Ryan은 바깥을 살폈지만 그는 그를 찾을 수 없었다.
➡ _____

18 그는 포스터를 만들어서 마을을 다니며 그것을 붙였다.
➡ _____

19 세 번째 밤이 지났다. 여전히 Bear는 나타나지 않았다.
➡ _____

20 Sheila가 그녀의 집 근처를 걷고 있었을 때, 그녀는 잃어버린 고양이에 대한 포스터를 보았다.
➡ _____

21 그녀는 그것을 자세히 읽고, 그녀의 눈은 커졌다.

➡ _____

22 "이 고양이는 꼭 Max 같아 보여. 너무 이상해."

➡ _____

23 그녀는 서둘러 집으로 돌아갔다.

➡ _____

24 "자, Max! 가자!"

➡ _____

25 그녀는 그를 포스터에 적힌 주소로 데려갔다.

➡ _____

26 "딩동." Ryan은 초인종이 울리는 소리를 듣고 문으로 달려가 문을 열었다.

➡ _____

27 "Bear야, 돌아왔구나!" Ryan이 외쳤다.

➡ _____

28 Max가 Ryan의 팔 안으로 뛰어올랐다.

➡ _____

29 "내가 맞춰 볼게," Sheila가 말했다.

➡ _____

30 "너의 고양이는 저녁에만 집에 오지, 그렇지?"

➡ _____

31 Ryan은 고개를 끄덕였다.

➡ _____

32 "그리고 너는 지난 금요일에 그를 잃어버렸지, 그렇지 않니?" Sheila가 말했다.

➡ _____

33 "응! "어떻게 알았니?"라고 Ryan은 말했다.

➡ _____

34 "이것은 또한 내 고양이이기 때문이야, 보통 낮에만 우리 집에 오거든."

➡ _____

35 "우리 고양이는 가족이 둘이야!" Ryan이 말했다.

➡ _____

36 이봐, 시간이 있으면 들어와서 쿠키 좀 먹어."

➡ _____

37 "그래," Sheila가 말했다.

➡ _____

38 "고마워, Max." 그녀는 생각했다.

➡ _____

39 "나는 네 덕분에 좋은 이웃을 만났어!"

➡ _____

※ 다음 우리말과 일치하도록 빈칸에 알맞은 말을 쓰시오.

Express Yourself C1~C2

1. C1: Do you _____ _____ _____ a magic show?

2. _____ you _____ the town festival on Monday, you _____ _____ Harry _____ magic tricks. _____ _____ at the festival!

3. C2: Do you want _____ _____ an _____ movie?

4. If you visit the town festival _____ _____, you _____ _____ Mr. Jackson, a director _____ _____ his new movie. It will _____ _____!

1. C1: 마술쇼를 보고 싶니?
2. 월요일에 마을 축제에 가면, Harry가 마술 묘기를 부리는 것을 볼 수 있을 거야. 축제 잘 보내!
3. C2: 야외 영화 보고 싶니?
4. 금요일에 마을 축제에 가면, 너는 영화감독 Jackson 씨가 그의 새 영화에 대해 이야기하는 것을 들을 거야. 그것은 재미있을 거야!

Project - Step 2

1. This is my _____ *tteokbokki* restaurant _____ _____ _____.

2. If you go there, you _____ _____ many students _____ *tteokbokki* and _____.

3. This is a _____ _____ _____ park near the school.

4. If you _____ _____ _____ a nice _____, please visit it.

5. You can _____ _____ _____ in the trees.

1. 이곳은 우리 동네에서 내가 제일 좋아하는 떡볶이 식당이다.
2. 그곳에 가면, 너는 많은 학생들이 떡볶이를 먹으면서 수다를 떨고 있는 것을 볼 수 있을 것이다.
3. 이곳은 학교 근처에 있는 작지만 아름다운 공원이다.
4. 편안한 휴식을 취하고 싶다면, 꼭 이곳을 방문하라.
5. 너는 나무에서 새들이 지저귀는 소리를 들을 수 있다.

Link to the World

1. _____ make a _____ _____!

2. In the U.S., there _____ a volunteer project _____ _____ houses for families _____ _____.

3. Many people _____ _____ the project to _____ _____ _____.

4. It's _____ _____ _____ _____ in Canada.

5. If you want to read books _____ _____ your neighbors, make one _____ _____ _____ your house!

6. It's a _____ refrigerator _____ _____.

7. People _____ _____ _____ in this refrigerator for people _____ _____.

1. 더 나은 마을을 만들자!
2. 미국에서는 도움이 필요한 가정을 위해 집을 짓는 자원봉사 프로젝트가 있다.
3. 많은 사람들이 그들에게 희망을 주기 위해 이 프로젝트에 참여하고 있다.
4. 그것은 캐나다에 있는 작은 무료 도서관이다.
5. 만약 여러분이 여러분의 이웃과 함께 책을 읽고 싶다면, 집 앞에 그것을 만들어라!
6. 그것은 독일에 있는 특별한 냉장고다.
7. 사람들은 도움이 필요한 사람들을 위해 이 냉장고 안에 음식을 두고 갈 수 있다.

※ 다음 우리말을 영어로 쓰시오.

Express Yourself C1~C2

1. C1: 마술쇼를 보고 싶니?
   ➡ _____

2. 월요일에 마을 축제에 가면, Harry가 마술 묘기를 부리는 것을 볼 수 있을 거야. 축제 잘 보내!
   ➡ _____

3. C2: 야외 영화 보고 싶니?
   ➡ _____

4. 금요일에 마을 축제에 가면, 너는 영화감독 Jackson 씨가 그의 새 영화에 대해 이야기하는 것을 들을 거야. 그것은 재미있을 거야.
   ➡ _____
   _____

Project - Step 2

1. 이곳은 우리 동네에서 내가 제일 좋아하는 떡볶이 식당이다.
   ➡ _____

2. 그곳에 가면, 너는 많은 학생들이 떡볶이를 먹으면서 수다를 떨고 있는 것을 볼 수 있을 것이다.
   ➡ _____

3. 이곳은 학교 근처에 있는 작지만 아름다운 공원이다.
   ➡ _____

4. 편안한 휴식을 취하고 싶다면, 꼭 이곳을 방문해라.
   ➡ _____

5. 너는 나무에서 새들이 지저귀는 소리를 들을 수 있다.
   ➡ _____

Link to the World

1. 더 나은 마을을 만들자!
   ➡ _____

2. 미국에서는 도움이 필요한 가정을 위해 집을 짓는 자원봉사 프로젝트가 있다.
   ➡ _____

3. 많은 사람들이 그들에게 희망을 주기 위해 이 프로젝트에 참여하고 있다.
   ➡ _____

4. 그것은 캐나다에 있는 작은 무료 도서관이다.
   ➡ _____

5. 만약 여러분이 여러분의 이웃과 함께 책을 읽고 싶다면, 집 앞에 그것을 만들어라!
   ➡ _____

6. 그것은 독일에 있는 특별한 냉장고다.
   ➡ _____

7. 사람들은 도움이 필요한 사람들을 위해 이 냉장고 안에 음식을 두고 갈 수 있다.
   ➡ _____

※ 다음 영어를 우리말로 쓰시오.

01	alone	22	behind
02	bite	23	someday
03	careful	24	join
04	dangerous	25	kind
05	direction	26	create
06	clothes	27	balance
07	exist	28	later
08	past	29	probably
09	far	30	rule
10	figure	31	search
11	climber	32	touch
12	actually	33	skill
13	following	34	yet
14	fun	35	hang up
15	safety	36	keep ~ in mind
16	real	37	over there
17	special	38	make noise
18	remember	39	be good for
19	climb	40	hear of
20	scenery	41	for the first time
21	harmony	42	for example
		43	go up

※ 다음 우리말을 영어로 쓰시오.

01	활동적인, 활발한	
02	표지판, 간판	
03	축제	
04	인물, 모습	
05	밀다	
06	곳, 장소	
07	풀, 잔디	
08	연습하다	
09	조언, 충고	
10	가까운, 친한	
11	안전한	
12	포즈[자세]	
13	정보	
14	길, 거리, 도로	
15	바위, 암석	
16	십대의	
17	공주	
18	헐거워진, 풀린, 헐렁한	
19	거울	
20	헬멧	
21	박물관, 미술관	

22	담소하다, 채팅하다	
23	과거, 지난날	
24	비결, 요령, 속임수	
25	~ 없이, ~하지 않고	
26	해변, 바닷가	
27	경치, 풍경	
28	균형, 평형	
29	조화, 화합	
30	옷, 의복	
31	조심하는, 주의 깊은	
32	위험한	
33	안전, 안전성	
34	특별한, 특수한	
35	예를 들면, 예를 들어	
36	처음으로	
37	~을 명심하다	
38	~에 좋다	
39	~ 앞에	
40	전화를 끊다	
41	떠들다	
42	~에 대해 듣다	
43	저쪽에, 저기에서	

※ 다음 영영풀이에 알맞은 단어를 <보기>에서 골라 쓴 후, 우리말 뜻을 쓰시오.

1 _____ : an artist who paints pictures: _____

2 _____ : able or likely to hurt or harm you: _____

3 _____ : moving around a lot or doing a lot of things: _____

4 _____ : an area of sand or stones beside the sea: _____

5 _____ : sit on a horse or bike and control its movements: _____

6 _____ : to talk to each other in an informal and friendly way: _____

7 _____ : a female member of a royal family, usually the daughter of a king or
queen: _____

8 _____ : a road in a city, town, or village, usually with houses along it: _____

9 _____ : aged between thirteen and nineteen years old: _____

10 _____ : the things that people wear, such as shirts, coats, trousers, and dresses:
_____

11 _____ : the hard substance which the Earth is made of: _____

12 _____ : a hat made of a strong material which you wear to protect your head:
_____

13 _____ : what you think someone should do in a particular situation: _____

14 _____ : to move towards the top of something such as a tree, mountain, or
ladder: _____

15 _____ : to use force to make something move away from you or away from its
previous position: _____

16 _____ : a flat piece of glass which reflects light, so that when you look at it you
can see yourself reflected in it: _____

※ 다음 우리말과 일치하도록 빈칸에 알맞은 말을 쓰시오.

Get Ready - 2

1. **G:** Look _____ that boy. He's _____.
   B: He's _____ an MTB. Do you _____ _____ it?
   G: No. _____ is it?
   B: It's a _____ bike _____ _____ _____ a mountain.

2. **G:** Wait. _____ jump _____ the water _____.
   B: _____ _____?
   G: You _____ swim _____ a life jacket. _____ it _____.

3. **G:** _____ _____ the beautiful flowers _____ _____! I'd _____ _____ _____ a selfie _____ _____ _____ them.
   B: You _____ go _____ there.
   G: Oh, _____.

4. **B:** I _____ _____ _____ _____ the birds _____ the trees.
   G: You _____ _____ _____ _____ too close to the _____.
   B: All _____, thanks.

Start Off - Listen & Talk A

1. **G:** Dad, _____ you _____ _____ _____ _____ Kim Soyun, the rock _____?
   M: Yes, I've _____ her _____ _____.
   G: She's _____ _____ _____ _____ at a _____ this Saturday. I _____ _____ _____ the camp.
   M: Okay, Miso, _____ you _____ _____ _____ too high.
   G: All _____. Thanks, Dad.

2. **G:** _____ you _____ of Rock Boys?
   M: _____, _____ _____.
   G: It's my _____ band. There's a _____ this Saturday. _____ _____ _____?
   M: Okay, Minju, but you _____ _____ _____ too late.
   G: All _____. Thanks, Dad.

1. G: 저 소년을 봐. 그는 대단하다.
   B: 그는 MTB를 타고 있어. 넌 그것에 대해 알고 있니?
   G: 아니. 그게 뭐지?
   B: 그것은 산에서 타는 특별한 자전거야.

2. G: 기다려. 아직 물속으로 뛰어들지 마.
   B: 왜 안 돼?
   G: 구명조끼 없이 수영하면 안 돼. 이 것을 입어.

3. G: 저기 있는 아름다운 꽃들을 봐! 그 꽃들 앞에서 셀피를 찍고 싶어.
   B: 거기 가면 안 돼.
   G: 아, 알았어.

4. B: 나는 나무에 있는 새들을 보고 싶어.
   G: 새들에게 너무 가까이 가지 마.
   B: 알았어, 고마워.

1. G: 아빠, 암벽 등반가인 김소윤에 대해 들어본 적 있으세요?
   M: 응, TV에서 봤어.
   G: 그녀가 이번 토요일에 캠프에서 암벽 등반을 가르쳐요. 저는 캠프 에 참가하고 싶어요.
   M: 알았어, 미소야, 하지만 너무 높이 올라가면 안 돼.
   G: 알았어요. 고마워요, 아빠.

2. G: Rock Boys에 대해 들어보셨어요?
   M: 아니, 듣지 못했다.
   G: 그건 제가 제일 좋아하는 밴드에 요. 이번 토요일에 콘서트가 있어 요. 가도 돼요?
   M: 좋아, 민주야, 하지만 너무 늦게 집에 오면 안 돼.
   G: 알았어요. 고마워요, 아빠.

Start Off - Listen & Talk B

B: _____ you _____ _____ bird watching?

M: Sure. I _____ it _____ I was a child.

B: That's nice. Actually, I'm _____ it _____ _____ _____ _____ this Saturday.

M: Are you? You _____ _____ warm clothes and _____ _____ _____.

B: Okay. What else _____ I _____ _____ _____?

M: You _____ _____ any noise _____ you watch the birds.

B: I'll _____ _____ _____ _____ _____. Thanks, Dad.

Step Up - Real-life Scene

Video Chat with Minjun from Jeju

A: Hello, Somin! _____ me! _____ you _____ _____?

B: Oh, _____, Minjun! What's _____?

A: This is so cool, _____ _____? We can video _____ on the phone! _____ you _____ _____ Jeju *Olle*?

B: _____, _____ _____. I really _____ to go there someday.

A: _____ _____? I'm on it now. Actually, I'm _____ _____ _____ _____ Seongsan Ilchulbong now.

B: That's _____!

A: Don't _____ _____. Enjoy the beautiful _____ with me.

B: _____ careful! You _____ _____ your cell phone _____ _____ _____.

A: Oh, _____. _____ you. I'll _____ you photos _____.

Express Yourself A

1. **G:** _____ _____ _____ _____ _____ Elvis Presley?

   B: _____, _____ _____ _____. _____ is he?

   G: He was a _____ _____ _____ and _____. We can see a _____ of Elvis here.

   B: _____ interesting. I want to _____ _____ with it.

   G: Okay. _____ _____.

2. **W:** You _____ _____ selfies here. Van Gogh's _____ is _____ you.

   B: _____ _____, Mom. It's not his _____ painting. _____ I can take selfies _____ _____ it.

   W: Really? Sounds interesting. _____ I take _____ here, too?

   B: Why _____?

B: 새 관찰에 대해 들어보셨어요?

M: 물론이지. 어렸을 때 해 봤어.

B: 그거 멋지네요. 사실, 전 이번 주 토요일에 처음으로 그것을 할 거예요.

M: 그래? 넌 따뜻한 옷과 먹을 것을 가져가야 해.

B: 알았어요. 그 밖에 또 무엇을 명심해야 하나요?

M: 너는 새들을 관찰할 때 아무 소리도 내지 말아야 해.

B: 그것을 명심할게요. 고마워요, 아빠.

제주에서 걸려온 민준과의 화상 채팅

A: 여보세요, 소민아! 나야! 나를 볼 수 있니?

B: 오, 안녕, 민준아! 무슨 일이니?

A: 이거 정말 멋지지 않니? 전화로 화상 채팅도 할 수 있어! 너 제주 올레에 대해 들어 본 적이 있니?

B: 응, 있어. 나는 언젠가 꼭 가 보고 싶어.

A: 그거 알아? 나 지금 올레에 있어. 사실은, 지금 성산 일출봉에 올라가려고 해.

B: 멋지다!

A: 끊지 마. 나와 함께 아름다운 경치를 즐겨.

B: 조심해! 걸을 때는 휴대폰을 사용해서는 안 돼.

A: 아, 맞다. 고마워. 나중에 사진 보내 줄게.

1. **G:** 엘비스 프레슬리에 대해 들어 본 적 있니?

   B: 아니, 없어. 그는 누구인데?

   G: 그는 유명한 미국 가수이자 배우였어. 우리는 여기서 엘비스의 모형을 볼 수 있어.

   B: 재미있을 것 같다. 그것과 함께 사진을 찍고 싶어.

   G: 좋아. 가자.

2. **W:** 넌 여기서 셀피를 찍으면 안 돼. 반 고흐의 그림이 네 뒤에 있어.

   B: 엄마, 걱정하지 마세요. 그건 그의 진짜 그림이 아니에요. 그래서 그 앞에서 셀피를 찍을 수 있어요.

   W: 정말이지? 재미있겠다. 나도 여기서 셀피를 찍을 수 있을까?

   B: 물론이죠.

해석

※ 다음 우리말에 맞도록 대화를 영어로 쓰시오.

Get Ready - 2

1. G: _____

   B: _____

   G: _____

   B: _____

2. G: _____

   B: _____

   G: _____

3. G: _____

   _____

   B: _____

   G: _____

4. B: _____

   G: _____

   B: _____

1. G: 저 소년을 봐. 그는 대단하다.
   B: 그는 MTB를 타고 있어. 넌 그것에 대해 알고 있니?
   G: 아니. 그게 뭐지?
   B: 그것은 산에서 타는 특별한 자전거야.

2. G: 기다려. 아직 물속으로 뛰어들지 마.
   B: 왜 안 돼?
   G: 구명조끼 없이 수영하면 안 돼. 이것을 입어.

3. G: 저기 있는 아름다운 꽃들을 봐! 그 꽃들 앞에서 셀피를 찍고 싶어.
   B: 거기 가면 안 돼.
   G: 아, 알았어.

4. B: 나는 나무에 있는 새들을 보고 싶어.
   G: 새들에게 너무 가까이 가지 마.
   B: 알았어, 고마워.

Start Off - Listen & Talk A

1. G: _____

   M: _____

   G: _____

   _____

   M: _____

   G: _____

2. G: _____

   M: _____

   G: _____

   M: _____

   G: _____

1. G: 아빠, 암벽 등반가인 김소윤에 대해 들어 본 적 있으세요?
   M: 응, TV에서 봤어.
   G: 그녀가 이번 토요일에 캠프에서 암벽 등반을 가르쳐요. 저는 캠프에 참가하고 싶어요.
   M: 알았어, 미소야, 하지만 너무 높이 올라가면 안 돼.
   G: 알았어요. 고마워요, 아빠.

2. G: Rock Boys에 대해 들어보셨어요?
   M: 아니, 듣지 못했다.
   G: 그건 제가 제일 좋아하는 밴드에요. 이번 토요일에 콘서트가 있어요. 가도 돼요?
   M: 좋아, 민주야, 하지만 너무 늦게 집에 오면 안 돼.
   G: 알았어요. 고마워요, 아빠.

Start Off - Listen & Talk B

B: _____

M: _____

B: _____

M: _____

B: _____

M: _____

B: _____

Step Up - Real-life Scene

Video Chat with Minjun from Jeju

A: _____

B: _____

A: _____
_____

B: _____

A: _____
_____

B: _____

A: _____

B: _____

A: _____

Express Yourself A

1. G: _____

   B: _____

   G: _____
   _____

   B: _____

   G: _____

2. W: _____

   B: _____

   W: _____

   B: _____

B: 새 관찰에 대해 들어보셨어요?

M: 물론이지. 어렸을 때 해 봤어.

B: 그거 멋지네요. 사실, 전 이번 주 토요일에 처음으로 그것을 할 거예요.

M: 그래? 넌 따뜻한 옷과 먹을 것을 가져가야 해.

B: 알았어요. 그 밖에 또 무엇을 명심해야 하나요?

M: 너는 새들을 관찰할 때 아무 소리도 내지 말아야 해.

B: 그것을 명심할게요. 고마워요, 아빠.

제주에서 걸려온 민준과의 화상 채팅

A: 여보세요, 소민아! 나야! 나를 볼 수 있니?

B: 오, 안녕, 민준아! 무슨 일이니?

A: 이거 정말 멋지지 않아? 전화로 화상 채팅도 할 수 있어! 너 제주 올레에 대해 들어 본 적이 있니?

B: 응, 있어. 나는 언젠가 꼭 가 보고 싶어.

A: 그거 알아? 나 지금 올레에 있어. 사실은, 지금 성산 일출봉에 올라가려고 해.

B: 멋지다!

A: 끊지 마. 나와 함께 아름다운 경치를 즐겨.

B: 조심해! 걸을 때는 휴대폰을 사용해서는 안 돼.

A: 아, 맞다. 고마워. 나중에 사진 보내줄게.

1. G: 엘비스 프레슬리에 대해 들어 본 적 있니?

   B: 아니, 없어. 그는 누구인데?

   G: 그는 유명한 미국 가수이자 배우였어. 우리는 여기서 엘비스의 모형을 볼 수 있어.

   B: 재미있을 것 같다. 그것과 함께 사진을 찍고 싶어.

   G: 좋아. 가자.

2. W: 넌 여기서 셀피를 찍으면 안 돼. 반 고흐의 그림이 네 뒤에 있어.

   B: 엄마, 걱정하지 마세요. 그건 그의 진짜 그림이 아니에요. 그래서 그 앞에서 셀피를 찍을 수 있어요.

   W: 정말이지? 재미있겠다. 나도 여기서 셀피를 찍을 수 있을까?

   B: 물론이죠.

※ 다음 우리말과 일치하도록 빈칸에 알맞은 것을 골라 쓰시오.

1 _____ you _____ _____ of a "selfie"?
A. heard   B. ever   C. have

2 _____ you _____ a photograph of _____, it's a selfie.
A. yourself   B. take   C. when

3 The students from Minji's photo club _____ searched _____ information _____ selfies for one month.
A. about   B. for   C. have

4 _____ are some of their _____ about _____.
A. selfies   B. presentations   C. here

5 Did _____ in the past _____ selfies?
A. take   B. people

6 _____ it wasn't easy _____ that time, the _____ is yes.
A. answer   B. at   C. though

7 _____ _____ this photo _____ Princess Anastasia.
A. of   B. at   C. look

8 She _____ a mirror to _____ a picture of _____.
A. herself   B. take   C. used

9 She _____ _____.
A. nervous   B. looks

10 Can you _____ _____?
A. why   B. guess

11 Well, I _____ it was her _____ selfie.
A. first   B. think

12 And it was _____ the world's first _____ selfie _____.
A. teenage   B. ever   C. probably

13 You can _____ selfies _____ world-famous places _____ Big Ben and the Leaning Tower of Pisa.
A. like   B. at   C. take

14 To _____ great pictures, just do fun _____ and use camera _____.
A. tricks   B. poses   C. take

15 You can _____ visit _____ museums to take _____ selfies.
A. fun   B. special   C. also

16 For _____, there _____ a _____ selfie museum in the Philippines.
A. is   B. famous   C. example

17 It has special _____ to _____ selfies.
A. take   B. spots

18 You can _____ the paintings and _____ inside them.
A. step   B. touch   C. even

19 Look _____ the _____ pictures.
A. following   B. at

20 _____ the boys are not really _____ horses, it looks _____ they are.
A. like   B. riding   C. though

1 여러분은 "셀피"에 대해 들어 본 적이 있나요?

2 여러분 자신의 사진을 찍을 때 그것이 셀피에요.

3 민지의 사진 동아리 학생들은 한 달 동안 셀피에 대한 정보를 찾았습니다.

4 여기 셀피에 대한 그들의 발표 내용이 있습니다.

5 과거의 사람들은 셀피를 찍었나 요?

6 그 때는 셀피를 찍는 것이 쉽지는 않았지만. 답은 '그렇다'입니다.

7 아나스타샤 공주의 이 사진을 보세요.

8 그녀는 거울을 사용하여 자신의 사진을 찍었습니다.

9 그녀는 긴장되어 보입니다.

10 왜인지 추측할 수 있나요?

11 글쎄, 나는 그것이 그녀의 첫 번 째 셀피였다고 생각해요.

12 그리고 그것은 아마도 세계 최초 의 10대 소녀의 셀피였을 거예요.

13 여러분은 빅벤과 피사의 사탑과 같은 세계적으로 유명한 장소에 서 셀피를 찍을 수 있습니다.

14 멋진 사진을 찍기 위해서, 단지 재미있는 포즈를 취하고 카메라 기술을 이용하세요.

15 여러분은 또한 재미있는 셀피를 찍기 위해 특별한 박물관을 방 문할 수 있습니다.

16 예를 들어, 필리핀에는 유명한 셀피 박물관이 있습니다.

17 그곳은 셀피를 찍기 위한 특별한 장소들이 있습니다.

18 여러분은 그림들을 만질 수 있 고 심지어 그림들 안으로 들어 갈 수도 있어요.

19 다음 사진들을 보세요.

20 비록 그 소년들은 말을 타고 있 는 것은 아니지만, 말을 타고 있 는 것처럼 보입니다.

21 Though the man is just _____ a big _____, it looks like he is _____ the Mona Lisa.
A. painting   B. brush   C. holding

22 Selfie museums _____ in Korea, _____.
A. too   B. exist

23 I have _____ one in Chuncheon _____.
A. before   B. visited

24 Why _____ you go there _____?
A. yourself   B. don't

25 These selfies _____ great, _____ _____ they a good idea?
A. were   B. but   C. look

26 I _____ think _____.
A. so   B. don't

27 They don't _____ _____.
A. safe   B. look

28 You _____ take special _____ when you take _____ in the wild or at high _____ like these.
A. places   B. selfies   C. care   D. should

29 A monkey could _____ you at any _____, or you _____ fall.
A. could   B. time   C. bite

30 Here _____ some _____ tips:
A. safety   B. are

31 1. _____ take selfies _____ you're _____.
A. walking   B. while   C. don't

32 2. _____ not _____ with or _____ wild animals.
A. near   B. pose   C. do

33 3. _____ take selfies _____ dangerous _____.
A. places   B. in   C. never

34 I think we can _____ selfies to _____ a _____ school life.
A. better   B. make   C. use

35 We _____ do good _____ at school and _____ selfies.
A. take   B. things   C. can

36 Then we can _____ the photos _____ our school _____.
A. website   B. on   C. post

37 I've _____ the _____ and flowers at school _____ one month.
A. for   B. plants   C. watered

38 I've _____ helped the teacher _____ the school library many _____.
A. times   B. at   C. also

39 _____ _____ my selfies of _____ things.
A. those   B. at   C. look

40 How _____ _____ me to _____ a better school life?
A. create   B. joining   C. about

---

21 비록 그 남자는 단지 커다란 붓을 잡고 있지만, 모나리자를 그리고 있는 것처럼 보입니다.

22 한국에도 셀피 박물관이 있습니다.

23 나는 전에 춘천에 있는 한 박물관을 방문한 적이 있습니다.

24 여러분도 직접 그곳에 가는 게 어때요?

25 이 셀피들은 멋져 보이지만, 그것들은 좋은 생각이었나요?

26 난 그렇게 생각하지 않아요.

27 그것들은 안전해 보이지 않습니다.

28 여러분은 야생이나 이와 같이 높은 곳에서 셀피를 찍을 때 특별한 주의를 기울여야 합니다.

29 원숭이가 언제든지 당신을 물거나 또는 당신은 떨어질 수 있습니다.

30 여기 몇 가지 안전 수칙이 있습니다.

31 1. 걸으면서 셀피를 찍지 마세요.

32 2. 야생 동물들과 함께 또는 가까이에서 포즈를 취하지 마세요.

33 3. 위험한 곳에서는 절대 셀피를 찍지 마세요.

34 나는 우리가 더 나은 학교생활을 만들기 위해 셀피를 이용할 수 있다고 생각해요.

35 우리는 학교에서 좋은 일을 할 수 있고 셀피를 찍을 수도 있습니다.

36 그리고 나서 우리는 학교 웹사이트에 사진을 올릴 수 있어요.

37 나는 한 달 동안 학교에서 식물과 꽃에 물을 주었습니다.

38 나는 또한 학교 도서관에서 선생님을 여러 번 도왔습니다.

39 그런 것들에 대한 내 셀피를 보세요.

40 저와 함께 더 나은 학교생활을 만들어 보는 건 어떨까요?

※ 다음 우리말과 일치하도록 빈칸에 알맞은 말을 쓰시오.

1 _____ you _____ _____ _____ a "selfie"?

2 When you _____ a photograph _____ _____, it's a selfie.

3 The students from Minji's photo _____ have _____ _____ _____ about selfies _____ one month.

4 _____ are some of _____ _____ about selfies.

5 Did _____ in the past _____ _____?

6 _____ it _____ easy at that time, the _____ is yes.

7 _____ _____ this photo of Princess Anastasia.

8 She _____ a mirror _____ _____ a picture of _____.

9 She _____ _____.

10 _____ you _____ _____?

11 Well, I _____ it was _____ _____ _____.

12 And it was _____ the world's first _____ selfie ever.

13 You _____ _____ _____ at world-famous places _____ Big Ben and the Leaning Tower of Pisa.

14 _____ _____ great _____, just do fun _____ and _____ _____.

15 You can _____ visit special museums to take _____ selfies.

16 For _____, there is a _____ selfie museum in the Philippines.

17 It _____ _____ _____ to _____ selfies.

18 You can _____ the paintings and _____ _____ inside them.

19 _____ _____ the _____ pictures.

20 _____ the boys are not really _____ horses, it _____ _____ they are.

1 여러분은 "셀피"에 대해 들어 본 적이 있나요?

2 여러분 자신의 사진을 찍을 때 그것이 셀피에요.

3 민지의 사진 동아리 학생들은 한 달 동안 셀피에 대한 정보를 찾았습니다.

4 여기 셀피에 대한 그들의 발표 내용이 있습니다.

5 과거의 사람들은 셀피를 찍었나요?

6 그 때는 셀피를 찍는 것이 쉽지는 않았지만, 답은 '그렇다'입니다.

7 아나스타샤 공주의 이 사진을 보세요.

8 그녀는 거울을 사용하여 자신의 사진을 찍었습니다.

9 그녀는 긴장되어 보입니다.

10 왜인지 추측할 수 있나요?

11 글쎄, 나는 그것이 그녀의 첫 번째 셀피였다고 생각해요.

12 그리고 그것은 아마도 세계 최초의 10대 소녀의 셀피였을 거예요.

13 여러분은 빅벤과 피사의 사탑과 같은 세계적으로 유명한 장소에서 셀피를 찍을 수 있습니다.

14 멋진 사진을 찍기 위해서, 단지 재미있는 포즈를 취하고 카메라 기술을 이용하세요.

15 여러분은 또한 재미있는 셀피를 찍기 위해 특별한 박물관을 방문할 수 있습니다.

16 예를 들어, 필리핀에는 유명한 셀피 박물관이 있습니다.

17 그곳은 셀피를 찍기 위한 특별한 장소들이 있습니다.

18 여러분은 그림들을 만질 수 있고 심지어 그림들 안으로 들어갈 수도 있어요.

19 다음 사진들을 보세요.

20 비록 그 소년들은 말을 타고 있는 것은 아니지만, 말을 타고 있는 것처럼 보입니다.

21 Though the man is _____ _____ a big _____, it _____ _____ he is _____ the Mona Lisa.

22 Selfie museums _____ in Korea, _____.

23 I _____ _____ one in Chuncheon _____.

24 _____ _____ you go there _____?

25 These selfies _____ great, _____ were they a good idea?

26 I _____ _____ _____.

27 They _____ _____ _____.

28 You _____ _____ _____ _____ when you take selfies in the wild or at high _____ _____ these.

29 A monkey _____ _____ you _____ _____ _____, or you _____ _____.

30 _____ _____ some _____ _____:

31 1. Don't _____ selfies _____ _____ _____.

32 2. Do _____ _____ with or near _____ animals.

33 3. _____ _____ _____ in dangerous _____.

34 I think we can _____ selfies to make a _____ school life.

35 We can do good _____ at school and _____ selfies.

36 Then we _____ _____ the photos on our school _____.

37 I've _____ the plants and flowers at _____ for one month.

38 I've _____ _____ the teacher _____ the school library _____ _____.

39 _____ _____ my selfies of _____ things.

40 _____ _____ joining me to _____ a better school life?

---

21 비록 그 남자는 단지 커다란 붓을 잡고 있지만, 모나리자를 그리고 있는 것처럼 보입니다.

22 한국에도 셀피 박물관이 있습니다.

23 나는 전에 춘천에 있는 한 박물관을 방문한 적이 있습니다.

24 여러분도 직접 그곳에 가는 게 어때요?

25 이 셀피들은 멋져 보이지만, 그것들은 좋은 생각이었나요?

26 난 그렇게 생각하지 않아요.

27 그것들은 안전해 보이지 않습니다.

28 여러분은 야생이나 이와 같이 높은 곳에서 셀피를 찍을 때 특별한 주의를 기울여야 합니다.

29 원숭이가 언제든지 당신을 물거나 또는 당신은 떨어질 수 있습니다.

30 여기 몇 가지 안전 수칙이 있습니다.

31 1. 걸으면서 셀피를 찍지 마세요.

32 2. 야생 동물들과 함께 또는 가까이에서 포즈를 취하지 마세요.

33 3. 위험한 곳에서는 절대 셀피를 찍지 마세요.

34 나는 우리가 더 나은 학교생활을 만들기 위해 셀피를 이용할 수 있다고 생각해요.

35 우리는 학교에서 좋은 일을 할 수 있고 셀피를 찍을 수도 있습니다.

36 그리고 나서 우리는 학교 웹사이트에 사진을 올릴 수 있어요.

37 나는 한 달 동안 학교에서 식물과 꽃에 물을 주었습니다.

38 나는 또한 학교 도서관에서 선생님을 여러 번 도왔습니다.

39 그런 것들에 대한 내 셀피를 보세요.

40 저와 함께 더 나은 학교생활을 만들어 보는 건 어떨까요?

※ 다음 문장을 우리말로 쓰시오.

1 Have you ever heard of a "selfie"? When you take a photograph of yourself, it's a selfie.
➡ _____

2 The students from Minji's photo club have searched for information about selfies for one month.
➡ _____

3 Here are some of their presentations about selfies.
➡ _____

4 Did people in the past take selfies?
➡ _____

5 Though it wans't easy at that time. the answer is yes.
➡ _____

6 Look at this photo of Princess Anastasia. She used a mirror to take a picture of herself.
➡ _____

7 She looks nervous. Can you guess why?
➡ _____

8 Well, I think it was her first selfie.
➡ _____

9 And it was probably the world's first teenage selfie ever.
➡ _____

10 You can take selfies at world-famous places like Big Ben and the Leaning Tower of Pisa.
➡ _____

11 To take great pictures, just do fun poses and use camera tricks.
➡ _____

12 You can also visit special museums to take fun selfies.
➡ _____

13 For example, there is a famous selfie museum in the Philippines.
➡ _____

14 It has special spots to take selfies.
➡ _____

15 You can touch the paintings and even step inside them.
➡ _____

16 Look at the following pictures.
➡ _____

17 Though the boys are not really riding horses, it looks like they are.

➡ _____

18 Though the man is just holding a big brush, it looks like he is painting the Mona Lisa.

➡ _____

19 Selfie museums exist in Korea, too. I have visited one in Chuncheon before.

➡ _____

20 Why don't you go there yourself? These selfies look great, but were they a good idea?

➡ _____

21 I don't think so. They don't look safe.

➡ _____

22 You should take special care when you take selfies in the wild or at high places like these.

➡ _____

23 A monkey could bite you at any time, or you could fall.

➡ _____

24 Here are some safety tips:

➡ _____

25 Don't take selfies while you're walking.

➡ _____

26 Do not pose with or near wild animals.

➡ _____

27 Never take selfies in dangerous places.

➡ _____

28 I think we can use selfies to make a better school life.

➡ _____

29 We can do good things at school and take selfies.

➡ _____

30 Then we can post the photos on our school website.

➡ _____

31 I've watered the plants and flowers at school for one month.

➡ _____

32 I've also helped the teacher at the school library many times.

➡ _____

33 Look at my selfies of those things.

➡ _____

34 How about joining me to create a better school life?

➡ _____

※ 다음 괄호 안의 단어들을 우리말에 맞도록 바르게 배열하시오.

1 (you / have / ever / of / heard / "selfie"? / a // when / take / you / photograph / of / a / yourself, / a / selfie. / it's)
➡ _____
_____

2 (students / the / from / photo / Minji's / club / searched / have / information / for / about / selfies / month. / one / for)
➡ _____

3 (are / here / of / some / their / presentations / selfies. / about)
➡ _____

4 (people / did / in / past / the / selfies? / take)
➡ _____

5 (it / though / wasn't / easy / that / at / time, / yes. / is / answer / the)
➡ _____

6 (at / look / photo / this / Princess / of / Anastasia. // used / she / mirror / a / take / to / picture / a / herself. / of)
➡ _____
_____

7 (looks / she / nervous. // you / can / guess / why?)
➡ _____

8 (well, / think / I / was / it / selfie. / first / her)
➡ _____

9 (and / was / it / the / probably / world's / teenage / first / ever. / selfie)
➡ _____

10 (you / take / can / selfies / at / places / world-famous / like / Big / Ben / and / Pisa. / of / Tower / the / Leaning)
➡ _____
_____

11 (take / great / to / pictures, / do / just / poses / fun / and / tricks. / camera / use)
➡ _____

12 (you / also / can / visit / museums / special / selfies. / take / to / fun)
➡ _____

13 (example, / for / is / there / famous / a / selfie / in / museum / Philippines. / the)
➡ _____

14 (has / it / spots / special / selfies. / take / to)
➡ _____

15 (can / you / touch / paintings / the / and / step / even / them. / inside)
➡ _____

16 (at / look / the / pictures. / following)
➡ _____

---

1 여러분은 "셀피"에 대해 들어 본 적이 있나요? 여러분 자신의 사진을 찍을 때 그것이 셀피에요.

2 민지의 사진 동아리 학생들은 한 달 동안 셀피에 대한 정보를 찾았습니다.

3 여기 셀피에 대한 그들의 발표 내용이 있습니다.

4 과거의 사람들은 셀피를 찍었나요?

5 그 때는 셀피를 찍는 것이 쉽지는 않았지만. 답은 '그렇다'입니다.

6 아나스타샤 공주의 이 사진을 보세요. 그녀는 거울을 사용하여 자신의 사진을 찍었습니다.

7 그녀는 긴장되어 보입니다. 왜 인지 추측할 수 있나요?

8 글쎄, 나는 그것이 그녀의 첫 번째 셀피였다고 생각해요.

9 그리고 그것은 아마도 세계 최초의 10대 소녀의 셀피였을 거예요.

10 여러분은 빅벤과 피사의 사탑과 같은 세계적으로 유명한 장소에서 셀피를 찍을 수 있습니다.

11 멋진 사진을 찍기 위해서, 단지 재미있는 포즈를 취하고 카메라 기술을 이용하세요.

12 여러분은 또한 재미있는 셀피를 찍기 위해 특별한 박물관을 방문할 수 있습니다.

13 예를 들어, 필리핀에는 유명한 셀피 박물관이 있습니다.

14 그곳은 셀피를 찍기 위한 특별한 장소들이 있습니다.

15 여러분은 그림들을 만질 수 있고 심지어 그림들 안으로 들어갈 수도 있어요.

16 다음 사진들을 보세요.

17 (the / though / boys / are / really / not / horses, / riding / looks / it / like / are. / they)
➡ _____

18 (the / man / though / is / holding / just / big / a / brush, / it / like / looks / is / he / painting / Lisa. / Mona / the)
➡ _____

19 (museums / selfie / in / exist / too. / Korea, // have / I / visited / in / one / before. / Chuncheon)
➡ _____

20 (you / don't / why / go / yourself? / there // selfies / these / great, / look / but / they / were / idea? / good / a)
➡ _____

21 (don't / so. / I / think // don't / they / safe. / look)
➡ _____.

22 (you / take / should / care / special / when / take / you / selfies / the / in / wild / or / high / at / these. / places / like)
➡ _____

23 (monkey / a / bite / could / you / at / time, / any / or / fall. / could / you)
➡ _____

24 (are / here / safety / tips: / some)
➡ _____

25 (selfies / don't / take / while / walking. / you're)
➡ _____

26 (pose / not / do / with / or / animals. / near / wild)
➡ _____

27 (take / never / selfies / places. / dangerous / in)
➡ _____

28 (we / think / I / use / can / selfies / make / to / a / school / better / life.)
➡ _____

29 (we / do / can / things / good / school / at / and / selfies. / take)
➡ _____

30 (then / we / post / can / photos / the / on / website. / school / our)
➡ _____

31 (I've / the / plants / watered / and / flowers / school / at / month. / one / for)
➡ _____

32 (I've / helped / also / teacher / the / at / school / the / library / times. / many)
➡ _____

33 (at / my / look / selfies / things. / those / of)
➡ _____

34 (about / how / joining / to / me / create / a / life? / school / better)
➡ _____

17 비록 그 소년들은 말을 타고 있는 것은 아니지만, 말을 타고 있는 것처럼 보입니다.

18 비록 그 남자는 단지 커다란 붓을 잡고 있지만, 모나리자를 그리고 있는 것처럼 보입니다.

19 한국에도 셀피 박물관이 있습니다. 나는 전에 춘천에 있는 한 박물관을 방문한 적이 있습니다.

20 여러분도 직접 그곳에 가는 게 어때요? 이 셀피들은 멋져 보이지만, 그것들은 좋은 생각이었나요?

21 난 그렇게 생각하지 않아요. 그것들은 안전해 보이지 않습니다.

22 여러분은 야생이나 이와 같이 높은 곳에서 셀피를 찍을 때 특별한 주의를 기울여야 합니다.

23 원숭이가 언제든지 당신을 물거나 또는 당신은 떨어질 수 있습니다.

24 여기 몇 가지 안전 수칙이 있습니다.

25 걸으면서 셀피를 찍지 마세요.

26 야생 동물들과 함께 또는 가까이에서 포즈를 취하지 마세요.

27 위험한 곳에서는 절대 셀피를 찍지 마세요.

28 나는 우리가 더 나은 학교생활을 만들기 위해 셀피를 이용할 수 있다고 생각해요.

29 우리는 학교에서 좋은 일을 할 수 있고 셀피를 찍을 수도 있습니다.

30 그러고 나서 우리는 학교 웹사이트에 사진을 올릴 수 있어요.

31 나는 한 달 동안 학교에서 식물과 꽃에 물을 주었습니다.

32 나는 또한 학교 도서관에서 선생님을 여러 번 도왔습니다.

33 그런 것들에 대한 내 셀피를 보세요.

34 저와 함께 더 나은 학교생활을 만들어 보는 건 어떨까요?

※ 다음 우리말을 영어로 쓰시오.

1 여러분은 "셀피"에 대해 들어 본 적이 있나요? 여러분 자신의 사진을 찍을 때 그것이 셀피에요.

➡ _____

2 민지의 사진 동아리 학생들은 한 달 동안 셀피에 대한 정보를 찾았습니다.

➡ _____

3 여기 셀피에 대한 그들의 발표 내용이 있습니다.

➡ _____

4 과거의 사람들은 셀피를 찍었나요?

➡ _____

5 그 때는 셀피를 찍는 것이 쉽지는 않았지만. 답은 '그렇다'입니다.

➡ _____

6 아나스타샤 공주의 이 사진을 보세요. 그녀는 거울을 사용하여 자신의 사진을 찍었습니다.

➡ _____

7 그녀는 긴장되어 보입니다. 왜인지 추측할 수 있나요?

➡ _____

8 글쎄, 나는 그것이 그녀의 첫 번째 셀피였다고 생각해요.

➡ _____

9 그리고 그것은 아마도 세계 최초의 10대 소녀의 셀피였을 거예요.

➡ _____

10 여러분은 빅벤과 피사의 사탑과 같은 세계적으로 유명한 장소에서 셀피를 찍을 수 있습니다.

➡ _____

11 멋진 사진을 찍기 위해서, 단지 재미있는 포즈를 취하고 카메라 기술을 이용하세요.

➡ _____

12 여러분은 또한 재미있는 셀피를 찍기 위해 특별한 박물관을 방문할 수 있습니다.

➡ _____

13 예를 들어, 필리핀에는 유명한 셀피 박물관이 있습니다.

➡ _____

14 그곳은 셀피를 찍기 위한 특별한 장소들이 있습니다.

➡ _____

15 여러분은 그림들을 만질 수 있고 심지어 그림들 안으로 들어갈 수도 있어요.

➡ _____

16 다음 사진들을 보세요.

➡ _____

17 비록 그 소년들은 말을 타고 있는 것은 아니지만, 말을 타고 있는 것처럼 보입니다.
➡ _____

18 비록 그 남자는 단지 커다란 붓을 잡고 있지만, 모나리자를 그리고 있는 것처럼 보입니다.
➡ _____

19 한국에도 셀피 박물관이 있습니다. 나는 전에 춘천에 있는 한 박물관을 방문한 적이 있습니다.
➡ _____

20 여러분도 직접 그곳에 가는 게 어때요? 이 셀피들은 멋져 보이지만, 그것들은 좋은 생각이었나요?
➡ _____

21 난 그렇게 생각하지 않아요. 그것들은 안전해 보이지 않습니다.
➡ _____

22 여러분은 야생이나 이와 같이 높은 곳에서 셀피를 찍을 때 특별한 주의를 기울여야 합니다.
➡ _____

23 원숭이가 언제든지 당신을 물거나 또는 당신은 떨어질 수 있습니다.
➡ _____

24 여기 몇 가지 안전 수칙이 있습니다.
➡ _____

25 걸으면서 셀피를 찍지 마세요.
➡ _____

26 야생 동물들과 함께 또는 가까이에서 포즈를 취하지 마세요.
➡ _____

27 위험한 곳에서는 절대 셀피를 찍지 마세요.
➡ _____

28 나는 우리가 더 나은 학교생활을 만들기 위해 셀피를 이용할 수 있다고 생각해요.
➡ _____

29 우리는 학교에서 좋은 일을 할 수 있고 셀피를 찍을 수도 있습니다.
➡ _____

30 그러고 나서 우리는 학교 웹사이트에 사진을 올릴 수 있어요.
➡ _____

31 나는 한 달 동안 학교에서 식물과 꽃에 물을 주었습니다.
➡ _____

32 나는 또한 학교 도서관에서 선생님을 여러 번 도왔습니다.
➡ _____

33 그런 것들에 대한 내 셀피를 보세요.
➡ _____

34 저와 함께 더 나은 학교생활을 만들어 보는 건 어떨까요?
➡ _____

※ 다음 우리말과 일치하도록 빈칸에 알맞은 말을 쓰시오.

Express Yourself-C

1. _____ you _____ of the pyramids in Egypt?

2. Though I _____ never _____ _____ _____ Egypt before, I'm standing _____ _____ _____ a pyramid in this picture.

3. I _____ it at the selfie _____.

1. 여러분은 이집트의 피라미드에 대해 들어 본 적이 있나요?
2. 나는 전에 이집트에 가 본 적이 없지만, 이 사진에서 나는 피라미드 앞에 서 있어요.
3. 나는 이 사진을 셀피 박물관에서 찍었어요.

Project-Step 2

1. Fire _____ _____

2. _____ you _____ _____ fire safety rules?

3. _____ there's a fire, you can _____ _____.

4. You _____ _____ the elevator.

5. You should _____ the teacher's _____.

1. 화재 안전 수칙
2. 당신은 화재 안전 수칙에 대해 들어 본 적이 있습니까?
3. 불이 났지만, 당신은 안전할 수 있어요.
4. 엘리베이터를 타지 마세요.
5. 선생님의 지시에 따라야 해요.

Link to the World

1. BMX Bike _____

2. _____ a BMX bike _____ very _____.

3. You can try _____ _____ _____.

4. You can _____ the bike _____ and _____ _____ with the bike.

5. _____ it's not _____, it's very _____.

6. You _____ _____ _____ standing skills.

7. _____ you try _____ skills, _____ is very important.

8. But _____ _____. You _____ _____ a helmet and gloves.

9. Also, you _____ _____ too fast _____ you're _____.

1. BMX 자전거 타기
2. BMX 자전거를 타는 것은 매우 흥미롭다.
3. 여러분은 많은 기술을 시도할 수 있다.
4. 여러분은 자전거를 자유롭게 돌릴 수 있고 심지어 자전거와 함께 점프할 수도 있다.
5. 쉽지는 않지만, 매우 흥미롭다.
6. 여러분은 서 있는 기술과 함께 시작하면 된다.
7. 서 있는 기술을 시도할 때, 균형을 잡는 것이 매우 중요하다.
8. 하지만 조심해라! 헬멧과 장갑을 착용해야 한다.
9. 또한, 자전거를 탈 때는 너무 빨리 가지 말아야 한다.

※ 다음 우리말을 영어로 쓰시오.

Express Yourself-C

1. 여러분은 이집트의 피라미드에 대해 들어 본 적이 있나요?
   ➡ _____

2. 나는 전에 이집트에 가 본 적이 없지만, 이 사진에서 나는 피라미드 앞에 서 있어요.
   ➡ _____

3. 나는 이 사진을 셀피 박물관에서 찍었어요.
   ➡ _____

Project - Step 2

1. 화재 안전 수칙
   ➡ _____

2. 당신은 화재 안전 수칙에 대해 들어 본 적이 있습니까?
   ➡ _____

3. 불이 났지만, 당신은 안전할 수 있어요.
   ➡ _____

4. 엘리베이터를 타지 마세요.
   ➡ _____

5. 선생님의 지시에 따라야 해요.
   ➡ _____

Link to the World

1. BMX 자전거 타기
   ➡ _____

2. BMX 자전거를 타는 것은 매우 흥미롭다.
   ➡ _____

3. 여러분은 많은 기술을 시도할 수 있다.
   ➡ _____

4. 여러분은 자전거를 자유롭게 돌릴 수 있고 심지어 자전거와 함께 점프할 수도 있다.
   ➡ _____

5. 쉽지는 않지만, 매우 흥미롭다.
   ➡ _____

6. 여러분은 서 있는 기술과 함께 시작하면 된다.
   ➡ _____

7. 서 있는 기술을 시도할 때, 균형을 잡는 것이 매우 중요하다.
   ➡ _____

8. 하지만 조심해라! 헬멧과 장갑을 착용해야 한다.
   ➡ _____

9. 또한, 자전거를 탈 때는 너무 빨리 가지 말아야 한다.
   ➡ _____

MEMO

MEMO

영어 기출 문제집

적중100

1학기

정답 및 해설

천재 | 정사열

중 2

영어 기출 문제집

적중¹⁰⁰

1학기

정답 및 해설

천재 | 정사열

중 2

적중100

Time to Start Again

01 ②   02 ②   03 ④   04 ⑤
05 interesting 06 ⑤   07 hurry   08 looking
for

01 ②는 반의어 관계이고 나머지는 유의어 관계이다.

02 find out: 알게 되다

03 많은 사람이 볼 수 있도록 표지판, 게시문 등을 붙이다: post(게시
하다)

04 can't wait for: ~이 몹시 기다려지다 / bump into: ~에 부
딪히다

05 반의어 관계이다. 강한 : 약한 = 흥미로운 : 지루한

06 • 그들은 가난한 사람들에게 음식을 제공한다. serve: 제공 하다
• 이 문장은 무엇을 의미하니? mean: 의미하다 • 나 는 오늘 풀
수학 문제가 있다. solve: 풀다 • 나는 다미를 데리고 갈 거야.
take: 데리고 가다

07 급히 움직이거나 행동하거나 가다: hurry(서두르다)

08 look for: ~을 찾다

서술형 시험대비   p.09

01 (1) continue   (2) forget   (3) wrong   (4) saying
02 (1) come over   (2) after school   (3) this year
03 (1) hard   (2) dish   (3) right
04 (1) strict   (2) boring   (3) fresh
05 (1) cut in on   (2) be good for   (3) bump into
06 (1) (f)inal   (2) (c)over   (3) (r)ealize

01 (1), (2), (3) 반의어 관계이다. (1) 흥미로운 : 지루한 = 계속 하
다 : 멈추다 (2) 쉬운 : 어려운 = 잊다 : 기억하다 (3) 기쁜 : 슬픈
= 맞는 : 틀린 (4) 친절한 : 친절한 = 속담 : 속담

02 (1) come over: 오다 (2) after school: 방과 후에 (3) this
year: 올해

03 (1) hard: 어려운; 열심히 (2) dish: 요리; 접시 (3) right: 알맞
은; 오른쪽의

04 (1) strict: 엄격한 (2) boring: 지루한 (3) fresh: 신선한

05 (1) cut in on: (말·대화에) 끼어들다 (2) be good for: ~ 에
좋다 (3) bump into: ~에 부딪히다

06 (1) final: 결승전 (2) cover: 표지 (3) realize: 깨닫다

1 (1) What, think of[about] / I think
   (2) What, opinion[view] on[about] / In, opinion[view]
2 (1) wait for
   (2) this year / looking forward

교과서 대화문 익히기

Check(√) True or False   p.12

1 T   2 F   3 F   4 T

교과서 확인학습   p.14~15

Get Ready - 2
1 think / looks, for / This year, going, with
2 Look at, going to / find out / excited, wait
3 your / to / What, think / a lot

Start Off - Listen & Talk A
1 good for, What / think, boring / which, to join /
plyaing
2 think of / right. to learn / too, first / wait for

Start Off - Listen & Talk B
Let's / growing / what / Let's, right now, with / on /
for

Step Up - Real-life Scene
what, think of / looks, strict / Don't judge, by / mean
/ with, exciting / During, class, with / can't wait for,
this year

Express Yourself A
1 What / I think, on / can eat / can't wait for
2 dishes, think of / bad / don't eat / Try, good

Check Yourself - Listen & Speak
Let's join, What, of / playing / playing / right now,
after school / going to, on / to play / too, wait for

시험대비 기본평가　　　　　　p.16

| 01 ② | 02 ⑤ | 03 ② | 04 ⑤ |

01 의견을 물을 때는 What do you think of ~?를 사용하고, 자신의 의견을 말할 때는 I think ~로 나타내므로, 빈칸에는 think가 들어가야 한다.

02 새로운 마술이 멋있다고 했으므로 마술 쇼가 기다려진다는 말이 와야 알맞다.

03 Emily에 대한 의견을 묻는 질문에 '나도 그녀를 좋아해.'라는 대답은 어울리지 않는다.

04 can't wait for와 같은 표현은 ⑤ look forward to이다.

시험대비 실력평가　　　　　　p.17~18

01 ②	02 ③	03 ③	04 ③
05 ②	06 ③	07 ①	08 ②
09 with	10 ③	11 ①, ③	12 cover
13 I can't wait for his birthday party.			

01 전치사 of의 목적어가 되는 의문대명사 what이 알맞다.

02 빈칸 다음의 말로 보아 의견 묻기에 대한 긍정의 대답이 와야 한다.

03 on+날짜

04 I can't wait for ~: 나는 ~이 매우 기다려진다.

05 의견을 묻는 표현인 What do you think of[about] ~? 는 What's your opinion on ~?으로 바꿔 쓸 수 있다.

06 be good for ~에 좋다

07 What do you think of ~?는 상대방의 생각이나 의견을 물을 때 사용한다.

08 by: ~으로, ~에 의해

09 with: ~와 함께, ~을 써서[이용하여]

10 ③ 세호는 박 선생님과의 첫 수업이 매우 흥미로웠다고 생각한다.

11 what do you think of[about] ~?: ~에 대해서 어떻게 생각하니?

12 책이나 잡지의 바깥 부분: 표지(cover)

13 can't wait for: ~이 매우 기다려지다

서술형 시험대비　　　　　　p.19

01 (A) good　(B) boring

02 What do you think of[about] it?

03 She thinks it's boring.

04 (B) – (D) – (C) – (A)　　05 what

06 They can have a party with fresh vegetables every month.

07 It's on April 30.

08 I can't wait for the party.

01 (A) look + 형용사: ~하게 보이다 (B) 주어가 지루한 감정을 느끼게 하는 원인이므로 현재분사형 형용사 boring이 알맞다.

02 '~에 대해 어떻게 생각하니?'는 What do you think of[about] ~?으로 표현한다.

03 소녀는 헬스 동아리가 지루하다고 생각한다고 했다.

04 (B) 봐! 이 수첩에 대해 어떻게 생각하니? - (D) 표지가 멋져. 그것은 민준에게 좋은 것 같아. - (C) 그래, 그는 그것을 아주 좋아할 거야. - (A) 나는 그의 생일 파티가 너무 기다려져!

05 ⓐ What do you think of ~?: 너는 ~에 대해 어떻게 생각하니? ⓑ You know what?: 너 그거 알아?(있잖아.)

06 그들은 매달 신선한 야채가 있는 파티를 열 수 있다고 언급되었다.

07 첫 번째 파티는 4월 30일이다.

08 I can't wait for ~: 나는 ~이 무척 기다려진다.

교과서
Grammar

핵심 Check　　　　　　p.20~21

1 (1) to go　(2) to write with　(3) to help　(4) cold to drink
2 (1) to listen　(2) to tell　(3) to visit
3 (1) that　(2) that
4 (1) hope⌵you　(2) says⌵the　(3) thinks⌵his

시험대비 기본평가　　　　　　p.22

01 (1) believes that　(2) thinks that
02 (1) to help us　(2) many things to do
03 (1) think that Jenny is at home
　　(2) hope that my parents are healthy.
　　(3) believed that he would come back.
04 (1) to drink　(2) to read　(3) to do

02 (1) to부정사구(to help us)는 앞에 나온 명사 the only person을 꾸며주는 형용사 역할을 한다. (2) '해야 할 많은 일'이라는 뜻으로 to do가 many things를 뒤에서 수식해 준다.

03 that이 접속사로 동사의 목적어가 되는 명사절을 이끄는 경우이다.

04 to부정사구가 앞에 나온 명사(구)를 꾸며주는 형용사 역할을 한다.

시험대비 실력평가　　　　　　p.23~25

01 ③	02 ②	03 ④	04 ⑤
05 to help	06 ③	07 ②	08 what →
that		09 taking → to take	10 ⑤

3

01 형용사적 용법의 to부정사가 들어가야 한다.

02 접속사는 절과 절을 연결해 주는 역할을 하므로 I hope 뒤와 I have의 앞인 ②에 오는 것이 적절하다.

03 나머지는 모두 형용사적 용법의 to부정사이고 ④는 명사적 용법의 to부정사이다.

04 ⑤ be동사 made 다음에 that이 이끄는 명사절이 나오는 것은 어색하다.

05 형용사적 용법의 to부정사가 들어가야 한다.

06 ③은 지시형용사이고, 나머지는 모두 명사절을 이끄는 접속사로 쓰였다.

07 to부정사의 형용사적 용법으로 앞의 부정대명사와 명사를 수식하고 있다.

08 접속사 that은 동사의 목적어 역할을 하는 명사절을 이끈다.

09 to부정사의 형태는 'to+동사원형'을 사용한다.

10 ①, ②, ③, ④의 that은 접속사의 목적어 역할로 쓰여서 생략이 가능하고 ⑤는 지시형용사로 쓰였으므로 생략할 수 없다.

11 to부정사의 형용사적 용법으로 앞의 (대)명사를 수식하고 'to + 동사원형'의 형태로 쓰인다. ③은 방향을 나타내는 전치사로 쓰였다.

12 목적어절을 이끄는 접속사 that이 필요하다.

13 '~에 살다'는 live in이므로 to live 다음에 전치사 in을 넣어야 한다.

14 명사+to부정사의 구문에서 sit이 자동사이고 의미상 의자 에 앉는 것이므로 전치사 on이나 in을 sit 뒤에 써야 한다.

15 '나는 ~라고 생각한다'는 I think that을 이용해서 나타낸다.

16 수식을 받는 명사가 전치사의 목적어일 경우에는 to부정사 뒤에 전치사를 써야 한다. play with: ~와 놀다 / write with: ~로 쓰다

17 주어진 문장과 ⑤의 that은 접속사로서 목적어절을 이끄는 역할을 한다.

18 ③은 to부정사의 형용사적 용법이고, 나머지는 모두 부사적 용법이다.

19 I don't know 뒤에 절이 따라올 때는 that 대신 if나 whether 를 쓴다.

20 ③ something reading → something to read

21 ③은 to부정사의 부사적 용법이고 나머지는 모두 형용사적 용법으로 쓰였다.

22 to부정사의 수식을 받는 명사가 전치사의 목적어일 경우 to부정사 뒤에 반드시 전치사를 써야 한다.

23 ①, ②, ③, ⑤: that[That] / ④: 접속사 When

24 ⓐ, ⓒ to부정사의 형용사적 용법 ⓑ to부정사의 명사적 용법 ⓓ to부정사의 부사적 용법

서술형 시험대비　　　　p.26~27

01 to

02 (1) They believe (that) there is an alien here.

　(2) I know (that) you came back home late.

03 (1) to eat　(2) to drink　(3) sit on[in]　(4) talk with

04 that

05 She needs something to put on.

06 (1) I think, he is Chinese

　(2) I know, she is a wise wife

07 (1) I want some snacks to eat in the afternoon.

　(2) They need four chairs to sit on.

08 Do you have something warm to wear?

09 (1) a chair to sit → a chair to sit on[in]

　(2) visiting → to visit

10 I think (that) my English teacher is pretty.

11 (1) She needs someone strong to help her.

　(2) He has no friends to play with.

12 (1) that you can do everything

　(2) you think that she is pretty

13 (1) We cannot find a place to park our car.

　(2) Dave wants to buy a bike to ride to school.

　(3) Kate has a lot of homework to do.

14 a pen to write with

15 (1) He knows that she is rich.

　(2) I don't think that he is American.

16 (1) They don't have anything to talk about.

　(2) We are looking for a hotel to stay at in Paris.

01 앞의 명사를 수식하는 형용사적 용법의 to부정사가 필요하다.

02 명사절 접속사 that을 사용하여 연결한다. 이때 that은 생략 가능하다.

03 앞의 명사를 꾸며주는 to부정사의 형용사적 용법을 이용한다.

04 첫 번째 문장의 that은 접속사, 두 번째 문장의 that은 지시형용사이다.

05 형용사 역할의 to부정사는 수식하는 명사나 부정대명사의 뒤에 위치한다.

06 접속사 that은 동사의 목적어절을 이끄는 역할을 한다.

07 (2) 의미상 to부정사구 뒤에 전치사 on이 와야 한다.

08 -thing으로 끝나는 부정대명사의 경우 형용사와 to부정사의 수식을 동시에 받을 때 「-thing+형용사+to부정사」 어순으로 쓰인다.

09 (1) to부정사의 수식을 받는 명사가 전치사의 목적어일 경우 to부정사 뒤에 반드시 전치사를 써야 한다. (to sit → to sit on[in]) (2) '~할'이라는 의미로 명사를 수식하는 to부정사가

와야 한다. (형용사적 용법)

10 I think (that)+주어+동사 ~: 나는 ~이 …라고 생각한다.

11 (1) -one+형용사+to부정사 (2) 명사+to부정사+전치사

12 that이 목적어가 되는 명사절을 이끄는 문장이다.

13 (1) 우리는 차를 주차할 장소를 찾을 수 없다. (2) Dave는 학교에 타고 갈 자전거를 사고 싶다. (3) Kate는 해야 할 숙제가 많다.

14 write with a pen의 구조이다.

16 (1) 형용사적 용법의 to부정사가 부정대명사(anything)를 수식 한다. (2) 명사+to부정사+전치사

교과서 Reading

확인문제 p.28

1 T 2 F 3 F 4 T 5 T 6 T

확인문제 p.29

1 T 2 F 3 T 4 T

교과서 확인학습 A p.30~31

01 were talking, when, over
02 said to
03 from
04 tickets
05 going, with
06 took, to
07 pay, back
08 what, in
09 isn't, fan, But
10 anyway, replied
11 won't, Trust
12 thought to herself
13 There's, later
14 hurried
15 on, to, run
16 At, bumped into
17 continued to
18 Just, on
19 but, was not
20 After, to, one of
21 happen to
22 answered
23 Isn't, in
24 not, lost
25 On, saw
26 had, in
27 angry, Why
28 Just then, shouted, in
29 yours
30 looking for
31 not, thought
32 were, saying
33 to say, asked
34 about, to, with
35 finals
36 looked, pleased, love to

교과서 확인학습 B p.32~33

1 Seho and Jihun were talking in the hallway when Dami came over.

2 "Happy birthday!" she said to Seho.

3 "Here. They're from my dad."

4 "Wow, two KBL tickets! Thanks!"

5 "Who are you going to take with you?" Dami asked.

6 "Minjun. He took me to a soccer game before.

7 So, it's time to pay him back."

8 "You know what?" Jihun cut in.

9 "Minjun isn't a fan of basketball. But I am!"

10 "Well, I'll ask him first anyway," replied Seho.

11 "He won't go with you. Trust me," said Jihun.

12 "Who is this guy?" Dami thought to herself, "He wants Minjun's ticket."

13 "Oh! There's the bell. See you later," said Dami.

14 She hurried to class.

15 "Come on, Jihun," said Seho, and he started to run.

16 At the corner, Seho bumped into someone.

17 "Sorry!" he said and continued to run.

18 Just then, Jihun saw something on the floor.

19 "Wait, Seho!" he said, but Seho was not there.

20 After class, Seho went to Dami and said, "I can't find one of my tickets.

21 Did you happen to see it?"

22 "No," she answered.

23 "Isn't it in your bag?"

24 "No, it's not there. I think I lost it," said Seho.

25 On her way home, Dami saw Jihun.

26 He had the ticket in his hand.

27 Dami got angry and said, "Hey! Why do you …?"

28 Just then, Jihun saw Seho and shouted, "Seho! I found a ticket in the hallway.

29 I think it's yours."

30 "Thanks! I was looking for that!" said Seho.

31 "He's not so bad," Dami thought.

32 "So, what were you saying?

33 Do you have something to say, Dami?" asked Jihun.

34 "Um, how about going to the school basketball game with me this Friday?

35 It's the finals."

36 Jihun looked really pleased. "I'd love to!"

시험대비 실력평가 p.34~37

01 ④
02 ②
03 one of my tickets
04 floor
05 He dropped one of his tickets.
06 ④
07 two KBL tickets
08 to

09 ⑤　　　10 ⑤　　　11 ③　　　12 ④
13 ②　　　14 the school basketball game
15 ④　　　16 ①　　　17 ②　　　18 (T)rust
19 to　　　20 the bell rang　　　21 ①
22 ③　　　23 (h)allway　24 I think that it's yours.
25 why don't you　　　26 ④　　　27 ⑤
28 ④　　　29 ②

01 bump into: ~에 부딪히다
02 but: 그러나
03 인칭대명사 it은 one of my tickets를 가리킨다.
04 당신이 건물 안에서 서 있는 평평한 표면: 바닥
05 세호는 바닥에 그의 입장권 중 하나를 떨어뜨렸다.
06 come over: 오다
07 They는 two KBL tickets를 의미한다.
08 take A to B: A를 B에 데려가다
09 so는 '그래서, 그 결과'의 의미로, 결과를 나타내는 접속사이다.
10 돈을 빌린 적이 있는 것이 아니라 전에 민준이가 축구 경기에 데려간 적이 있어서 신세를 갚아야 한다고 언급되었다.
11 on one's way home: 집에 오는 길에
12 나머지는 모두 Jihun을 가리키고 ④는 Dami를 가리킨다.
13 ⓑ와 ②는 to부정사의 형용사적 용법, ①③⑤는 부사적 용법, ④는 명사적 용법이다.
14 인칭대명사 it은 앞 문장에 나온 the school basketball game을 가리킨다.
15 위 글을 통해서는 학교 농구 경기를 몇 시에 하는지는 알 수 없다.
16 cut in: (말·대화에) 끼어들다
17 ②는 민준이를 가리키고 나머지는 지훈이를 가리킨다.
18 어떤 사람이 정직하거나 또는 나쁜 일이나 그릇된 일을 하지 않을 것이라고 믿다
19 think to oneself: 마음속으로 생각하다
20 다미가 서둘러 수업에 간 이유는 종이 울렸기 때문이다.
21 on one's way home: 집으로 가는 도중에 (이때의 home은 부사이므로 전치사 to는 붙지 않음)
22 문맥상 입장권을 가지고 있는 이유를 묻는 의문사 why가 알맞다.
23 많은 방들로 이어지는 건물이나 집의 통로: 복도
24 목적어절을 이끄는 접속사 that은 생략할 수 있다.
25 How about -ing ~?는 Why don't you ~?로 바꿔 쓸 수 있다.
26 ④ 다미는 지훈이가 하는 말을 듣고 그가 나쁘지 않다고 생각했다.
27 (A) on: ~ 위에
　　(B) one of: ~ 중 하나
28 주어진 문장의 it은 one of my tickets를 가리키므로 ④번이 적절하다.
29 ⓑ의 he는 지훈이를 가리킨다.

서술형 시험대비　　　　　　　　　p.38~39

01 (A) over　(B) in　　02 She gave them to Seho.　　03 He wants to go to a basketball game with Minjun.　　04 it's time to pay him back　　05 He bumped into someone at the corner.　　06 그는 그의 입장권 중 하나를 찾을 수 없다. 그녀에게 혹시 그것을 보았는지 물었다.　　07 in my bag　　08 I think (that) I lost it.　　09 in
10 I am a fan of basketball!　11 Dami thought to herself.　　12 class　　13 On her way
14 Because Jihun had the ticket in his hand.　15 He found the ticket in the hallway.　　16 finals

01 (A) come over: 오다 (B) cut in: (말·대화에) 끼어들다
02 다미는 세호에게 두 장의 농구 입장권을 주었다.
03 세호는 민준이와 함께 농구 경기에 가고 싶어 한다.
04 it은 비인칭 주어 it이고 to pay는 명사 time을 수식하는 to부정사의 형용사적 용법이다. pay someone back: ~에게 신세를 갚다
05 세호는 모퉁이에서 누군가와 부딪혔다고 언급되어 있다.
06 I can't find one of my tickets. Did you happen to see it?라고 말했다.
07 장소 부사 there는 in my bag을 의미한다.
08 I think (that) + 주어 + 동사 ~의 구문을 쓴다.
09 cut in: (말·대화에) 끼어들다
10 be동사 am 다음에는 a fan of basketball이 생략되었다.
11 think to oneself: 마음속으로 생각하다
12 학생들이 특정한 과목이나 활동을 배우는 일련의 모임: 수업
13 on one's way home: 집으로 오는 도중에
14 다미는 지훈이가 입장권을 그의 손에 갖고 있었기 때문에 화가 났다고 언급되었다.
15 지훈이는 복도에서 입장권을 찾았다고 언급되었다.
16 시합에서 마지막이자 가장 중요한 경기 : finals(결승)

영역별 핵심문제　　　　　　　　p.41~45

01 ⑤　　02 ①　　03 ③　　04 (s)erious　　05 (s)erve　06 this year　07 ④
08 ④　　09 (B) – (D) – (C) – (A)　　10 What, think of[about]　　11 ⑤　　12 on
13 ⑤　　14 ⑤　　15 think that　16 ⑤
17 ③　　18 ②　　19 We don't believe that she will come to the party.　20 to talk → to talk with[to]
21 ④　　22 ④　　23 ⑤　　24 didn't think that he was handsome　25 ②　26 I need a book to read.　27 ④　　28 with　29 ②
30 ③　　31 ③　　32 later　33 ②
34 ③　　35 in　　36 many　37 ④

01 주의 깊이 생각한 후에 무언가 또는 누군가에 대한 견해를 형성하다: 판단하다(judge)

02 on one's way to: ~로 가는 도중에

03 ③은 유의어 관계이고 나머지는 반의어 관계이다.

04 serious: 진지한

05 serve: 제공하다, 봉사하다

06 this year: 올해

07 A가 I agree with you. I enjoyed it a lot이라고 말했으므로 B도 긍정적인 의견을 말했음을 알 수 있다.

08 영화를 볼 예정이라고 말한 다음에 기대를 표현하는 말이 이어지는 것이 자연스럽다.

09 (B) 오늘 점심에 대해 어떻게 생각하니? - (D) 괜찮은 것 같아. 내일 메뉴는 뭐니? - (C) 와! 내일 우리는 스파게티를 먹을 수 있어. - (A) 내일 점심시간이 기다려진다.

10 '~에 대해 어떻게 생각하니?'라고 상대방의 의견을 묻는 표현으로 What do you think of[about] ~?를 쓸 수 있다.

11 right now: 지금 당장

12 on + 날짜

13 I can't wait for ~는 I'm looking forward to ~.로 바꿔 쓸 수 있다.

14 ⑤ 첫 번째 파티가 무슨 요일에 열리는지는 알 수 없다.

15 I think that ~: ~라고 생각하다

16 to부정사의 형용사적 용법이므로, 'to+동사원형' 형태가 쓰인다. take care of: ~을 돌보다

17 ①, ②, ④, ⑤는 명사절을 이끄는 접속사 that이고 ③은 지시형용사이다.

18 ①, ③, ④, ⑤는 형용사적 용법의 to부정사로 각각 앞의 명사를 수식하고 있다. ②는 decided의 목적어 역할을 하는 명사적 용법의 to부정사이다.

19 접속사 that 이하의 내용이 부정일 때, that 앞에 있는 동사를 부정으로 만든다.

20 명사+to부정사+전치사 구문이다.

21 ④ 명사절 접속사 that 뒤에 주어(the girl)는 있지만 동사가 빠져 있으므로 동사 is를 넣어야 한다.

22 <보기>, ④: 명사절을 이끄는 접속사 ①, ②, ⑤: 지시대명사, ③: 지시형용사

23 to부정사인 to live가 앞의 명사 a good house를 수식한다. 수식을 받는 명사가 전치사의 목적어인 경우 to부정사 뒤에 전치사가 와야 한다.

24 think는 that절을 목적어로 취하는 동사로, 「주어+think+주어+동사 ~」의 어순으로 쓰는데, 과거형 부정문이므로 think 앞에 didn't가 온다.

25 to부정사의 수식을 받는 명사가 전치사의 목적어인 경우 to부정사 뒤에 반드시 전치사를 써야 한다. live → live in

26 to부정사의 형용사적 용법: ~할

27 ⓐ when: ~할 때 ⓔ You know what?: 너 그거 알아?

28 with: ~와 함께

29 ⓒ so: 그래서 ⓕ but: 그러나

30 ⓓ와 ③은 형용사적 용법의 to부정사이고, ①, ②, ④는 명사적 용법, ⑤는 부사적 용법의 to부정사이다.

31 think to oneself: 마음속으로 생각하다

32 미래의 어느 때에: 나중에(later)

33 ② 다미의 아빠가 농구 입장권을 누구에게서 받았는지는 알 수 없다.

34 주어진 문장은 '그러면 그들도 나에게 좋은 말을 할 것이다.'라는 의미로 '내가 먼저 다른 사람들에게 좋은 말을 할 것이다'라는 문장 다음에 오는 것이 적절하다.

35 in English: 영어로

36 lots of: 많은(=many)

37 Nice words for nice words.는 가는 말이 고와야 오는 말이 곱다는 영어 속담이다.

단원별 예상문제   p.46~49

01 forget   02 for   03 ③   04 thought to herself   05 ④   06 (f)inal   07 ⑤
08 I think it's the right club for me.   09 (t)ricks
10 the magic club   11 ③   12 ②
13 ⑤   14 (1) She thinks that her daughter is sick. (2) I don't believe that Nick will come to the party.   15 ②   16 to play with   17 ⑤
18 ③, ⑤   19 We need more flour to bake a cake with.   20 Dami gave two basketball tickets to Seho.   21 ④   22 지훈이는 입장권을 세호에게 돌려주었다.   23 that   24 wrong
25 ⑤   26 ④   27 ④   28 yours
29 ⓓ to say ⓔ going   30 지훈이가 입장권 한 장을 세호에게 주는 것을 보았기 때문이다.

01 반의어 관계이다. 위험한 : 안전한 = 기억하다 : 잊다

02 look for: ~을 찾다 / be good for: ~에 좋다

03 ③은 ceiling(천장)의 영영풀이다.

04 think to oneself: 마음속으로 생각하다

05 bump into: ~에 부딪히다 / on one's way home: 집으로 가는 도중에

06 final: 마지막의, 결승전

07 의견을 표현하는 답변이 나오므로 의견을 묻는 질문이 들어가야 자연스럽다.

08 의견 묻기와 자신의 의견을 표현하는 대화이다.

09 사람들을 즐겁거나 재미있게 하려고 하는 기발하고 교묘한 동작: 마술

10 인칭대명사 it은 the magic club을 가리킨다.

11 I can't wait for ~는 '나는 ~이 무척 기다려진다'는 뜻으로 기대를 나타내는 표현이다.

12 빈칸 뒤에 이어지는 문장이 says의 목적어 역할을 하므로 빈칸에는 '~하는 것'을 뜻하는 명사절 접속사 that이 적절하다.

13 to부정사인 to save가 앞의 명사 a way를 꾸며주는 형용사 역할을 한다.

14 (2) 접속사 that 이하의 내용이 부정일 때, that 앞에 있는 동사를 부정으로 만든다.

15 ②는 to부정사의 형용사적 용법이고 나머지는 부사적 용법이다.

16 앞의 명사를 수식하는 to부정사를 이용하여 한 문장으로 만들도록 한다. 수식을 받는 명사가 전치사의 목적어인 경우 to부정사 뒤에 전치사가 와야 한다.

17 ①~④는 명사절을 이끄는 접속사 that으로, that 이하가 문장에서 동사의 목적어의 역할을 하며 생략 가능하다. ⑤의 that은 동격의 명사절을 이끄는 접속사로 쓰였다.

18 to부정사의 형용사적 용법을 찾는다. ① 명사적 용법 ② 부사적 용법(결과) ④ 부사적 용법(목적)

19 밀가루를 가지고 케이크를 구워야 하므로 전치사 with를 써야 한다.

20 수여동사 give + 간접목적어 + 직접목적어(4형식) → 수여동사 give + 직접목적어 + to + 간접목적어(3형식)

21 on one's way to: ~로 가는 도중에

22 give someone back something: 누군가에게 어떤 것을 되돌려주다

23 목적어절을 이끄는 접속사 that이 알맞다.

24 사실이나 진실과 일치하지 않는 방식으로 말하거나 행동하거나 판단하는: 틀린, 잘못 알고 있는(wrong)

25 학교 농구 경기가 몇 시에 하는지는 알 수 없다.

26 ④의 me는 Dami를 가리킨다.

27 ⓐ on one's way home: 집으로 가는 도중에 ⓒ look for: ~을 찾다

28 yours: 너의 것

29 ⓓ something을 꾸며 주는 형용사적 용법의 to부정사가 되어야 한다. ⓔ How about + 동명사 ~?: ~하는 게 어때?

서술형 실전문제   p.50~51

01 can't wait 02 What do you think of[about] your English teacher? 03 I'm looking forward to it. 04 (C) – (B) – (D) – (A) 05 to write → to write with 06 (1) I know that she was a teacher. (2) I think that he is honest. (3) He believes that it will be a lot of fun. 07 (1) She has a strong desire to be a singer. (2) We had something to talk about. (3) I want a sheet[piece] of paper to write on. (4) Please give me something hot to drink. 08 On her way home, Dami saw Jihun. 09 I think that it's yours. 10 It's on this Friday. 11 (p)leased 12 (s)aying 13 (A) too (B) to remember 14 내가 먼저 다른 사람들에게 좋은 말을 하고 그러면 다른 사람들도 나에게 좋은 말을 해서 15 가는 말이 고와야 오는 말이 곱다.

01 I can't wait for ~는 '나는 ~이 무척 기다려져.'라는 의미로 기대를 나타내는 표현이다.

02 '~에 대해 어떻게 생각하니?'는 What do you think of[about] ~?으로 표현한다.

03 I'm looking forward to ~: 나는 ~이 무척 기대돼.

04 (C) 이 동아리는 너에게 맞는 것 같아. 그것에 대해 어떻게 생각하니? - (B) 헬스 동아리? 지루하다고 생각해. - (D) 그럼 넌 어떤 동아리에 가입하고 싶니? - (A) 난 축구 동아리에 가입할 거야. 나는 축구를 좋아해.

05 to부정사인 to write가 앞의 명사 a pen을 수식한다. 이때는 write with a pen이라는 전치사의 목적어 관계이므로 write 다음의 전치사 with를 빠뜨리지 않도록 주의한다.

06 that: 명사절(목적어)을 이끄는 접속사

07 (1), (2) to부정사의 형용사적 용법을 이용해 「명사+to부정사」의 형태로 쓴다. (3) to부정사의 목적어가 있고 to부정사의 동사가 자동사일 때는 전치사가 필요하다. (4) -thing으로 끝나는 부정대명사는 「-thing+형용사+to부정사」의 어순을 따른다.

08 on one's way home: 집으로 가는 도중에

09 I think that + 주어 + 동사 ~: 나는 ~가 …라고 생각한다.

10 학교 농구 경기는 이번 주 금요일에 있다고 언급되었다.

11 어떤 것에 대해 행복해하는: 기쁜

12 대부분의 사람이 옳다고 믿고 있는 생각을 표현하는 오래되고 유명한 어구: 속담

13 too: (긍정문에서) ~도 (B) try to+동사원형: ~하려고 노력하다

15 Nice words for nice words는 '가는 말이 고와야 오는 말이 곱다'는 영어 속담이다.

창의사고력 서술형 문제   p.52

|모범답안|

01 (1) I want a bicycle to ride on weekends.
   (2) I want a hat to wear when I go out.

02 (1) He thinks that Jenny is kind.
   (2) She heard that they need help.
   (3) Tony says that it's delicious.
   (4) They know that many children are hungry.

03 (1) I need a chair to sit on.
   (2) I need a friend to talk with.
   (3) I need some food to eat.

(4) I need ski gloves to put on.

02 동사의 목적어가 되는 명사절을 이끄는 접속사 that을 사용하여 내용상 어울리는 것끼리 연결한다.

03 앞의 명사를 꾸며주는 to부정사의 형용사적 용법을 이용한다.

단원별 모의고사
p.53~56

01 ④	02 ⑤	03 ②	04 ②
05 (f)an	06 cut in	07 ④	08 ②
09 ⑤	10 ③	11 I can't wait for the concert.	
12 Tuesday, Thursday / July 15			
13 ③	14 ④	15 something cold to drink	
16 ③	17 ④	18 ②	
19 didn't know that	20 ④	21 Why do you have the ticket in your hand?	
22 ③			
23 (B) a ticket (C) the school basketball game			
24 (1) F (2) T	25 ③	26 I can't find one of my tickets.	
27 너 혹시 그것(내 입장권 하나)을 보았니?			
28 fan	29 ②	30 to	

01 식사할 때나 식당 등에서 먹을 것과 마실 것을 사람에게 주다: 제공하다(serve)

02 find out: ~을 알게 되다

03 • 여기에 너의 메모를 게시해라. • 이 문제 푸는 방법을 말해 줄래? • 나는 3일 내에 그 돈을 갚을 것이다. • 네가 믿을 수 있는 사람들과 시간을 보내라.

04 look at: ~을 보다 / be good for: ~에 좋다

05 fan: 팬, 선풍기

06 cut in: (말·대화에) 끼어들다

07 ④는 시합을 걱정한다는 의미이고, 나머지는 모두 '게임을 기대하고 있다'는 의미이다.

08 ②는 '학교 밴드 동아리에 대해 생각해 보는 게 어때?'라는 의미이고, 나머지는 학교 밴드 동아리에 대한 의견을 묻는 표현이다.

09 주어진 문장은 '나는 콘서트에서 연주하기를 희망한다.'라는 의미로, Me. too.(나도 콘서트에서 연주하기를 희망한다) 앞에 와야 한다.

10 on +날짜

11 I can't wait for ~: 나는 ~이 무척 기다려지다

12 매주 화요일과 목요일 방과 후에 연습을 하고, 7월 15일에 첫 번째 콘서트를 열 것이다.

13 명사 뒤에서 to+동사원형은 앞의 명사를 꾸며주며, '~할, ~할 수 있는'으로 해석한다.

14 ①, ②, ③, ⑤: 명사절을 이끄는 접속사 ④: 지시형용사

15 「-thing+형용사+to부정사」의 어순으로 쓴다.

16 think 뒤에 절이 올 경우 접속사 「that+주어+동사」의 어순으로

쓰고, 이때 접속사 that은 생략 가능하다. ③은 의문문의 어순으로 되어 있으므로 that절 뒤에 이어질 수 없다.

17 부정사인 to write가 앞의 명사 paper를 수식한다. 이때 paper는 write on의 목적어이므로 write 다음에 전치사 on을 붙여야 한다.

18 <보기>와 ②는 앞에 나오는 명사나 부정대명사를 꾸며주는 to부정사의 형용사적 용법이다. ① 명사적 용법(주어) ③ 명사적 용법(목적어) ④ 명사적 용법(보어) ⑤ 명사적 용법(목적어)

19 목적어절을 이끄는 접속사 that이 필요하다.

20 주어진 문장은 '나는 그것(입장권 한 장)을 찾고 있었어.'라는 의미로 '고맙다!'는 말 다음에 오는 것이 적절하다.

22 something을 수식하는 to부정사의 형용사적 용법이 되어야 한다.

23 (B)는 a ticket을 가리키고, (C)는 the school basketball game을 가리킨다.

24 (1) 다미는 세호의 손에 있는 입장권을 보고 화가 났다.

25 ⓐ bump into: ~에 부딪히다 ⓑ on: ~위에

26 one of: ~ 중 하나

27 Do you happen to+동사원형 ~?: 너 혹시 ~하니?

28 누군가 또는 무엇가를 숭배하거나 누군가 또는 무엇가를 보거나 듣는 것을 즐기는 사람: 팬

29 ②는 민준이를 가리키고 나머지는 지훈이를 가리킨다.

30 ⓑ think to oneself: 마음속으로 생각하다 ⓒ to: ~에

9

Lesson 2

I Love My Town!

시험대비 실력평가
p.60

01 ④	02 ①	03 ④	04 borrow
05 neighbor	06 ④	07 ④	08 address

01 ④는 부사형이고 나머지는 형용사형이다.

02 clean up: 청소하다

03 특히 동의나 이해를 나타내기 위해 머리를 위아래로 움직이다: (고개를) 끄덕이다(nod)

04 반의어 관계이다. 배고픈 : 배부른 = 빌려주다 : 빌리다

05 neighbor: 이웃

06 look at: ～을 보다 / put up: ～을 붙이다

07 ④는 유의어 관계이고 나머지는 반의어 관계이다.

08 누군가가 살거나 일하는 곳과 편지 등을 보낼 수 있는 곳에 대한 세부사항: 주소

서술형 시험대비
p.61

01 (1) rest (2) lend (3) sell (4) laugh 02 (1) a pair of (2) in front of 03 (1) pass (2) cut (3) miss 04 (1) enough (2) elderly (3) lonely 05 (1) be good at (2) take care of (3) prepare for 06 (1) (b)lock (2) (p)erfect (3) (v)olunteer

01 (1)은 유의어 관계이다. 맛있는 : 맛있는 = 휴식 : 휴식 (2), (3), (4)는 반의어 관계이다. (2) 쉬운 : 어려운 = 빌리다 : 빌려주다 (3) 옳은 : 틀린 = 사다 : 팔다 (4) 기억하다 : 잊다 = 울다 : 웃다

02 (1) a pair of: 한 켤레의 (2) in front of: ～ 앞에서

03 (1) pass: 합격하다; 통과하다 (2) cut: 상처; 베다 (3) miss: 그리워하다; 놓치다

04 (1) enough: 충분한 (2) elderly: 연세가 드신 (3) lonely: 외로운

05 (1) be good at: ～을 잘하다 (2) take care of: ～을 돌보다 (3) prepare for: ～을 준비하다

06 (1) block: 블록, 구획 (2) perfect: 완벽한 (3) volunteer: 자원봉사자

교과서 Conversation

핵심 Check
p.62~63

1 (1) What, going[planning] / I'm going[planning] to
  (2) What, plans / plan to
2 (1) make it, / Sure, then (2) How about going, problem
  (3) Let's play / Sorry, I can't

교과서 대화문 익히기

Check(√) True or False
p.64

1 F 2 T 3 T 4 F

교과서 확인학습
p.66~67

Get Ready - 2
1 going to take, front of / Sounds, over
2 It's, get / Let's, at, in
3 planning, for / selling, over there / Let's, around

Start Off - Listen & Talk A
1 any, for / planning to, dancing / Sounds, Can, join / not
2 planning to, to prepare / mean, with / make it / then

Start Off - Listen & Talk B
are, going to / clean up, with / like, Can, join / make it, at / not, about / with, a pair of / See, on

Start Off - Speak Up - Look and talk.
planning to, at / Can, with / Why not, make / Let's, front of

Step Up - Real-life Scene
to volunteer, care / mean, near / Will, with, take care of / love, walking, good at / bring, with, too / neighbor, too, shall, meet / make, at, at / on

Express Yourself A
1 I'm planning to, to watch / interesting, with / Of, Can, make, at / No, then
2 to enter / Don't, can win / Thank

Learning Diary - Listen & Speak
are, going to / planning, at / great / Will, with / shall, meet / make it / afraid, about / See, then

시험대비 기본평가　　　　　　　　p.68

01 ③　　　02 ③　　　03 ⑤　　　04 ④

01 계획을 묻는 표현이다.

02 Can you make it at ~?은 약속 시간을 정할 때 쓰는 표현이다.

03 여행을 갈 계획이라는 B의 대답으로 보아 계획을 묻는 질문이 들어가야 한다.

04 B가 동의하고 5시에 만나자고 말했으므로 약속 시간을 정하는 표현인 ④가 알맞다.

시험대비 실력평가　　　　　　　　p.69~70

01 ③　　02 ④　　03 ④　　04 ③
05 ③　　06 dancing　07 ④　　08 ③
09 the animal care center　　10 ②　　11 ④
12 ⑤　　13 How[What] about　　14 ④

01 주어진 문장은 '같이 가도 될까?'라는 의미로, Sure.(물론.)의 질문으로 오는 것이 적절하다.

02 be going to =will: ~할 예정이다

03 빈칸 다음의 문장으로 보아 제안에 거절하는 표현이 알맞다.

04 ③ 소년이 오후 1시에 만날 수 없는 이유는 알 수 없다.

05 be planning to ~: ~할 계획이다(=be going to)

06 practice는 목적어로 동명사를 취한다.

07 Why not?은 요청에 수락하는 표현이다. Not at all.: 천만에.

08 주어진 문장의 them은 animals를 가리킨다.

09 the one은 앞 문장의 the animal care center를 가리킨다.

10 take care of: ~을 돌보다

11 ⓒ와 ④는 '허가', ①은 '추측', ②③⑤는 '가능, 능력'을 나타낸다.

12 지나가 오전 8시에 만나자고 하는 것으로 보아 몇 시에 만날지를 묻는 질문이 알맞다.

13 Can you make it ~?은 How[What] about meeting ~? 으로 바꿔 쓸 수 있다.

14 ④ Alex가 동물을 몇 마리 기르는지는 알 수 없다.

서술형 시험대비　　　　　　　　p.71

01 meeting　　02 Let's meet in front of the library.
03 소년은 이번 화요일에 도서관에서 자원봉사를 할 계획이다.
04 (C) – (B) – (D) – (A)　　05 What are you going
to do this Saturday?　　06 make it　　07 They
will meet at the bus stop at 2 p.m.　　08 on

01 오후 3시에 만날 수 있느냐는 의미이다.

02 Let's+동사원형 ~.: ~하자. / in front of: ~ 앞에서

03 volunteer: 자원봉사를 하다

04 (C) 주말에 무슨 계획 있니? (B) 응. 청소년 센터에서 춤을 연습할 계획이야. (D) 좋은데. 같이 가도 될까? (A) 그거 좋지.

05 What are you going to+동사원형 ~?: 너는 ~에 무엇을 할 거니?

06 make it은 시간이나 장소의 표현과 함께 쓰여 '시간에 맞춰 가다, 도착하다'라는 의미를 갖는다.

07 그들은 오후 2시에 버스 정류장에서 만날 것이다.

08 on + 요일

교과서
Grammar

핵심 Check　　　　　　　　p.72~73

1 (1) will miss　(2) If　(3) takes　(4) studies
2 (1) play　(2) knocking　(3) shaking　(4) broken

시험대비 기본평가　　　　　　　　p.74

01 (1) felt, touch[touching]　(2) heard, arrive[arriving]
　　(3) saw, run[running]
02 (1) If you hurry up, you will catch the bus.
　　(2) If it is fine tomorrow, we will go on a picnic.
　　(3) If you are tired, you can sit here.
03 (1) She watched her husband paint[painting] the
　　　wall.
　　(2) The dog heard the baby cry[crying].
　　(3) The police officer sees a girl pick[picking] up
　　　a bottle.
04 (1) If you study hard　(2) If it rains

01 「지각동사+목적어+동사원형[현재분사]」의 형태로 써야 한다.

02 「If+주어+현재시제, 주어+will[can/may]+동사원형 ~.」의 어순이다.

03 「지각동사 + 목적어 + 목적격 보어(동사원형/현재분사)」 어순이다.

04 '만약 ~한다면'이라는 의미로 조건을 나타내는 표현은 「if+주어+동사의 현재형」으로 나타낸다.

시험대비 실력평가　　　　　　　　p.75~77

01 ③　　02 ②　　03 ⑤　　04 ②
05 If it is, will go　　06 ①, ②　　07 ③
08 ④　　09 ④　　10 touched → touch
[touching]　11 ①　　12 ③　　13 We
heard the rain falling on the roof.　　14 ④

15 If, don't / Unless   16 ③   17 will rain → rains   18 ②   19 felt somebody hit her   20 ⑤   21 If you get tickets, we can go to the concert.   22 ③   23 ④   24 Can you hear him go down the stairs?

01 지각동사는 목적격 보어로 동사원형과 현재분사를 쓸 수 있는데, 동작의 진행을 강조하는 경우에는 현재분사를 쓴다.

02 조건을 나타내는 if절은 미래의 의미이더라도 현재시제로 나타내지만, 주절은 미래시제로 써야 한다.

03 5형식 문장에서 지각동사는 목적격 보어로 동사원형이나 현재분사를 취한다.

04 현재나 미래에 실현 가능성이 있는 조건의 if 문장이다.

05 조건의 부사절에서는 현재가 미래시제를 대신한다. 날씨를 말할 때는 비인칭 주어 it을 사용한다.

06 지각동사 see는 목적격 보어로 동사원형이나 현재분사를 취한다.

07 조건을 나타내는 접속사 if가 이끄는 절에서는 미래의 일을 나타내는 경우일지라도 동사는 현재형을 쓴다. ③ will snow → snows

08 지각동사 see, hear 등은 목적격 보어로 동사원형 또는 현재분사를 쓸 수 있다.

09 • '~하지 않으면'의 의미인 Unless가 알맞다. • '~이기 때문에'라는 의미의 because나 as가 알맞다.

10 지각동사 feel의 목적격 보어로 동사원형 또는 현재분사를 쓸 수 있다.

11 ① 지각동사 hear는 목적격 보어로 동사원형이나 현재분사를 취한다. (sang → sing[singing])

12 ③은 '~인지 아닌지'의 의미이고 나머지는 '만일 ~이라면'의 뜻이다.

13 비가 떨어지고 있는 것을 들었으므로 진행의 의미를 갖는 현재분사를 쓴다.

14 목적격 보어로 동사원형과 현재분사를 쓸 수 있는 동사는 지각동사이다. / get, want+목적어+to부정사 / make, have+목적어+동사원형 / hear+목적어+동사원형[현재분사]

15 if ~not은 unless(~하지 않으면)로 바꿔 쓸 수 있다

16 '경험'을 나타내므로 현재완료시제가 적합하고, 지각동사가 쓰였으므로 목적격 보어로 동사원형을 쓴다.

17 조건을 나타내는 if절에서는 현재시제가 미래시제를 대신한다.

18 <보기>와 나머지는 '만약 ~라면'이라는 의미로 조건을 나타내는 접속사로 쓰였고, ②는 '~인지 아닌지'라는 의미로 명사절을 이끄는 접속사로 쓰였다.

19 「지각동사+목적어+동사원형」의 어순으로 써야 한다.

20 조건을 나타내는 if절에서는 현재시제가 미래시제를 대신한다. (⑤ it will be → it is)

21 조건을 나타내는 if절에서는 현재시제가 미래시제를 대신한다.

22 ① touched → touch[touching] ② called → call[calling] ④ shook → shake[shaking] ⑤ stole → steal[stealing]

23 ④는 이유를 나타내는 접속사 because가 와야 한다.

24 'Can you+지각동사(hear)+목적어(him)+목적격 보어(go) ~?'의 어순으로 배열한다. '계단을 내려가다'는 go down the stairs이다.

서술형 시험대비
p.78~79

01 (1) I saw a strange man enter my house.
  (2) I saw my brother meeting a lady in the bakery.
  (3) I felt something crawl up my arm.
  (4) I heard the church bells ring out in the distance.

02 (1) If it is sunny tomorrow,
  (2) If it doesn't stop raining,

03 (1) to read → read / reading
  (2) sang → sing / singing

04 (1) If the weather is nice, I always walk to school.
  (2) If it rains on weekends, we watch TV.
  (3) If I am late for class, my teacher gets very angry.

05 (1) saw the boys playing baseball
  (2) felt somebody hit her

06 (1) If (2) when (3) Unless

07 I heard a famous singer sing[singing] on the stage yesterday.

08 (1) Unless you leave (2) If it doesn't

09 (1) I watched my dad wash[washing] his car.
  (2) Jisu saw Tom ride[riding] a bike.
  (3) He felt a warm hand touch[touching] his back.

10 (1) will have → have (2) have gone → go
  (3) won't send → don't send

11 (1) If you don't hurry up, you'll be late.
  (2) If you go straight three blocks, you will find a supermarket.

12 (1) I felt the building shake.
  (2) I have never heard my sister play the piano.

01 지각동사의 목적격 보어로 동사원형이나 현재분사를 써서 두 문장을 한 문장으로 쓸 수 있다.

02 조건을 나타내는 If절에서는 미래의 의미이더라도 현재시제로 써야 한다. stop+-ing: ~하는 것을 멈추다

03 지각동사의 목적격 보어는 동사원형이나 현재분사를 사용한다.

04 if는 종속절을 이끄는 접속사이다.

05 「지각동사+목적어+현재분사/동사원형」 어순으로 써야 한다.

06 when은 때, if는 조건을 나타낸다. unless는 if ~ not의 뜻이다.

07 「지각동사 hear+목적어(a famous singer)+목적격 보어(원형
　동사/현재분사)」 구문으로 만든다.

08 unless는 if ~ not과 같은 뜻이다.

09 watch, see, feel 등은 지각동사로 목적격 보어로 동사원형이
　나 현재분사 형태를 쓸 수 있다.

10 if 조건절에서는 현재시제가 미래시제를 대신한다.

11 If 조건문 – If+주어+동사(현재형), 주어+will[won't]+동사
　원형

12 주어+지각동사+목적어+목적보어(동사원형)의 어순이다.

교과서 Reading

확인문제 　　　　　　　　　　　　　p.80

1 F　2 F　3 T　4 T　5 F

확인문제 　　　　　　　　　　　　　p.81

1 T　2 T　3 F　4 F

교과서 확인학습 A 　　　　　　　　　p.82~83

01 with　　　　　02 with

03 always thought, perfect, because, spot

04 outside, run after　　　　05 in, for

06 away, lived with　　　　07 to, lonely

08 no　　　　　09 after, followed

10 One day, sitting　　　　11 was making

12 wrong　　　13 at, closely, cut 14 took, to

15 get better, enough, inside　　16 at, was

17 outside, couldn't　　　　18 put, up

19 third, Still　　20 When, walking, lost

21 read, big　　22 looks, like, strange

23 hurried　　24 on, Let's　　25 to, on

26 Ding–Dong, heard, ring, ran, opened

27 back, cried　　28 jumped up　　29 Let, guess

30 in, doesn't　　31 nodded　　32 last, didn't you

33 How, know　　34 Because, too, during

35 Our, has　　36 if, come in, have

37 Sure　　　38 Thank, thought

39 met, thanks to

교과서 확인학습 B 　　　　　　　　　p.84~85

1 Bear was a black and brown cat with green eyes.

2 He lived with a boy, Ryan.

3 Ryan always thought that "Bear" was a perfect
　name for the cat because he had a black spot in
　the shape of a bear.

4 Bear liked to go outside every morning and run
　after butterflies.

5 He always came home just in time for dinner.

6 Five blocks away, Max the cat lived with a girl,
　Sheila.

7 When Sheila moved to this town last month, she
　was lonely.

8 She had no friends there.

9 But, after Max followed her home, he became a
　good friend to her.

10 One day, Sheila saw Max sitting under the desk.

11 He was making a strange sound.

12 "What's wrong?" asked Sheila.

13 She looked at him closely and found a bad cut
　on his leg.

14 She took him to the animal hospital.

15 The doctor said, "He will get better if he gets
　enough rest. Keep him inside for a week."

16 That night, at Ryan's house, there was no Bear.

17 Ryan checked outside, but he couldn't find him.

18 He made posters and put them up around town.

19 A third night passed. Still no Bear.

20 When Sheila was walking near her house, she
　saw a poster about the lost cat.

21 She read it closely, and her eyes got big.

22 "This cat looks exactly like Max. It's so strange."

23 She hurried home.

24 "Come on, Max! Let's go!"

25 She took him to the address on the poster.

26 "Ding–Dong." When Ryan heard the doorbell
　ring, he ran to the door and opened it.

27 "Bear, you're back!" Ryan cried.

28 Max jumped up into Ryan's arms.

29 "Let me guess," said Sheila.

30 "Your cat comes home only in the evenings,
　doesn't he?"

31 Ryan nodded.

32 "And you lost him last Friday, didn't you?" Sheila
　said.

33 "Yes! How did you know?" said Ryan.

34 "Because this is my cat, too, and he usually
　comes to my home only during the day."

35 "Our cat has two families!" said Ryan.
36 "Hey, if you have time, please come in and have some cookies."
37 "Sure," said Sheila.
38 "Thank you, Max," she thought.
39 "I met a good neighbor thanks to you!"

시험대비 실력평가
p.86~89

01 with 　　02 ⑤ 　　03 ② 　　04 spot
05 ④ 　　06 ④ 　　07 ② 　　08 to sit →
sitting[sit] 　09 ③ 　　10 ⑤ 　　11 ④
12 ① 　　13 a poster 　14 like 　15 ③
16 to ring → ring[ringing] 　17 ② 　18 doesn't
19 comes usually → usually comes 　20 ⑤
21 ② 　　22 ⑤ 　　23 ④ 　　24 ②
25 ⑤ 　　26 cut 　　27 were → was
28 포스터에 있는 고양이가 Max와 꼭 닮은 것 29 ③

01 with: ~와 함께
02 이유를 나타내는 접속사 because가 알맞다.
03 in time for: ~에 시간 맞춰
04 다른 부분과 달리 보이는 표면의 작은 부분: 점, 반점(spot)
05 ④ Bear가 왜 나비를 쫓아다녔는지는 알 수 없다.
06 Sheila는 친구가 없었다고 했으므로 외로웠을 것이다. lonely: 외로운
07 but: 그러나
08 지각동사 see는 목적격 보어로 현재분사 또는 동사원형을 쓴다.
09 ⓓ look at: ~을 보다 ⓔ take A to B: A를 B로 데려가다
10 Max가 왜 다쳤는지는 알 수 없다.
11 but: 그러나
12 ⓑ put up: ~을 붙이다 ⓔ on: ~에
13 인칭대명사 it은 앞 문장에 나온 a poster를 가리킨다.
14 look like: ~처럼 보이다
15 ③ 왜 Ryan이 Bear를 잃어버렸는지는 알 수 없다.
16 지각동사 hear는 목적격 보어로 동사원형이나 현재분사를 쓴다.
17 jump up: 뛰어오르다 / in the evenings: 저녁마다
18 평서문의 동사가 일반동사 현재형이고 주어가 3인칭 단수이므로 doesn't가 알맞다.
19 빈도부사는 일반동사 앞에 위치한다.
20 Max가 Ryan의 고양이인 것을 Sheila가 어떻게 알았는지는 알 수 없다.
21 목적어절을 이끄는 접속사 that이 알맞다.
22 저녁 식사 시간에 맞춰 집에 왔다고 언급되었다.
23 주어진 문장은 '그녀는 그를 동물 병원에 데려갔다.'는 의미로 그

의 다리에 심한 상처를 발견했다는 문장 다음에 오는 것이 자연스럽다.
24 ⓐ on: ~에 ⓒ for a week: 일주일 동안
25 get better는 '(병이) 좋아지다, 호전되다'는 뜻으로 recover와 바꿔 쓸 수 있다.
26 날카로운 것에 의해 사람의 몸에 생긴 상처: cut
27 주어가 Bear로 단수이므로 was가 되어야 한다.
28 인칭대명사 It은 앞 문장을 받는다.
29 Sheila는 그녀의 집 근처를 걷고 있었을 때 포스터를 보았다고 언급되었다.

서술형 시험대비
p.90~91

01 with 　　02 His eyes are green. 　　03 (p)erfect 　　04 Because "Bear" had a black spot in the shape of a bear. 　05 When Ryan heard the doorbell ring 　　06 He lost him last Friday. 　　07 didn't you 　08 He usually comes to her home only during the day. 　　09 She moved to this town last month. 　　10 lonely
11 (A) after 　(B) sitting 　(C) gets 　　12 he had a big cut on his leg 　　13 He made posters and put them up around town. 　　14 ⓐ closely 　ⓑ like 　　15 She saw it when she was walking near her house. 　　16 address

01 with: ~을 가진
02 Bear의 눈은 초록색이라고 언급되었다.
03 결점이나 약점이 없는 완전한: 완벽한
04 곰 모양의 검은 반점이 있었기 때문에 "Bear"가 그 고양이에 대한 완벽한 이름이라고 생각했다.
05 when+주어+지각동사 hear+목적어+동사원형
06 Ryan은 그의 고양이를 지난 금요일에 잃어버렸다고 언급되었다.
07 평서문의 주어가 you이고 일반동사 과거형이므로 부가의문문은 didn't you가 알맞다.
08 Sheila의 고양이는 보통 그녀의 집에 낮 동안에만 온다고 언급되었다.
09 Sheila는 지난달에 이 마을로 이사를 왔다고 언급되었다.
10 말할 친구나 사람이 없어서 행복하지 않은: 외로운
11 (A) 문맥상 after가 알맞다. (B) 지각동사 see+목적어+현재분사 (C) if 조건절에서는 미래시제 대신 현재시제를 쓴다.
12 Sheila는 Max가 다리에 심한 상처를 입었기 때문에 Max를 병원에 데려갔다.
13 Ryan은 포스터를 만들어서 그것들을 마을 주위에 붙였다고 언급되었다.
14 ⓐ 동사를 수식하는 부사가 되어야 한다. ⓑ look like: ~처럼

보이다

15 Sheila는 그녀의 집 근처를 걷고 있을 때 잃어버린 고양이에 대한 포스터를 보았다고 언급되었다.

16 누군가가 살거나 일하는 곳과 편지 등을 보낼 수 있는 곳에 대한 세부사항: 주소

영역별 핵심문제　　　　　　　　　　　　　　p.93~97

01 ④	02 ③	03 ④	04 (s)trange
05 in	06 butterfly	07 ④	
08 ②	09 (D) - (B) - (C) - (A)		10 ③

11 What are you planning to do this Saturday?

12 ②　　13 make　　14 They will meet at the bus stop at 2 p.m.　　15 ④　　16 ①

17 to get → get[getting]　　18 ②　　19 won't → don't　　20 ⑤　　21 ④　　22 I saw an old man get off the train.　　23 If Susan does not get up now, she will miss the train. 또는 Susan will miss the train if she does not get up now.　　24 ④　　25 ⑤　　26 Kate heard someone shouting[shout] at her.　　27 ④

28 ③	29 ④	30 blocks	31 ③
32 ④	33 ③	34 closely	35 ⑤
36 rest	37 ③		

01 색이 다르거나 그것이 있는 표면과 다른 느낌이 드는 작고 둥근 부분: 점, 반점(spot)

02 ③은 유의어 관계이고 나머지는 반의어 관계이다.

03 take a break: 휴식을 취하다 / take care of: ~을 돌보다

04 strange: 이상한

05 in need: 어려움에 처한 / in front of: ~ 앞에

06 길고 얇은 몸과 보통 밝은 색상의 날개들을 가진 날아다니는 곤충: 나비(butterfly)

07 A: 너는 이번 방학에 무엇을 할 계획이니? ① 나는 할머니를 방문했어. ② 나는 미국에 갔다. ③ 응. 나는 미국에 갈 계획이야. ④ 나는 오스트레일리아에 갈 계획이야. ⑤ 아니. 나는 미국에 가지 않을 예정이야.

08 9시에 만나자는 제안에 학교 체육관에서 보자고 했으므로 제안에 수락하는 말이 와야 한다.

09 (D) 나는 댄스 쇼를 보기 위해 마을 축제에 갈 계획이야. (B) 흥미롭구나. 같이 가도 될까? (C) 물론이지. 오후 6시에 학교 정문에서 만날까? (A) 그래. 그럼 그때 보자.

10 박물관 앞에서 만나자는 말에 '그 박물관은 좋은 곳이었어.'라고 대답하는 것은 어색하다.

11 '~할 계획이다'는 「be planning to+동사원형」으로 나타낼 수 있다. / this Saturday: 이번 토요일

12 공원을 청소할 계획이라는 말에 멋진 계획인 것 같다고 답했으

므로 이어질 말로 함께할 수 있는지 묻는 표현이 자연스럽다.

13 make it: 시간에 대다, 만나다

14 소년이 오후 2시에 버스 정류장에서 만나자고 제안하자 소녀는 괜찮다고 했다.

15 「지각동사+목적어+동사원형」 어순이다.

16 '만약 ~한다면'을 의미하는 접속사 if를 이용하며, if절에서는 미래의 일이라도 will을 쓸 수 없고 현재시제를 쓴다.

17 「지각동사+목적어+동사원형/현재분사」 형태이다.

18 '만약 ~하면'의 뜻으로 조건절을 이끄는 접속사와 '~인지 아닌지'의 뜻으로 명사절을 이끄는 접속사 역할을 하는 if가 알맞다.

19 if절에서는 미래의 일을 현재시제로 나타낸다.

20 모두 지각동사가 있는 5형식 문장이다. 목적격 보어로 현재분사, 동사원형이 올 수 있다. ⑤는 cried를 cry 또는 crying으로 고쳐 써야 한다.

21 '만약 ~라면'의 뜻으로 조건을 나타내지 않는 문장을 찾는다. ④ if절은 '~인지 아닌지'의 뜻으로 명사절을 이끄는 접속사로 쓰였다.

22 「주어(I)+지각동사(saw)+목적어(an old man)+동사원형(get off) ~」의 어순으로 쓴다.

23 첫 문장이 두 번째 문장의 조건이 되므로 접속사 if를 이용하여 연결한다.

24 지각동사 watch의 목적격 보어로 동사원형이나 현재분사가 와야 한다.

25 ①~④는 내용상 조건을 나타내는 접속사 if가 와야 하고, ⑤는 동사 think의 목적어 역할을 하는 접속사 that이 적절하다.

26 지각동사+목적어+목적격 보어(목적어와 능동 관계이면 현재분사나 동사원형이 쓰인다.)

27 with: ~을 가진

28 ①, ②, ④, ⑤는 명사절을 이끄는 접속사 that이고 ③은 지시형용사이다.

29 because: ~ 때문에

30 사방에 거리가 있는 건물들의 그룹: 구획, 블록

31 문맥상 after가 알맞다.

32 Sheila가 이 마을로 왜 이사를 왔는지는 알 수 없다.

33 지각동사 + 목적어 + 현재분사

34 동사를 수식하는 부사가 되어야 한다.

35 on: ~에 / put up: ~을 붙이다

36 활동하거나 일을 한 후에 쉬거나 잠을 자거나 아무 일도 하지 는 기간: 휴식

37 Sheila의 집 근처에 동물 병원이 있었는지는 알 수 없다.

단원별 예상문제　　　　　　　　　　　　　　p.98~101

01 ②	02 up	03 ②	04 look around
05 ④	06 (d)irector	07 ⑤	
08 ②	09 ⑤	10 volunteer	11 Can

15

you make it at 3 p.m.? 　12 They will meet at 4 p.m. 　13 ③ 　14 ①, ⑤ 　15 to cry → cry[crying] 　16 ③ 　17 ⑤ 　18 Unless you like the food 　19 ③ 　20 ④ 　21 ③ 　22 ② 　23 nod 　24 He comes to his home only in the evenings. 　25 ③ 　26 shape 　27 (A) because　(B) after 　28 ④ 　29 ③

01 날카로운 것에 의해 사람의 몸에 생긴 상처: cut

02 put up: ~을 붙이다 / clean up: ~을 청소하다

03 get better: (병 따위가) 좋아지다 / get enough rest: 충분한 휴식을 취하다

04 look around: ~을 둘러보다

05 neighbor: 이웃 / strange: 이상한 / nervous: 긴장되는 / brown: 갈색의

06 director: 감독

07 콘서트에 가자는 A의 제안에 B가 동의를 했으므로, 뒤에는 만나는 시간 약속을 하는 내용이 이어지는 것이 자연스럽다.

08 미래에 할 계획이나 의도를 묻는 표현에 대한 응답으로 ②의 할 수 있다는 표현은 어색하다.

09 Aria가 오후 3시에 만나자고 제안하자 Eric이 안 된다고 하고, 오후 4시에 만나자는 제안을 하는 흐름이 알맞다.

10 어떤 보상을 기대하지 않고 무언가를 하겠다고 제안하다: 자원봉사를 하다

11 '시간에 맞춰 가다'는 make it이다. '너는 오후 3시에 올 수 있니?'라는 뜻의 의문문을 만든다.

12 Eric이 오후 4시에 만나자고 제안하자 Aria가 좋다고 했다.

13 조건을 나타내는 if절에서는 현재시제가 미래의 일을 나타내므로 ③이 알맞다.

14 지각동사의 목적격 보어로는 동사원형이나 현재분사가 쓰인다.

15 heard는 지각동사이므로 목적격 보어 자리에 동사원형이나 현재분사를 사용한다.

16 조건의 부사절에서는 현재시제로 미래를 나타낸다. ③ will pass → pass

17 지각동사(hear, see, feel, watch) + 목적어 + 목적격 보어: 목적어와 능동 관계인 경우 동사원형이나 현재분사를 쓴다. ⑤의 to move는 move나 moving으로 고쳐야 바른 문장이 된다.

18 '만약 ~하지 않는다면'이라는 의미의 「If+주어+don't [doesn't]+동사원형 ~」은 「Unless+주어+동사의 현재형 ~」으로 바꿔 쓸 수 있다.

19 ③ 평서문의 일반동사가 현재형이고 주어가 3인칭 단수이므로 부가의문문은 doesn't he가 되어야 한다.

20 because: ~ 때문에

21 during the day: 낮 동안에 / thanks to: ~ 덕분에

22 '만약 ~하면'의 조건절을 이끄는 접속사 if가 알맞다.

23 특히 동의나 이해를 보여주기 위해 머리를 위아래로 움직이다: (고개를) 끄덕이다

24 Ryan의 고양이는 저녁에만 집에 온다고 언급되었다.

25 thought 다음에 나오는 내용이 목적어의 역할을 하고 있으므로 명사절을 이끄는 접속사 that이 와야 한다.

26 사물의 형태나 윤곽: 모양

27 (A) because + 주어 + 동사: ~ 때문에 (B) after: ~한 후에

28 run after: ~을 쫓아다니다

29 ③ Bear는 항상 저녁 시간에 맞춰 Ryan의 집에 왔다고 언급되었다.

서술형 실전문제 　p.102~103

01 I'm planning to visit my grandparents.

02 are you going to do / are you planning to do

03 What time shall we meet? 　04 meet

05 (1) to play → play[playing] 　(2) will go → goes (3) drew → draw[drawing]

06 Unless 　07 Hana saw her cat climbing the wall.

08 If you arrive on time, your friend won't have to wait for you.

09 He made posters and put them up around town.

10 still 　11 This cat looks exactly like Max.

12 She took him to the address on the poster.

13 Sheila saw Max sitting under the desk.

14 (c)ut 　15 She took him to the animal hospital.

16 그가 충분한 휴식을 취하면 좋아질 거야.

01 be planning to: ~할 계획이다

02 미래의 계획을 묻는 표현은 What will you do ~? = What are you going to do ~? = What are you planning to do ~? 등이다.

03 What time shall we meet?: 우리 몇 시에 만날까?

04 Can you make it ~?은 Can we meet ~?으로 바꿔 쓸 수 있다.

05 (1), (3) 지각동사+목적어+목적격 보어(동사원형/현재분사) (2) 조건의 부사절에서는 의미가 미래일지라도 미래시제를 쓰지 않고 현재시제를 쓴다.

06 If ~ not은 '~하지 않는다면'이라는 의미로 Unless와 같다.

07 지각동사 saw가 있으므로 목적어와 목적격 보어를 차례로 쓴다. 목적격 보어는 climbing으로 현재분사 형태로 주어져 있다.

08 주절이 먼저 나오고 if절이 뒤로 가도 상관없다.

09 이어동사의 목적어가 인칭대명사일 때 목적어는 동사와 부사 사이에 위치해야 한다.

10 전에 일어나거나 존재해서 현재도 계속되는: 여전히(still)

11 look exactly like: 꼭 ~처럼 보이다

12 Sheila는 Max를 포스터에 있는 주소로 데려갔다.

13 「지각동사+목적어+현재분사」의 어순으로 써야 한다.

14 날카로운 것에 의해 몸에 생긴 상처

15 Sheila는 Max를 동물 병원으로 데려갔다고 언급되었다.

16 get better: 좋아지다, 나아지다 / get enough rest: 충분한 휴식을 취하다

|모범답안|

01 (1) I saw a man plant[planting] trees.

(2) I heard a phone ring[ringing].

(3) I felt somebody touch[touching] my leg.

02 (1) If I get an A on the math test, my parents will be happy.

(2) If it is sunny tomorrow, I will go hiking with my friends.

(3) If I find an abandoned dog on the street, I will bring it to my house.

03 (1) My mother saw me wash[washing] the dishes.

(2) I felt the ground move[moving] under me.

(3) I heard my mom call[calling] my name.

(4) I watched a girl swim[swimming] in the sea.

01 「지각동사+목적어+동사원형/현재분사」 구문을 이용하여 문장을 만들어 본다.

02 '만약 ~이라면'의 뜻의 if를 활용하여 조건절을 만든다. if가 이끄는 절이 부사절일 때는 미래시제 대신 현재시제를 쓰는 것에 유의한다.

01 ④	02 ④	03 (m)iss	04 ⑤
05 ②	06 (1) over (2) in		07 ②, ⑤
08 ③	09 동물 보호 센터에서 근무하는 사람들		
10 ④	11 make it at	12 ②	13 ②
14 ②	15 If Mary sleeps early, we will go to the theater at night.		16 ⑤　17 (1) cutting → cut (2) to burn → burn[burning] 18 ⑤
19 ②	20 ⑤		21 He will get better if he gets enough rest.　22 enough　23 ④
24 ④	25 didn't you	26 ②	27 ①
28 posters	29 ④	30 ③	

01 ④는 유의어 관계이고 나머지는 반의어 관계이다.

02 take care of: ~을 돌보다 / thanks to ~덕분에

03 miss: 놓치다, 그리워하다.

04 ⑤는 lend(빌려주다)의 영영풀이다.

05 take[have] a break: 휴식을 취하다 / put up: ~을 내붙이다, 게시하다

06 (1) over there: 저쪽에서 (2) in need: 어려움에 처한

07 '나는 ~할 예정이다'라는 뜻의 I'm going to ~, I'm planning to ~.로 표현할 수 있다.

08 주어진 문장은 '너는 다른 친구들도 데려와도 돼.'라는 의미로, ' 알겠어. 내 이웃인 Nancy에게 물어볼게.'라는 문장 앞에 와야 한다.

09 They는 동물 보호 센터에서 근무하는 사람들을 가리킨다.

10 take care of: ~을 돌보다 / be good at: ~을 잘하다

11 make it: 시간에 대다, 만나다 / at + 시각

12 ② 지나가 어떤 동물을 기르는지는 알 수 없다.

13 saw가 지각동사이므로 목적격 보어로 동사원형이나 현재분사가 와야 한다. '테니스 치다'는 play tennis로 한다.

14 조건을 나타내는 if절에서는 현재시제가 미래시제를 대신한다. ② will go → go

15 조건을 나타내는 if절에서는 현재시제가 미래시제를 대신한다.

16 ⑤에서 목적어 your number와 목적보어의 관계가 수동이므로 현재분사(calling) 대신 과거분사(called)가 와야 한다.

17 (1) 나무가 베어진 것은 수동의 의미이므로 과거분사형인 cut이 적절하다. (2) 지각동사 saw의 목적격 보어로 원형동사나 -ing형이 온다.

18 ⑤는 '만일 ~라면'의 의미의 접속사이고, 나머지는 '~인지 아닌지'라는 의미의 접속사로 쓰였다.

19 주어진 문장은 '그는 이상한 소리를 내고 있었다.'는 의미로, 무슨 문제가 있는지 묻는 말 앞에 오는 것이 적절하다.

20 상대방의 증상을 묻는 표현이 쓰여야 한다. ⑤는 '너는 왜 그렇게 무서워하는 거야?'라는 뜻이다.

21 if 조건절은 의미상 미래이더라도 현재시제를 쓴다.

22 필요하거나 원하는 만큼 많은: 충분한

23 when: ~할 때

24 Let me ~: 내가 ~하겠다

25 주어가 you이고 동사가 일반동사 과거형이므로 부가의문문은 didn't you가 맞다.

26 too: 또한

27 역접의 접속사 but이 알맞다.

28 인칭대명사 them은 앞에 나온 복수명사를 가리킨다.

29 about: ~에 대한 / on: ~(위)에

30 Sheila는 그녀의 집 근처를 걷고 있을 때, 잃어버린 고양이에 대한 포스터를 보았다고 언급되었다.

Be Active, Be Safe!

Conversation

핵심 Check
p.114~115

1 (1) Have, read / have   (2) Have, heard / haven't
2 (1) shouldn't use, sorry   (2) Don't / not / shouldn't
   (3) think, cold / better not drink

교과서 대화문 익히기

Check(√) True or False
p.116

1 T   2 F   3 T   4 F

시험대비 실력평가
p.112

01 ⑤	02 ②	03 ④	04 careless
05 ③	06 teenage	07 make	08 ②

01 ①, ②, ③, ④는 모두 clothes(옷)에 속한다.

02 for the first time: 처음으로 / look at: ~을 보다

03 대개 그것을 따라 집들이 있는, 도시나 읍 또는 마을의 도로: street(길, 도로)

04 반의어의 관계이다. 기억하다 : 잊다 = 주의 깊은 : 부주의한

05 over there: 저기에

06 열세 살에서 열아홉 살 사이의 나이인: teenage(십대의)

07 make noise: 떠들다, 소란 피우다

08 out of: ~에서 / lots of: 많은

교과서 확인학습
p.118~119

Get Ready - 2
1 at, great / riding, know / What / special, riding
2 Don't, into / Why / shouldn't, without, Put, on
3 Look, over, like, take, front / over / okay
4 watch, in / up, birds / right

Start Off - Listen & Talk A
1 ever, climber / seen, on / climbing, camp, join / but, climb / right
2 Have, heard / haven't / favorite, concert, Can / shouldn't, too / right

Start Off - Listen & Talk B
heard of / when / doing, for / should bring / should, keep / shouldn't, when / in mind

Step Up - Real-life Scene
It's, see / hi, up / isn't, chat, heard / want / Guess, going / great / up, scenery / Be, use, while / right. Thank, send, later

Express Yourself A
1 heard, haven't. Who / singer, actor, figure / Sounds, take / Let's
2 take, painting / worry, real, So, front / Can, selfies, not

서술형 시험대비
p.113

01 (1) colorful   (2) princess   (3) safe
02 (1) for example   (2) had, fun   (3) look at
03 (1) during   (2) Even   (3) following   (4) someday
04 (1) actually   (2) advice   (3) dangerous
05 (1) good at   (2) hear of   (3) look for   (4) keep in mind
06 (1) (r)ide   (2) (c)limb   (3) (p)ast

01 (1) 명사에 -ful을 붙이면 형용사가 된다. (2) 남성명사에 -ess를 붙이면 여성명사가 된다. (3) 반의어 관계이다. 위험한 : 안전한 = 강한 : 약한

02 (1) for example: 예를 들면 (2) have a lot of fun: 아주 재미있게 지내다 (3) look at: ~을 보다

03 (1) during: ~ 중에 (2) even: ~도, ~조차 (3) following: 다음에 나오는 (4) someday: 언젠가

04 (1) actually: 실제로, 사실 / actual: 실제의 (2) advice: 충고 / advise: 충고하다 (3) dangerous: 위험한 / danger: 위험

05 (1) be good at: ~을 잘하다 (2) hear of: ~에 대해 듣다 (3) look for: ~을 찾다 (4) keep in mind: ~을 명심하다

06 (1) ride: 타다 (2) climb: 오르다 (3) past: 과거

시험대비 기본평가
p.120

01 better not	02 ③	03 ②	04 ③

01 금지를 나타낼 때는 should not[shouldn't]이나 had better not
을 쓴다.

02 '~에 가 본 적 있니?'라고 경험을 물을 때는 Have you been ~?
표현을 사용한다. '전에'는 before로 쓴다.

03 B의 답변으로 보아, 빈칸에는 금지를 나타내는 should not을
사용한 문장이 들어가야 한다.

04 현재완료로 경험을 묻는 말에 부정으로 답할 때는 No, I
haven't.라고 한다.

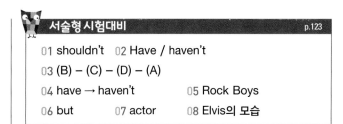

시험대비 실력평가   p.121~122

01 ⑤	02 Have, ever / have	03 ③
04 ④	05 ④	06 heard	07 ②
08 ①, ③	09 ⑤	10 ④	11 ⑤
12 Actually	13 scenery	14 ⑤

01 금지의 표현은 명령문 「Don't+동사원형 ~.」을 쓰거나 You
shouldn't + 동사원형 ~. / You'd better not + 동사원형 ~
을 쓸 수 있다.

02 경험을 묻는 현재완료를 쓴다.

03 넌 여기서 셀피를 찍으면 안 돼. 반 고흐의 그림이 네 뒤에 있어.
- 엄마, 걱정하지 마세요. 그건 그의 진짜 그림이 아니에요. 그래
서 그 앞에서 셀피를 찍을 수 있어요. - 정말이지? 재미있겠다.
나도 여기서 셀피를 찍을 수 있을까? - 물론이죠.

04 영화를 본 경험이 있는지 묻는 말에 본 적이 없다고 답하며 '너는
봤니?'라고 상대방에게 되묻는 표현이다. 대화의 흐름상 현재완
료형으로 물어야 하므로 ④ Have you (seen it)?가 적절하다.

05 B가 자기의 행동을 사과하고 있으므로 잘못된 행동을 금지하는
말이 와야 알맞다. ④ leave computers on: 컴퓨터를 켠 채로
두다

06 현재완료이므로 'have+과거분사'의 형이 알맞다.

07 on TV: 텔레비전으로

08 금지의 표현인 must not, should not, had better not가 들어가
야 한다.

09 ⑤ 암벽 등반을 반대한 것이 아니라 너무 높이 올라가지 말라고
말했다.

10 What is up?: 무슨 일 있니?

11 부가의문문이므로 is의 부정형인 isn't가 오고, this는 인칭대명
사 it으로 바꾼다.

12 문장 전체를 수식하는 부사가 되어야 한다.

13 여러분 주위에서 볼 수 있는 땅, 물, 식물들: scenery(경치, 풍경)

14 ⑤ 민준이가 얼마나 많은 사진을 소민에게 보낼지는 위 대화를
통해 알 수 없다.

서술형 시험대비   p.123

01 shouldn't	02 Have / haven't
03 (B) – (C) – (D) – (A)	
04 have → haven't	05 Rock Boys
06 but	07 actor	08 Elvis의 모습

01 금지를 나타낼 때는 should not[shouldn't]나 must not[mustn't]
등을 쓸 수 있다.

02 경험을 나타내는 현재완료 문장이다.

03 저 소년을 봐. 그는 대단하다. - 그는 MTB를 타고 있어. 넌 그
것에 대해 알고 있니? - 아니. 그게 뭐지? - 산에 오르기 위한 특
별한 자전거야.

04 No로 시작하는 부정문이므로 haven't로 고쳐야 한다.

05 It은 인칭대명사로 앞에 나온 단수명사를 받는다. Rock Boys는
그룹의 명칭이므로 단수 취급한다.

06 앞뒤의 내용이 반대되는 개념이므로 but이 알맞다.

07 연극이나 영화에서 연기하는 것이 직업인 사람: actor(배우)

08 it은 위 문장의 a figure of Elvis를 받는다.

교과서

Grammar

1 (1) done   (2) have / eaten   (3) has lived   (4) for
2 (1) Though   (2) Though   (3) Though   (4) Although

01 (1) has been   (2) been   (3) finished
   (4) has just finished   (5) arrived   (6) did you reach
02 (1) Because → Though / Although
   (2) since → though / although
   (3) As → Though / Although
03 (1) He has been sick in bed since last Friday.
   (2) How long have you known Miss Smith?
   (3) Have you ever read the Christmas Carol?
   (4) My father hasn't read the newspaper yet.

01 (1) 부사구 since ~가 있으므로 현재완료가 맞다. (2) '~에 다
녀오다'=have been to (3) two hours ago와 같이 명백한 과
거 시점을 나타내는 부사구가 있으므로 현재완료가 아닌 과거시
제로 써야 한다. (4) just와 함께 '이제 막 마쳤다'라는 의미이므
로 현재완료가 맞다. (5) yesterday와 같이 명백한 과거 시점

19

을 나타내는 부사가 있으므로 현재완료가 아닌 과거시제로 써야 한다. (6) 의문사 when은 특정 시점에 대해 묻는 의문사이므로 현재완료와 함께 쓸 수 없다.

02 '비록 ~이지만'의 의미를 나타내는 접속사 though나 although를 사용해야 한다.

03 (1) 계속 용법의 현재완료이다. (2) 계속 용법의 현재완료이다. (3) 경험 용법의 현재완료이다. (4) 완료 용법의 현재완료이다.

시험대비 실력평가   p.127~129

01 ⑤	02 ⑤	03 ④	04 t(T)
hough	05 have	06 ①, ④	07 ④

08 Though the traffic was heavy, we arrived on time. / We arrived on time though the traffic was heavy.

09 ④	10 ④	11 not
12 ③	13 since	14 ①	15 ②

16 Although[Even though/Though] he played well, he lost the soccer game.

17 ③	18 ④
19 ②	20 has been absent	21 yet
22 ②	23 ④	

01 계속을 나타내는 현재완료이다.

02 though: 비록 ~이지만

03 계속을 나타내는 현재완료이다.

04 though: ~이지만(접속사); 그러나, 하지만(부사)

05 「have+p.p.」로 현재완료 시제로 쓰인 문장이다.

06 whether: ~인지 아닌지 / as though: 마치 ~처럼

07 현재완료의 경험 용법이 사용된 문장에서 빈도부사 never는 have와 been 사이에 위치해야 한다.

08 though로 시작하는 부사절은 주절의 앞이나 뒤에 올 수 있다.

09 계속을 나타내는 현재완료이다.

10 although: 비록 ~이지만

11 앞 문장이 현재완료 결과의 문장이므로 '나의 엄마는 쇼핑에 가고 여기 없다.'의 뜻이 되어야 한다.

12 though는 but을 써서 같은 의미로 바꿔 쓸 수 있다.

13 '~한 이래로'는 since로 나타낸다.

14 빈칸 뒤의 내용이 '나는 잠을 자지 않으려고 노력했다'의 의미이므로 문맥상 졸렸다는 내용이 들어가야 한다.

15 현재완료형으로 물었으므로 현재완료형으로 대답해야 한다.

16 While은 Though[Even though/Although] 등의 양보 접속사로 바꿔 써야 한다.

17 though는 '비록 ~이지만'의 뜻으로 although, even though 등과 같은 의미로 사용된다.

18 ④와 같이 when ~이 명백한 과거의 시점을 나타낼 때는 현재완료 시제는 쓸 수 없다. (has been → was)

19 ② though를 이유를 나타내는 접속사 as나 because로 고쳐야

자연스럽다.

20 결석을 얼마나 오랫동안 했는지 물었으므로 현재완료(have+p.p.)로 쓴다.

21 yet: 1. 이미, 벌써(의문문) 2. 아직(부정문)

22 첫 번째 빈칸에는 양보의 접속사 though, although, even though 등이 들어가고, 두 번째 빈칸에는 이유의 접속사 as, because 등이 들어간다.

23 ④의 has gone은 '~에 가고 없다'는 의미의 현재완료 결과 용법이다. 나머지는 모두 현재완료 경험의 용법으로 쓰였다.

서술형 시험대비   p.130~131

01 (1) have, finished   (2) has not returned
   (3) has gone to

02 (1) Though[Although]   (2)though[although]

03 (1) has gone → went   (2) already → yet

04 t(T)hough

05 (1) has seen → saw   (2) is → has been

06 (1) He has been to Italy many times.
   (2) I have been very busy these days.
   (3) I have never visited Paris before.

07 (1) before   (2) that   (3) since   (4) because   (5) if
   (6) though

08 (1) I went to London four years ago.
   (2) When did you see a white lion?
   (3) I often played with her when I was a child.
   (4) He was ill in bed last month.

09 (1) Because → Although / Though
   (2) (2) as → although / though

10 (1) He has lived in New York since 1970.
   (2) Have you finished reading this story yet?
   (3) I have seen the movie once.

11 (A)lthough

01 (1) 현재완료 완료 용법 (2) yet은 과거에서 현재까지 아직 완료되지 않은 상태를 말한다. (3) 현재완료 결과 용법

02 양보의 접속사는 though, although, even though 등이 쓰인다.

03 (1) 과거를 나타내는 부사구가 있으므로 현재완료 시제가 아니라 과거시제를 써야 한다. (2) 부정문에서 '아직'의 뜻으로는 yet을 쓴다.

04 though가 문장 끝에 올 때는 부사로 '그러나, 하지만'의 뜻으로 쓰인다.

05 (1) 과거를 나타내는 부사구가 있으므로 현재완료 시제가 아니라 과거시제를 써야 한다. (2) 계속을 나타내는 현재완료가 알맞다.

06 (1) 현재완료 경험 용법 (2) 일정한 기간을 나타내는 부사구 (these days)는 현재완료와 함께 쓰일 수 있다. (3) 현재완료 경

07 (1) before: ~하기 전에 (2) so ~ that ...: 아주 ~해서 …하다 (3) since: ~부터, ~한 이래 (4) because: ~이기 때문에 (5) if: 만일 ~한다면 (6) though: 비록 ~이지만

08 (1) 과거 시점을 나타내는 four years ago가 있으므로 과거시 제로 쓴다. (2) when은 과거의 특정 시점을 묻는 표현이므로 과거시제로 써야 한다. (3) when 이하의 절이 과거의 특정 시 점을 나타내므로 과거시제로 쓴다. (4) '지난달(last month)'이 라는 명백한 과거 시점이 있으므로 과거시제로 나타낸다.

09 '비록 ~이지만'의 의미를 나타내는 접속사 though나 although 를 사용해야 한다.

10 (1) 현재완료 계속 용법 (2) 현재완료 완료 용법 (3) 현재완료 경험 용법

11 although: 비록 ~이지만(= though, even though)

교과서 Reading

확인문제   p.132

1 T   2 F   3 F   4 T   5 F

확인문제   p.133

1 T   2 T   3 F   4 T   5 F

교과서 확인학습 A   p.134~135

01 Have, heard   02 take, yourself
03 club, for, for   04 Here, about   05 people, take
06 Though, answer   07 Look
08 used, herself   09 nervous
10 why   11 think, first
12 probably, teenage   13 take, like
14 take, tricks   15 also, fun
16 example, famous   17 special, take
18 touch, even   19 following
20 Though, riding, like
21 just, brush, painting   22 exist
23 visited, before 24 don't, yourself 25 look, but
26 so   27 safe
28 should, when, places
29 could, time, fall   30 safety
31 take, while   32 pose, wild   33 Never, places
34 use, better   35 things, take   36 post, website

37 watered, school   38 also, at, times
39 at, those   40 about, create

교과서 확인학습 B   p.136~137

1 Have you ever heard of a "selfie"? When you take a photograph of yourself, it's a selfie.

2 The students from Minji's photo club have searched for information about selfies for one month.

3 Here are some of their presentations about selfies.

4 Did people in the past take selfies?

5 Though it wasn't easy at that time. the answer is yes.

6 Look at this photo of Princess Anastasia. She used a mirror to take a picture of herself.

7 She looks nervous. Can you guess why?

8 Well, I think it was her first selfie.

9 And it was probably the world's first teenage selfie ever.

10 You can take selfies at world-famous places like Big Ben and the Leaning Tower of Pisa.

11 To take great pictures, just do fun poses and use camera tricks.

12 You can also visit special museums to take fun selfies.

13 For example, there is a famous selfie museum in the Philippines.

14 It has special spots to take selfies.

15 You can touch the paintings and even step inside them.

16 Look at the following pictures.

17 Though the boys are not really riding horses, it looks like they are.

18 Though the man is just holding a big brush, it looks like he is painting the Mona Lisa.

19 Selfie museums exist in Korea, too. I have visited one in Chuncheon before.

20 Why don't you go there yourself? These selfies look great, but were they a good idea?

21 I don't think so. They don't look safe.

22 You should take special care when you take selfies in the wild or at high places like these.

23 A monkey could bite you at any time, or you

could fall.

24 Here are some safety tips:

25 Don't take selfies while you're walking.

26 Do not pose with or near wild animals.

27 Never take selfies in dangerous places.

28 I think we can use selfies to make a better school life.

29 We can do good things at school and take selfies.

30 Then we can post the photos on our school website.

31 I've watered the plants and flowers at school for one month.

32 I've also helped the teacher at the school library many times.

33 Look at my selfies of those things.

34 How about joining me to create a better school life?

시험대비 실력평가   p.138~141

01 ③	02 ④	03 ③	04 ⑤
05 ②	06 her → herself		07 여러분은

그녀가 왜 긴장돼 보이는지 추측할 수 있나요?   08 ⑤

09 ⑤	10 ②	11 ③	12 ①, ④
13 ③	14 Why	15 ②	16 ③

17 ②   18 여러분은 야생이나 이와 같이 높은 곳에서 셀피를 찍을 때 특별한 주의를 기울여야 합니다.   19 ⑤

20 ⑤   21 그리고 나서 우리는 학교 웹사이트에 사진을 올릴 수 있다.   22 ①   23 What

24 ⑤	25 ①	26 ①, ④	27 ③

28 ①   29 She used a mirror to take a picture of herself.   30 ③

01 '~할 때'의 뜻을 나타내는 접속사 when이 알맞다.

02 search for: ~을 찾다 / for+수사가 붙은 기간

03 ⓓ, ③ 1문형 ① 3문형 ② 2문형 ④ 5문형 ⑤ 4문형

04 마지막 문장에 민지의 사진 동아리 학생들의 셀피에 대해 수집한 정보가 제시될 것이라고 서술하고 있다.

05 거울로 셀피를 찍은 Anastasia 공주의 사진을 보라는 뜻이므로 과거에도 셀피를 찍었다고 서술하는 문장 다음에 와야 한다.

06 전차사 of의 목적어가 주어 자신이므로 재귀대명사를 써야 한다.

07 why 뒤에는 she looks nervous가 생략된 것이다.

08 주어진 문장의 It은 a famous selfie museum을 받는다.

09 ⓐ와 ⑤는 전치사로 쓰였고, 나머지는 모두 동사로 쓰였다.

10 빈칸 뒤에 special museums에 대한 구체적인 예가 나오고 있다.

11 위 글은 셀피를 찍기 위한 재미있는 장소를 소개하고 있다.

12 문맥상 '비록 ~이지만'의 뜻인 양보의 접속사가 알맞다.

13 exist: ~에 있다, 존재하다

14 Why don't you ~?: ~하지 그래?

15 ② 소년들은 말을 타고 있는 것처럼 보인다고 언급되어 있다.

16 위험한 장소에서 셀피를 찍을 때는 주의해야 한다는 문장 앞에 와야 한다.

17 상반되는 절을 연결해 주는 접속사 but이 알맞다.

18 should: ~해야 한다 / like: ~와 같은

19 '~하는 동안'의 뜻인 while이 알맞다.

20 ⓐ, ⑤ 목적을 나타내는 부사적 용법 ①, ③, ④ 명사적 용법 ② 형용사적 용법

21 then: 그 다음에 / post: 올리다

22 for+수사가 붙은 기간

23 How[What] about -ing?: ~하는 게 어때?

24 ⑤ 소윤이가 왜 선생님을 도왔는지는 알 수 없다.

25 hear of: ~에 대해 듣다 / take a photograph of: ~의 사진을 찍다

26 ⓒ, ①, ④ 계속 ② 경험 ③ 완료 ⑤ 결과

27 문맥상 '비록 ~이지만'의 뜻인 though가 알맞다.

28 look at: ~을 보다

29 to take a picture of: ~의 사진을 찍기 위해

30 ③ 민지는 Anastasia 공주가 처음으로 셀피를 찍었다고 생각한다.

서술형 시험대비   p.142~143

01 여러분은 빅벤과 피사의 사탑과 같은 세계적으로 유명한 장소에서 셀피를 찍을 수 있습니다.   02 poses

03 For   04 필리핀에 있는 유명한 셀피 박물관

05 I can go to special museums to take fun selfies.

06 at   07 비록 그 소년들은 말을 타고 있는 것은 아니지만, 말을 타고 있는 것처럼 보입니다.   08 a selfie museum   09 yourself   10 they were a good idea   11 safely → safe   12 at

13 dangerous 14 야생 동물이 물거나 높은 데서 떨어질 위험이 있기 때문이다.   15 나는 우리가 더 나은 학교생활을 만들기 위해 셀피를 이용할 수 있다고 생각해요.

16 watered   17 for   18 about

01 like: ~와 같은

02 예를 들면 당신을 사진 찍거나 그릴 때 당신이 서 있거나, 앉거나, 또는 누워 있거나 하는 특별한 방법: pose(자세, 포즈)

03 for example: 예를 들면

06 look at: ~을 보다

07 it looks like (that) ~: ~처럼 보이다

08 부정대명사 one은 앞에 나온 'a+보통명사'를 받는다.

09 주어진 you를 강조하는 재귀대명사로 고쳐야 한다.

10 so는 지시대명사로 앞 문장에 나온 긍정의 내용을 받는다.

11 감각동사 look의 보어로 형용사가 와야 한다.

12 at any time: 어느 때고

13 danger의 형용사형으로 고쳐야 한다.

15 I think 뒤에는 명사절을 이끄는 접속사 that이 생략되었다.

16 현재완료 구문이므로 water의 과거분사형인 watered로 고쳐야 한다.

17 for+수사가 붙은 기간

18 How about -ing?: ~하는 게 어때요?

01 ①, ③, ④, ⑤는 반의어의 관계이고, ②는 유의어의 관계이다.

02 • Kate는 그에게서 아직 편지를 받지 못했다. • 그가 몸을 돌려 뒤를 보았다. • 그는 그 장소를 어려움 없이 찾았다. • 그가 또 무슨 다른 말을 했나요?

03 과거 : 현재 : 미래

04 be good for: ~에 좋다

05 어떤 사람을 속이기 위해 의도된 행위: trick(속임수, 장난)

06 for the first time: 처음으로 / for example: 예를 들면

07 hang up: 전화를 끊다

08 경험을 묻고 대답하는 대화이다.

09 You'd better not + 동사원형 ~은 '~하지 않는 게 좋겠다.'라는 의미로 금지하는 표현이다.

10 What's up?: 무슨 일이니? / hang up: 전화를 끊다

11 this는 부가의문문에서 인칭대명사 it으로 바뀐다.

12 Guess what?: 있잖아., 알겠니?

13 be동사 다음은 보어 자리이므로 형용사가 되어야 한다. care에 -ful을 붙이면 형용사형이 된다.

14 문맥상 '~하는 동안'의 뜻인 while이 알맞다.

15 ④ 소민은 민준에게 걸는 동안은 전화기를 사용하지 말라고 충고했다.

16 과거에서 지금까지의 경험을 나타내는 문장이므로 현재완료

(have+p.p.) 시제로 써야 한다.

17 though: 비록 ~이지만

18 계속을 나타내는 현재완료이다.

19 although: 비록 ~이지만

20 ③ last week라는 특정 과거 시점이 있으므로 현재완료가 아니라 과거시제로 써야 한다. (have climbed → climbed)

21 although: 비록 ~이지만(= though, even though)

22 have[has] gone to ~: ~에 갔다(그래서 여기 없다) 결과를 나타내는 현재완료이다.

23 보기, ② 경험 ①, ④ 계속 ③ 완료 ⑤ 결과

24 ③ though를 이유를 나타내는 접속사 as나 because로 고쳐야 한다.

25 ① ~ ago라는 과거 시점이 있으므로 과거시제 went가 맞다.

26 though: 비록 ~이지만(= although, even though)

27 사물이 사람을 흥미 있게 하는 것이므로 현재분사형의 형용사를 써야 한다.

28 '많은'의 뜻이지만 뒤에 복수명사가 오므로 much는 쓸 수 없다.

29 문맥상 '~할 때'의 뜻인 when이 알맞다.

30 ② BMX의 가격은 언급되지 않았다.

31 for example: 예를 들면

32 it은 인칭대명사로 앞에 나온 단수명사를 받는다.

33 it looks like (that): ~처럼 보이다

34 Why don't you ~?: ~하지 그래요?

35 ③ 그림들에 손을 댈 수 있다고 언급되어 있다.

36 safe: 안전한 / safety: 안전

37 since와 as though는 양보를 나타내는 접속사가 아니다.

01 ④는 유의어 관계이고 나머지는 남성명사 - 여성명사 관계이다.

02 be fond of: ~을 좋아하다 / in front of: ~ 앞에

03 동사 : 명사의 관계이다.

04 ④는 push(밀다)의 영영풀이다.

05 keep in mind: ~을 명심하다, ~을 잊지 않다

06 shouldn't는 '~해서는 안 된다'의 뜻으로 금지를 나타낼 때 쓰

는 표현이다.

07 No, I haven't.로 답했으므로 현재완료를 이용해서 경험을 묻는 질문이 와야 알맞다.

08 주어진 문장은 그밖에 또 무엇을 명심해야 하느냐고 묻는 질문이므로 새들을 관찰할 때 아무 소리도 내지 말아야 한다는 문장 앞에 와야 한다.

09 it은 앞에 나온 단수명사를 받는다.

10 for the first time: 처음으로

11 make noise: 떠들다

12 that은 앞에 나온 문장의 내용을 받는다.

13 ⑤ 소년은 처음으로 들새 관찰을 하는 것이므로 취미라고 말할 수 없다.

14 현재완료의 경험 용법이 사용된 문장에서 빈도부사 never는 have[has]와 been 사이에 위치해야 한다.

15 although: 비록 ~이지만

16 since 이하가 과거에서 현재에 이르는 기간을 말하므로 현재완료의 계속 용법이 필요하다.

17 since는 현재완료 시제와 함께 쓰이므로 didn't see는 have not seen이 되어야 한다.

18 though는 but을 써서 같은 의미로 바꿔 쓸 수 있다.

19 시계를 잃어버려 현재 가지고 있지 않다는 것을 나타낸다. 결과를 나타내는 현재완료이다.

20 ⑤ Because 대신에 Though 또는 Although를 써야 한다.

21 ③의 has gone은 '~에 가고 없다'는 의미의 현재완료 결과 용법이다. 나머지는 모두 현재완료 경험 용법으로 쓰였다.

22 이유를 묻는 문장이므로 그녀가 긴장하고 있는 것처럼 보인다는 문장 다음에 와야 한다.

23 it은 앞에 나온 문장의 내용을 받는다.

24 ⓑ, ⑤ 목적을 나타내는 부사적 용법 ①, ③ 명사적 용법 ②, ④ 형용사적 용법

26 주어진 문장은 헬멧과 장갑을 착용하라는 뜻이므로 주의하라는 문장 다음에 와야 한다.

27 사물이 사람을 흥분시키는 것이므로 현재분사형의 형용사를 써야 한다.

28 much는 양을 나타내는 명사에 쓰인다. a few는 '조금'이라는 뜻이다.

29 though와 but은 같은 뜻의 문장으로 바꿔 쓸 수 있다.

30 문맥상 '~할 때'의 뜻인 when이 알맞다.

31 be동사의 보어인 형용사형을 써야 한다.

서술형 실전문제 p.154~155

01 climber 02 seen 03 She will teach rock climbing at a camp. 04 (B) – (C) – (D) – (A)
05 (1) Peter has lived in Peking since 2010.

(2) Tom has been in hospital for a week.

(3) My mother has gone shopping.

06 (1) Though it was windy, it wasn't very cold.

(2) Although Tim often annoyed Anne, she was fond of him.

(3) You must do it though you don't like it.

07 (1) has gone → went (2) have you seen → did you see

(3) have often played → often played

08 heard 09 you → yourself 10 for

11 자기 자신의 사진을 직접 찍는 것이다. 12 to make

13 take 14 plants 15 joining

01 스포츠나 취미로 바위나 산을 오르는 사람: climber(등반가)

02 현재완료 구문이므로 see의 과거분사로 고쳐야 한다.

04 잠깐, 지민. - 왜? - 저 표지판 좀 봐. 여기서 사진 찍으면 안 돼. - 아, 알았어.

05 현재완료(have+p.p.)를 이용해 문장을 완성한다. (1) 현재완료의 계속 용법 (2) 현재완료의 계속 용법 (3) 현재완료의 결과 용법

07 (1) 과거 시점을 나타내는 last year가 있으므로 과거시제로 쓴다. (2) 의문사 when으로 시작하므로 과거시제로 쓴다. (3) when 이하의 부사절이 과거의 특정 시점을 나타내므로 과거시제로 쓴다.

08 현재완료이므로 hear의 과거분사를 쓴다.

09 전치사 of의 목적어가 주어 자신이므로 재귀대명사를 써야 한다.

10 search for: ~을 찾다 / for+수사가 붙은 기간

12 목적을 나타내는 부사적 용법의 to부정사가 알맞다.

13 take selfies: 셀피를 찍다

14 줄기, 잎, 뿌리를 가지고 있으며 땅에서 자라는 살아 있는 것, 특히 나무나 덤불보다 작은 것: plant(식물)

15 전치사 다음에는 동명사형을 써야 한다.

창의사고력 서술형 문제 p.156

|모범답안|

01 (1) I have just sent an e-mail to Jane.

(2) Kate has just cleaned her room.

(3) Mike has already finished his job.

(4) Have you taken your medicine yet?

(5) Mary hasn't sung yet.

(6) You haven't studied enough yet.

(7) Has Tom done his homework yet?

02 (1) Though my mother was sick, she tried to clean the house. / My mother tried to clean the house though she was sick.

(2) Although the food smelled delicious, I didn't feel like eating it. / I didn't feel like eating the food although it smelled delicious.

(3) Even though I was sick, I didn't want to go to hospital. / I didn't want to go to hospital even though I was sick.

01 ④	02 ②	03 ④	04 pull
05 of	06 ②	07 ②	08 ⑤
09 ③	10 ③	11 What else should I keep in mind?	
		12 ①	13 ②
14 ④	15 ③	16 ①	17 ④
18 have lost	19 ②, ④	20 ③	21 ③
22 ②	23 He or she took it at the selfie museum.		
	24 나는 이 셀피들이 좋은 생각이었다고 생각하지 않습니다.		
		25 ①	26 ③
27 ③	28 rules	29 ④	30 ` fire, elevator

01 be good for: ~에 좋다

02 다른 사람들이나 다른 것들보다 더 좋거나 더 중요한: 특별한 (special)

03 during: ~ 중에, ~ 동안 / else 또[그 밖의] 다른, 다른

04 반의어 관계이다. 안전한 : 위험한 = 밀다 : 끌다

05 hear of: ~에 대해 소식을 듣다 / lots of: 많은

06 너 말을 타본 적 있니? - 응, 있어. 너는 어때? - 아니, 난 없어. 말 타는 거 어땠어? - 재미있었지만, 조금 무섭기도 했어.

07 Have you ever+과거분사 ~?에 대한 응답은 Yes, I have. / No, I haven't.이다. 빈칸 다음의 말로 보아 부정의 대답이 와야 한다.

08 You'd better not+동사원형 ~은 '~하지 않는 게 좋겠다'는 뜻으로 금지하는 표현이므로 You shouldn't + 동사원형 ~.으로 바꿔 쓸 수 있다.

09 hear of: ~에 관해 듣다 / for the first time: 처음으로

10 ⓒ, ③ 형용사적 용법 ①, ④ 명사적 용법 ②, ⑤ 부사적 용법

11 else는 '또[그 밖의] 다른'의 뜻으로 의문대명사 what 뒤에 위치한다.

12 문맥상 '~할 때'의 뜻을 나타내는 when이 알맞다.

13 ② 소년이 들새 관찰을 좋아하는지는 언급되지 않았다.

14 완료를 나타내는 현재완료의 부정문이다.

15 even though: 비록 ~이지만(= though, although)

16 ① ~ ago라는 과거 시점이 있으므로 과거시제 went가 맞다.

17 though: 비록 ~이지만

18 열쇠를 잃어버린 결과가 현재까지 영향을 미치므로 현재완료의 결과 용법으로 나타낸다.

19 though: 비록 ~이지만 (= although, even though)

20 과거에서 지금까지의 경험을 나타내는 문장이므로 현재완료 (have+p.p.) 시제로 써야 한다.

21 hear of: ~에 관해 듣다 / in front of: ~ 앞에서

22 ⓑ, ② 경험 ①, ④ 계속 ③ 완료 ⑤ 결과

23 셀피를 박물관에서 찍었다고 언급되어 있다.

24 so는 지시대명사로 앞 문장의 they were a good idea를 받는다.

25 문맥상 '안전한'이 알맞다.

26 '아니면, 또는'의 뜻으로 선택을 나타내는 접속사 or가 알맞다.

27 ③ 원숭이가 사람을 잘 따르는지는 알 수 없다.

28 당신이 할 수 있는 일과 할 수 없는 일을 알려주는 지침: rule(규칙)

29 문맥상 '비록 ~이라도'의 뜻으로 양보를 나타내는 접속사가 알맞다.

교과서 파헤치기

Lesson **1**

01 게시[공고]하다	02 깨닫다	03 계속하다
04 수첩, 일기	05 접시; 요리	06 표지
07 팬; 부채	08 결승전	09 바닥
10 정말	11 건강	12 풀다
13 믿다	14 표, 입장권	15 엄격한
16 종	17 신선한	18 맛있는
19 재미있는	20 구석	21 판단하다
22 친절한	23 활동	24 메모
25 수학	26 맞는, 알맞은	27 함께
28 말, 단어	29 어쨌든	30 외치다
31 기쁜	32 대답하다	33 기르다, 재배하다
34 연습하다	35 (말·대화에) 끼어들다	
36 ~에 대해 생각하다		37 ~에 부딪히다
38 ~이 몹시 기다려지다		39 ~을 알게 되다
40 ~에 좋다	41 ~으로 가는 길에[도중에]	
42 ~에게 신세를 갚다		43 마음속으로 생각하다

01 boring	02 problem	03 practice
04 hurry	05 take	06 excited
07 magic	08 cafeteria	09 busy
10 shout	11 present	12 remember
13 grow	14 always	15 serious
16 anyway	17 hard	18 cool
19 homeroom teacher		20 join
21 reply	22 serve	23 exciting
24 class	25 pleased	26 mean
27 saying	28 trick	29 health
30 floor	31 strict	32 continue
33 judge	34 cover	35 be good for
36 bump into	37 cut in	38 after school
39 think of	40 find out	41 look for
42 right now	43 think to oneself	

1 grow, 재배하다   2 hurry, 서두르다, 서둘러 가다
3 cover, 표지   4 reply, 대답하다   5 strict, 엄격한
6 dish, 접시   7 final, 결승전   8 realize, 깨닫다
9 serve, 제공하다   10 judge, 판단하다   11 magic, 마술
12 post, 게시[공고]하다   13 trust, 믿다   14 saying, 속담
15 cafeteria, 구내식당   16 fan, 팬

Get Ready - 2

1 what, think of / looks, for / This year, going to study, with
2 Look at, going to, homeroom teacher / find out / excited, can't wait
3 everyone, your English teacher / Glad to meet / What, think of / interesting, a lot

Start Off - Listen & Talk A

1 looks good for, What, think of it / think, boring / which club, to join / join the soccer, plyaing
2 think of / think, right, to learn many interesting tricks / too, first meeting / can't wait for

Start Off - Listen & Talk B

Let's, What do you think of / growing vegetables / what, eating / Let's join, right now, with, every month / on April 30 / can't wait for

Step Up - Real-life Scene

what, think of / looks, strict, serious / Don't judge, by / What, mean / with, was great, exciting / During, class, math activities with / can't wait for, this year

Express Yourself A

1 What do you think / I think, on / can eat / can't wait for lunchtime
2 dishes, think of / not bad, vegetables / don't eat / Try, good for our health

Check Yourself - Listen & Speak

Let's join, What, of / playing the flute / like playing / right now, after school, Tuesday, Thursday / going to have, on / to play / too, can't wait for

Get Ready - 2

1 G: Hey, what do you think of this notebook?
   B: It looks great! Is it for science?
   G: Yes. This year I'm going to study science harder with this notebook.

2 B: Look at the teachers. Who's going to be our new homeroom teacher?

G: We'll find out in 10 minutes.

B: I'm very excited. I can't wait!

3 M: Hello, everyone! My name is Yun Kihun. I'm your English teacher.

G&B: Glad to meet you, Mr. Yun.

M: What do you think of English?

G: It's interesting. I like English a lot.

Start Off - Listen & Talk A

1 B: This club looks good for you. What do you think of it?

G: The health club? I think it's boring.

B: Then which club do you want to join?

G: I'll join the soccer club. I like playing soccer.

2 G: What do you think of the magic club?

B: I think it's the right club for me. I want to learn many interesting tricks.

G: I'll join it, too. When is the first meeting?

B: Next Wednesday. I can't wait for the first meeting!

Start Off - Listen & Talk B

B: Let's join the Green Garden club together. What do you think of it?

G: Okay. I like growing vegetables.

B: You know what? I like eating vegetables.

G: Let's join the club right now. We can have a party with fresh vegetables every month.

B: Great. The first party is on April 30.

G: I can't wait for the party.

Step Up - Real-life Scene

Seho: Miso, what do you think of Mr. Park?

Miso: The new math teacher? He looks very strict and serious.

Seho: Don't judge a book by its cover.

Miso: What do you mean, Seho?

Seho: My first class with Mr. Park was great. He was very kind, and his class was so exciting.

Miso: Really?

Seho: Yes. During the first class, we did interesting math activities with our cell phones.

Miso: Wow! I can't wait for his class tomorrow. It's my first math class this year.

Express Yourself A

1 B: What do you think of today's lunch?

G: I think it's okay. What's on tomorrow's menu?

B: Wow! We can eat spaghetti tomorrow.

G: I can't wait for lunchtime tomorrow

2 G: Look! Two dishes of vegetables! What do you think of today's menu?

B: It's not bad. I like vegetables.

G: I don't eat vegetables.

B: Try some. They are good for our health.

Check Yourself - Listen & Speak

B: Let's join the School Band club together. What do you think of it?

G: Okay. I like playing the flute.

B: I like playing the ukulele.

G: Let's join the club right now. They practice after school every Tuesday and Thursday.

B: They're going to have the first concert on July 15.

G: Great. I hope to play in the concert.

B: Me, too. I can't wait for the concert.

본문 TEST Step 1   p.09~10

01 talking, when, came

02 Happy, said to   03 from, my

04 two, tickets   05 going, take, asked

06 took, to, before   07 time, back

08 what, cut   09 isn't, fan, am

10 ask, anyway, replied

11 won't, with, Trust

12 thought, herself, wants   13 bell, See, later

14 hurried, class 15 on, started to

16 At, bumped into

17 said, continued to   18 then, saw, on

19 Wait, but, not

20 After, went, can't, find   21 happen, see

22 she, answered 23 Isn't, your   24 not, think, lost

25 On, way, saw 26 had, in

27 got angry, Why

28 saw, shouted, found   29 think, yours

30 looking for, said   31 not, thought

32 were, saying   33 something say, asked

34 about going to   35 It's, finals

36 looked, pleased, to

본문 TEST Step 2   p.11~12

01 were talking, when, came over

02 Happy birthday, said to   03 from my dad

04 two KBL tickets   05 going to take

06 took me to   07 time to pay him back

27

08 know what, cut in   09 isn't, fan, But

10 ask, anyway, replied

11 won't go with, Trust

12 thought to herself, wants, ticket

13 There's, See you later

14 hurried to class

15 on, started to run

16 At, bumped into someone

17 continued to run   18 Just then, on

19 but, was not

20 After class, went to, one of my tickets

21 happen to   22 answered

23 Isn't, in your bag   24 not, think, lost

25 On her way home

26 had, in his hand

27 got angry, Why

28 Just then, shouted, found a ticket in

29 think, yours   30 was looking for

31 not so bad, thought   32 were, saying

33 have, to say, asked

34 about going to, with me   35 finals

36 looked, pleased, love to

---

19 "기다려, 세호야!" 그가 말했지만 세호는 거기에 없었다.

20 수업이 끝난 후, 세호는 다미에게 가서 말했다. "내 입장권 한 장을 찾을 수 없어.

21 너 혹시 입장권을 봤니?"

22 "아니." 그녀가 대답했다.

23 "네 가방 안에 있지 않니?"

24 "아니, 거기에 없어. 내 생각에 그것을 잃어버린 것 같아." 세호가 말했다.

25 집으로 돌아오는 길에 다미는 지훈을 보았다.

26 그는 손에 입장권을 가지고 있었다.

27 다미는 화가 나서 "이봐! 너가 왜 ...?"라고 말했다.

28 바로 그때, 지훈이는 세호를 보고 소리쳤다. "세호야! 내가 복도에서 입장권을 찾았어.

29 네 것 같아."

30 "고마워! 나는 그것을 찾고 있었어!" 세호가 말했다.

31 "그는 그렇게 나쁘진 않아." 다미는 생각했다.

32 "그래서, 무슨 말을 하고 있었던 거야?

33 너 할 말이 있니, 다미야?" 지훈이가 물었다.

34 "음, 이번 금요일에 나랑 학교 농구 경기에 같이 가는 게 어때?

35 그것은 결승전이야."

36 지훈은 정말 기뻐 보였다. "가고 싶어!"

---

1 세호와 지훈이는 다미가 왔을 때 복도에서 이야기를 나누고 있었다.

2 생일 축하해!" 다미가 세호에게 말했다.

3 "이거 받아. 우리 아빠가 주신 거야."

4 "와, KBL 입장권 두 장. 고마워!"

5 "넌 누구를 데려 갈 거니?" 다미가 물었다.

6 "민준이. 그가 전에 나를 축구 경기에 데려갔어.

7 그래서 그에게 신세를 갚아야 할 때야."

8 "그거 알아?" 지훈이가 끼어들었다.

9 "민준이는 농구 팬이 아니야. 하지만 난 농구 팬이야!"

10 "음, 어쨌든 먼저 민준이에게 물어볼 거야." 세호가 대답했다.

11 "그는 너와 함께 가지 않을 거야. 날 믿어." 지훈이가 말했다.

12 "이 녀석은 누구지?" 다미는 "그는 민준이의 입장권을 원하는구나."라고 마음속으로 생각했다.

13 "아, 종이 울린다. 나중에 보자,"라고 다미가 말했다.

14 그녀는 서둘러 수업에 들어갔다.

15 "어서, 지훈아." 세호는 말하고 달리기 시작했다.

16 모퉁이에서, 세호는 누군가와 부딪혔다.

17 그는 "미안해!"라고 말하고는 계속 달렸다.

18 바로 그때, 지훈이가 바닥에 있는 무언가를 보았다.

---

1 Seho and Jihun were talking in the hallway when Dami came over.

2 "Happy birthday!" she said to Seho.

3 "Here. They're from my dad."

4 "Wow, two KBL tickets! Thanks!"

5 "Who are you going to take with you?" Dami asked.

6 "Minjun. He took me to a soccer game before.

7 So, it's time to pay him back."

8 "You know what?" Jihun cut in.

9 "Minjun isn't a fan of basketball. But I am!"

10 "Well, I'll ask him first anyway," replied Seho.

11 "He won't go with you. Trust me," said Jihun.

12 "Who is this guy?" Dami thought to herself, "He wants Minjun's ticket."

13 "Oh! There's the bell. See you later," said Dami.

14 She hurried to class.

15 "Come on, Jihun," said Seho, and he started to run.

16 At the corner, Seho bumped into someone.

17 "Sorry!" he said and continued to run.

18 Just then, Jihun saw something on the floor.

19 "Wait, Seho!" he said, but Seho was not there.

20 After class, Seho went to Dami and said, "I can't find one of my tickets.

21 Did you happen to see it?"

22 "No," she answered.

23 "Isn't it in your bag?"

24 "No, it's not there. I think I lost it," said Seho.

25 On her way home, Dami saw Jihun.

26 He had the ticket in his hand.

27 Dami got angry and said, "Hey! Why do you ...?"

28 Just then, Jihun saw Seho and shouted, "Seho! I found a ticket in the hallway.

29 I think it's yours."

30 "Thanks! I was looking for that!" said Seho.

31 "He's not so bad," Dami thought.

32 "So, what were you saying?

33 Do you have something to say, Dami?" asked Jihun.

34 "Um, how about going to the school basketball game with me this Friday?

35 It's the finals."

36 Jihun looked really pleased. "I'd love to!"

2. I will say nice words to others first.

3. Then they will say nice words to me, too.

4. I believe that I can make lots of good friends this way.

5. This year, I will always try to remember this saying and say nice words to others.

Check Yourself - Read & Write

1. Dami gave Seho two basketball tickets.

2. Jihun wanted to go to the basketball game with Seho.

3. Seho dropped one of the tickets on his way to go class.

4. Jihun found Seho's ticket in the hallway.

5. Dami saw Seho's ticket in Jihun's hand, and she thought, "He's a bad boy."

6. Jihun gave the ticket back to Seho, and Dami realized that she was wrong.

7. Dami wanted to go to the school basketball game with Jihun.

8. Jihun was really pleased.

구석구석지문 TEST Step 1   p.19

Project - Link to the World

1. means, words, in

2. will say, others

3. nice words, too

4. believe, make, friends

5. always try to, saying, others

Check Yourself - Read & Write

1. Seho two basketball tickets

2. wanted to go, with

3. dropped, on his way to

4. found, hallway

5. saw, thought

6. gave, back to, realized, was wrong

7. wanted to go to

8. pleased

구석구석지문 TEST Step 2   p.20

Project - Link to the World

1. This saying means "Nice words for nice words" in English.

11 cut, 상처   12 nod, (고개를) 끄덕이다   13 rest, 휴식

14 spot, 점, 반점   15 borrow, 빌리다

16 doorbell, 초인종

단어 TEST Step 1   p.21

01 연세가 드신	02 자세히, 면밀히	03 구역, 블록
04 이웃	05 나비	06 주소
07 귀여운	08 감독	09 초인종
10 먹이를 주다	11 무료의, 한가한	12 살피다, 확인하다
13 문	14 초록색의	15 급히[서둘러] 가다
16 ~을 두고 오다[가다]		17 상처; 자르다, 베다
18 잃어버린	19 짓다, 건축하다	20 수다를 떨다
21 자원봉사자; 자원봉사하다		22 희망
23 갈색의	24 휴식	25 울다
26 이상한	27 씻다	28 빌리다
29 옷, 의복	30 외로운	31 완벽한
32 긴장되는	33 꼭, 정확히	34 밖에, 밖에서
35 ~을 쫓아다니다, ~을 뒤쫓다		36 휴식을 취하다
37 둘러보다	38 좋아지다, 호전되다	
39 A를 B로 데려가다		40 충분한 휴식을 취하다
41 ~을 붙이다	42 ~을 잘하다	43 ~을 돌보다

단어 TEST Step 2   p.22

01 around	02 nod	03 shape
04 perfect	05 care	06 clothes
07 practice	08 special	09 enough
10 follow	11 spot	12 stage
13 exactly	14 hard	15 inside
16 return	17 lonely	18 miss
19 still	20 move	21 nervous
22 outside	23 pass	24 sell
25 guess	26 used	27 borrow
28 strange	29 chat	30 neighbor
31 feed	32 elderly	33 address
34 doorbell	35 be late for	36 prepare for
37 take A to B	38 in front of	39 look around
40 take a break	41 put up	42 clean up
43 thanks to		

단어 TEST Step 3   p.23

1 perfect, 완벽한   2 build, 짓다   3 feed, 먹이를 주다

4 lonely, 외로운   5 return, 돌아오다[가다]

6 volunteer, 자원봉사자   7 address, 주소

8 block, 구역, 블록   9 neighbor, 이웃   10 butterfly, 나비

대화문 TEST Step 1   p.24~25

Get Ready - 2

1 going to take, in front of / Sounds, over there

2 It's, think, get / Let's meet at, in front of

3 planning, for / selling, over there / Let's go, look around

Start Off - Listen & Talk A

1 any plans for / planning to, dancing / Sounds, Can, join / not

2 planning to go, to prepare for / mean, to study / make it at / See you then

Start Off - Listen & Talk B

are, going to do / to clean up, with / like, Can, join / make it, at / afraid not, How about / Fine with, bring a pair of / See, on Saturday

Start Off - Speak Up - Look and talk.

planning to Saturday / Can, come with you / Why not, can, make it / Let's meet in front of

Step Up - Real-life Scene

planning to volunteer, animal care center / mean, near / Will, come with, volunteers to take care of / love to, feeding, walking, good at washing / bring, with, too / ask my neighbor, too, shall, meet / make, at, at / see, on Sunday

Express Yourself A

1 I'm planning to go to, to watch / interesting, come with / Of course, Can you make it, at / No, See you then

2 planning to enter, nervous / Don't worry, If, practice, can win / Thank

Learning Diary - Listen & Speak

are you going to / planning to volunteer / great / Will, come with / When shall, meet / Can you make it / afraid not, How about / See you then

대화문 TEST Step 2   p.26~27

Get Ready - 2

1 B: I'm going to take some pictures in front of the flower gate.

G: Sounds good. It's over there.

2 B: Hello. It's me, Jamie. I think I'll get there in 20 minutes.

G: Okay. Let's meet at 2 p.m. in front of the clock tower.

3 B: I'm planning to buy some clothes for a school picnic.

G: Look. They're selling old books and clothes over there.

B: Great. Let's go and look around.

Start Off - Listen & Talk A

1 G: Do you have any plans for the weekend?

B: Yes. I'm planning to practice dancing at the youth center.

G: Sounds great. Can I join you?

B: Why not?

2 G: I'm planning to go to the library to prepare for the exam.

B: You mean City Library? I want to study with you.

G: Great. Can you make it at 3 p.m. tomorrow?

B: Sure. See you then.

Start Off - Listen & Talk B

B: What are you going to do this Saturday?

G: I'm planning to clean up the park with my dad.

B: Sounds like a wonderful plan. Can I join you?

G: Sure. Can you make it at the bus stop at 1 p.m.?

B: I'm afraid not. How about 2?

G: Fine with me. Please bring a pair of gloves and a big plastic bag.

B: Okay. See you on Saturday.

Start Off - Speak Up - Look and talk.

A: I'm planning to volunteer at the library this Tuseday.

B: Great. Can I come with you?

A: Why not? Can you make it at 3 p.m.?

B: Sure. Let's meet in front of the library.

Step Up - Real-life Scene

Jina: I'm planning to volunteer at the animal care center this Sunday morning.

Alex: You mean the one near Grand Park, Jina?

Jina: Right. Will you come with me, Alex? They need volunteers to take care of the animals.

Alex: I'd love to join. I like feeding and walking animals. I'm also good at washing them.

Jina: Great. You can bring other friends with you, too.

Alex: Okay. I'll ask my neighbor Nancy. She loves animals, too. What time shall we meet?

Jina: Can you make it at 8 a.m. at the Grand Park bus stop?

Alex: Sure. I'll see you on Sunday.

Express Yourself A

1 M: I'm planning to go to the town festival to watch a dance show.

W: Sounds interesting. Can I come with you?

M: Of course. Can you make it at the school gate at 6 p.m.?

W: No problem. See you then.

2 W: I'm planning to enter a singing contest in my town, but I'm nervous.

M: Don't worry. If you practice hard, you can win the contest.

W: Thank you.

Learning Diary - Listen & Speak

B: What are you going to do this Friday, Aria?

G: I'm planning to volunteer at the post office.

B: Sounds great!

G: Will you come with me, Eric?

B: Sure. When shall we meet ?

G: Can you make it at 3 p.m.?

B: I'm afraid not. How about 4 p.m.?

G: Good. See you then.

본문 TEST Step 1   p.28~29

01 black, brown, with   02 lived with

03 perfect, because, spot, shape

04 outside, run after

05 always came, in

06 away, lived with

07 moved, last, lonely

08 had no   09 after, followed, became

10 One, saw, under

11 making, sound   12 wrong, asked

13 at, closely, found, cut

14 took, to, hospital

15 better, gets rest, Keep   16 at, was no

17 outside, couldn't find   18 made, put, up

19 third, passed, no

20 walking near, saw, lost

21 read, closely, got

22 looks, like, strange   23 hurried, home

24 on, Let's   25 took, to, on

26 heard, ring, ran, opened   27 back, cried

28 jumped, into, arms   29 Let, guess

30 comes, only, doesn't
31 Ryan nodded
32 lost, last, didn't
33 How, know
34 Because, too, only during
35 Our, has, said
36 if, in, have
37 Sure, said
38 Thank, thought
39 met, thanks to

본문 TEST Step 2

p.30~31

01 with green eyes
02 lived with
03 always thought, perfect, because, spot, shape
04 liked to go outside, run after
05 always, in, for
06 away, lived with
07 When, moved to, last month, lonely
08 had no friends
09 after, followed her home, became
10 One day, saw, sitting
11 was making a strange sound
12 wrong, asked
13 looked at, closely, found a bad cut
14 took, to, animal hospital
15 get better, gets enough rest, Keep him inside
16 at, was no
17 checked outside, couldn't find
18 made, put, up
19 third, night passed, Still
20 When, was walking near, saw, the lost cat
21 read, closely, got big
22 looks, like, strange
23 hurried, home
24 on, Let's go
25 took, to
26 When, heard, ring, ran to, opened
27 back, cried
28 jumped, up, into
29 Let me guess
30 comes home, in, doesn't
31 nodded
32 lost, last, didn't you
33 How did, know
34 Because, too, usually comes, during the day
35 has two families
36 if you have time, come in, have
37 Sure
38 Thank, thought
39 met, thanks to you

본문 TEST Step 3

p.32~33

1 Bear는 초록색 눈을 가진 검은색과 갈색의 고양이였다.
2 그는 소년 Ryan과 함께 살았다.
3 Ryan은 항상 "Bear"가 곰 모양의 검은 반점이 있기 때문에 그 고양이에게 딱 맞는 이름이라고 생각했다.
4 Bear는 매일 아침 밖으로 나가 나비를 쫓아다니는 것을 좋아했다.
5 그는 항상 저녁 식사 시간에 맞춰 집에 왔다.
6 다섯 블록 떨어진 곳에, 고양이 Max는 Sheila라는 소녀와 함께 살았다.
7 지난달에 Sheila가 이 마을로 이사 왔을 때, 그녀는 외로웠다.
8 그녀는 그곳에 친구가 없었다.
9 하지만 Max가 그녀를 따라 집으로 온 후, 그는 그녀에게 좋은 친구가 되었다.
10 어느 날, Sheila는 책상 밑에 앉아 있는 Max를 보았다.
11 그는 이상한 소리를 내고 있었다.
12 "무슨 일 있니?" Sheila가 물었다.
13 그녀는 그를 자세히 살펴보고 그의 다리에 심한 상처가 난 것을 발견했다.
14 그녀는 그를 동물 병원으로 데려갔다.
15 의사는 "충분한 휴식을 취하면 좋아질 거야. 그를 일주일 동안 안에 있도록 해라."라고 말했다.
16 그날 밤, Ryan의 집에는 Bear가 없었다.
17 Ryan은 바깥을 살폈지만 그는 그를 찾을 수 없었다.
18 그는 포스터를 만들어서 마을을 다니며 그것을 붙였다.
19 세 번째 밤이 지났다. 여전히 Bear는 나타나지 않았다.
20 Sheila가 그녀의 집 근처를 걷고 있었을 때, 그녀는 잃어버린 고양이에 대한 포스터를 보았다.
21 그녀는 그것을 자세히 읽고, 그녀의 눈은 커졌다.
22 "이 고양이는 꼭 Max 같아 보여. 너무 이상해."
23 그녀는 서둘러 집으로 돌아갔다.
24 "자, Max! 가자!"
25 그녀는 그를 포스터에 적힌 주소로 데려갔다.
26 "딩동." Ryan은 초인종이 울리는 소리를 듣고 문으로 달려가 문을 열었다.
27 "Bear야, 돌아왔구나!" Ryan이 외쳤다.
28 Max가 Ryan의 팔 안으로 뛰어올랐다.
29 "내가 맞춰 볼게." Sheila가 말했다.
30 "너의 고양이는 저녁에만 집에 오지, 그렇지?"
31 Ryan은 고개를 끄덕였다.
32 "그리고 너는 지난 금요일에 그를 잃어버렸지, 그렇지 않니?" Sheila가 말했다.
33 "응! "어떻게 알았니?"라고 Ryan은 말했다.
34 "이것은 또한 내 고양이이기 때문이야. 보통 낮에만 우리 집에 오거든."
35 "우리 고양이는 가족이 둘이야!" Ryan이 말했다.
36 이봐, 시간이 있으면 들어와서 쿠키 좀 먹어."
37 "그래." Sheila가 말했다.
38 "고마워, Max." 그녀는 생각했다.
39 "나는 네 덕분에 좋은 이웃을 만났어!"

본문 TEST Step 4-Step 5

p.34~37

1 Bear was a black and brown cat with green eyes.
2 He lived with a boy, Ryan.

3 Ryan always thought that "Bear" was a perfect name for the cat because he had a black spot in the shape of a bear.

4 Bear liked to go outside every morning and run after butterflies.

5 He always came home just in time for dinner.

6 Five blocks away, Max the cat lived with a girl, Sheila.

7 When Sheila moved to this town last month, she was lonely.

8 She had no friends there.

9 But, after Max followed her home, he became a good friend to her.

10 One day, Sheila saw Max sitting under the desk.

11 He was making a strange sound.

12 "What's wrong?" asked Sheila.

13 She looked at him closely and found a bad cut on his leg.

14 She took him to the animal hospital.

15 The doctor said, "He will get better if he gets enough rest. Keep him inside for a week."

16 That night, at Ryan's house, there was no Bear.

17 Ryan checked outside, but he couldn't find him.

18 He made posters and put them up around town.

19 A third night passed. Still no Bear.

20 When Sheila was walking near her house, she saw a poster about the lost cat.

21 She read it closely, and her eyes got big.

22 "This cat looks exactly like Max. It's so strange."

23 She hurried home.

24 "Come on, Max! Let's go!"

25 She took him to the address on the poster.

26 "Ding-Dong." When Ryan heard the doorbell ring, he ran to the door and opened it.

27 "Bear, you're back!" Ryan cried.

28 Max jumped up into Ryan's arms.

29 "Let me guess," said Sheila.

30 "Your cat comes home only in the evenings, doesn't he?"

31 Ryan nodded.

32 "And you lost him last Friday, didn't you?" Sheila said.

33 "Yes! How did you know?" said Ryan.

34 "Because this is my cat, too, and he usually comes to my home only during the day."

35 "Our cat has two families!" said Ryan.

36 "Hey, if you have time, please come in and have

some cookies."

37 "Sure," said Sheila.

38 "Thank you, Max," she thought.

39 "I met a good neighbor thanks to you!"

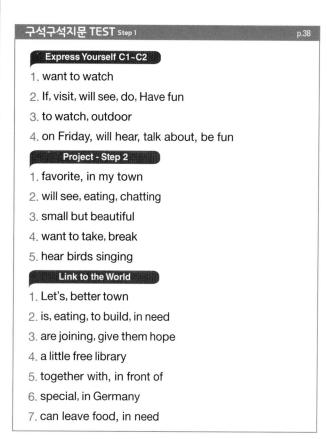

구석구석지문 TEST Step 1 p.38

Express Yourself C1~C2

1. want to watch
2. If, visit, will see, do, Have fun
3. to watch, outdoor
4. on Friday, will hear, talk about, be fun

Project - Step 2

1. favorite, in my town
2. will see, eating, chatting
3. small but beautiful
4. want to take, break
5. hear birds singing

Link to the World

1. Let's, better town
2. is, eating, to build, in need
3. are joining, give them hope
4. a little free library
5. together with, in front of
6. special, in Germany
7. can leave food, in need

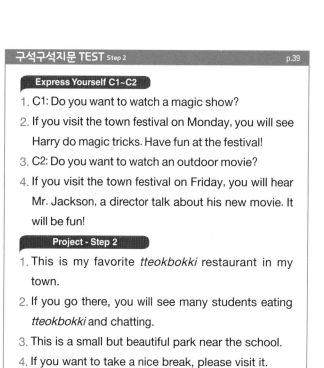

구석구석지문 TEST Step 2 p.39

Express Yourself C1~C2

1. C1: Do you want to watch a magic show?
2. If you visit the town festival on Monday, you will see Harry do magic tricks. Have fun at the festival!
3. C2: Do you want to watch an outdoor movie?
4. If you visit the town festival on Friday, you will hear Mr. Jackson, a director talk about his new movie. It will be fun!

Project - Step 2

1. This is my favorite *tteokbokki* restaurant in my town.
2. If you go there, you will see many students eating *tteokbokki* and chatting.
3. This is a small but beautiful park near the school.
4. If you want to take a nice break, please visit it.
5. You can hear birds singing in the trees.

Link to the World

1. Let's make a better town!
2. In the U.S., there is a volunteer project to build houses for families in need.
3. Many people are joining the project to give them hope.
4. It's a little free library in Canada.
5. If you want to read books together with your neighbors, make one in front of your house!
6. It's a special refrigerator in Germany.
7. People can leave food in this refrigerator for people in need.

단어 TEST Step 1   p.40

01 혼자	02 (이빨로) 물다, 베어 물다
03 조심하는, 주의 깊은	04 위험한
05 방향, (주로 복수로) 지시	06 옷, 의복
07 ~에 있다, 존재하다	08 과거, 지난날
09 먼, 멀리	10 인물, 모습 11 등반가
12 실제로, 정말로	13 다음에 나오는, 그 다음의
14 재미; 재미있는 15 안전, 안전성	16 진짜의, 현실적인
17 특별한, 특수한 18 기억하다	19 오르다, 올라가다
20 경치, 풍경 21 조화, 화합	22 ~ 뒤에, 뒤에
23 언젠가, 훗날 24 함께하다, 가입하다	
25 종류 26 창조하다, 만들다 27 균형, 평형	
28 나중에, 후에 29 아마 30 규칙	
31 찾다, 수색하다 32 만지다, 건드리다 33 기술, 기량	
34 아직 35 전화를 끊다	
36 ~을 명심하다, ~을 잊지 않다 37 저쪽에, 저기에서	
38 떠들다, 소란 피우다 39 ~에 좋다	
40 ~에 대해 듣다 41 처음으로	
42 예를 들면, 예를 들어 43 오르다	

단어 TEST Step 2   p.41

01 active	02 sign	03 festival
04 figure	05 push	06 place
07 grass	08 practice	09 advice
10 close	11 safe	12 pose
13 information	14 street	15 rock
16 teenage	17 princess	18 loose
19 mirror	20 helmet	21 museum
22 chat	23 past	24 trick
25 without	26 beach	27 scenery
28 balance	29 harmony	30 clothes
31 careful	32 dangerous	33 safety
34 special	35 for example	
36 for the first time		37 keep ~ in mind
38 be good for	39 in front of	40 hang up
41 make noise	42 hear of	43 over there

단어 TEST Step 3   p.42

1 painter, 화가   2 dangerous, 위험한
3 active, 활동적인, 활발한   4 beach, 해변, 바닷가

5 ride, 타다　6 chat, 담소[이야기]하다　7 princess, 공주

8 street, 길, 도로　9 teenage, 십대의　10 clothes, 옷, 의복

11 rock, 바위, 암석　12 helmet, 헬멧

13 advice, 조언, 충고　14 climb, 오르다, 올라가다

15 push, 밀다　16 mirror, 거울

대화문 TEST Step 1　　　　　p.43~44

Get Ready - 2

1 at, great / riding, know about / What / special, for riding on

2 Don't, into, yet / Why not / shouldn't, without, Put, on

3 Look at, over there, like to take, in front of / shouldn't, over / okay

4 want to watch, in / shouldn't go up, birds / right

Start Off - Listen & Talk A

1 have, ever heard of, climber / seen, on TV / teaching rock climbing, camp, want to join / but, shouldn't climb up / right

2 Have, heard / No, I haven't / favorite, concert, Can I go / shouldn't come home / right

Start Off - Listen & Talk B

Have, heard of / tried, when / doing, for the first time / should bring, something to eat / should, keep in mind / shouldn't make, when / keep that in mind

Step Up - Real-life Scene

It's, Can, see me / hi, up / isn't it, chat, Have, heard of / Yes, I have, want / Guess what, going to go up / great / hang up, scenery / Be, shouldn't use, while you're walking / right. Thank, send, later

Express Yourself A

1 Have you heard of, No, I haven't. Who / famous American singer, actor, figure / Sounds, take pictures / Let's go.

2 shouldn't take, painting, behind / Don't worry, real, So, in front of / Can, selfies, not

대화문 TEST Step 2　　　　　p.45~46

Get Ready - 2

1 G: Look at that boy. He's great.

　B: He's riding an MTB. Do you know about it?

　G: No. What is it?

　B: It's a special bike for riding on a mountain.

2 G: Wait. Don't jump into the water yet.

　B: Why not?

　G: You shouldn't swim without a life jacket. Put it on.

3 G: Look at the beautiful flowers over there! I'd like to take a selfie in front of them.

　B: You shouldn't go over there.

　G: Oh, okay.

4 B: I want to watch the birds in the trees.

　G: You shouldn't go up too close to the birds.

　B: All right, thanks.

Start Off - Listen & Talk A

1 G: Dad, have you ever heard of Kim Soyun, the rock climber?

　M: Yes, I've seen her on TV.

　G: She's teaching rock climbing at a camp this Saturday. I want to join the camp.

　M: Okay, Miso, but you shouldn't climb up too high.

　G: All right. Thanks, Dad.

2 G: Have you heard of Rock Boys?

　M: No, I haven't.

　G: It's my favorite band. There's a concert this Saturday. Can I go?

　M: Okay, Minju, but you shouldn't come home too late.

　G: All right. Thanks, Dad.

Start Off - Listen & Talk B

B: Have you heard of bird watching?

M: Sure. I tried it when I was a child.

B: That's nice. Actually, I'm doing it for the first time this Saturday.

M: Are you? You should bring warm clothes and something to eat.

B: Okay. What else should I keep in mind?

M: You shouldn't make any noise when you watch the birds.

B: I'll keep that in mind. Thanks, Dad.

Step Up - Real-life Scene

A: Hello, Somin! It's me! Can you see me?

B: Oh, hi, Minjun! What's up?

A: This is so cool, isn't it? We can video chat on the phone! Have you heard of Jeju Olle?

B: Yes, I have. I really want to go there someday.

A: Guess what? I'm on it now. Actually, I'm going to go up Seongsan Ilchulbong now.

B: That's great!

A: Don't hang up. Enjoy the beautiful scenery with me.

B: Be careful! You shouldn't use your cell phone while you're walking.

A: Oh, right. Thank you. I'll send you photos later.

Express Yourself A

1 G: Have you heard of Elvis Presley?

  B: No, I haven't. Who is he?

  G: He was a famous American singer and actor. We can see a figure of Elvis here.

  B: Sounds interesting. I want to take pictures with it.

  G: Okay. Let's go.

2 W: You shouldn't take selfies here. Van Gogh's painting is behind you.

  B: Don't worry, Mom. It's not his real painting. So I can take selfies in front of it.

  W: Really? Sounds interesting. Can I take selfies here, too?

  B: Why not?

본문 TEST Step 1   p.47~48

01 Have, ever heard
02 When, take, yourself
03 have, for, about
04 Here, presentations, selfies   05 people, take
06 Though, at, answer   07 Look at, of
08 used, take, herself   09 loos nervous
10 guess why   11 think, first
12 probably, teenage, ever   13 take, at, like
14 take, poses, tricks
15 also, special, fun
16 example, is, famous   17 spots, take
18 touch, even step   19 at, following
20 Though, riding, like
21 holding, brush, painting   22 exist, too
23 visited, before 24 don't, yourself 25 look, but were
26 don't, so   27 look safe
28 should, care, selfies, places
29 bite, time, could   30 are, safety
31 Don't, while, walking
32 Do, pose, near
33 Never, in, places
34 use, make, better
35 can, things, take
36 post, on, website

---

37 watered, plants, for   38 also, at, times
39 Look at, those 40 about joining, create

본문 TEST Step 2   p.49~50

01 Have, ever heard, of
02 take, of yourself
03 club, searched for information, for
04 Here, their presentations
05 people, take selfies
06 Though, wasn't, answer   07 Look at
08 used, to take, herself   09 loos nervous
10 Can, guess why
11 think, her first selfie
12 probably, teenage
13 can take selfies, like
14 To take, pictures, poses, use camera tricks
15 also, fun   16 example, famous
17 has special spots, take
18 touch, even step
19 Look at, following
20 Though, riding, looks like
21 just holding, brush, looks like, painting
22 exist, too   23 have visited, before
24 Why don't, yourself   25 look, but
26 don't think so 27 don't look safe
28 should take special care, places like
29 could bite, at any time, could fall
30 Here are, safety tips
31 take, while you're walking
32 not pose, wild 33 Never take selfies, places
34 use, better   35 things, take
36 can post, website
37 watered, school
38 also helped, at many times   39 Look at, those
40 How about, create

본문 TEST Step 3   p.51~52

1 여러분은 "셀피"에 대해 들어 본 적이 있나요? 여러분 자신의 사진을 찍을 때 그것이 셀피에요.

2 민지의 사진 동아리 학생들은 한 달 동안 셀피에 대한 정보를 찾았습니다.

3 여기 셀피에 대한 그들의 발표 내용이 있습니다.

4 과거의 사람들은 셀피를 찍었나요?

5 그 때는 셀피를 찍는 것이 쉽지는 않았지만, 답은 '그렇다' 입니다.

6 아나스타샤 공주의 이 사진을 보세요. 그녀는 거울을 사용하여 자신의 사진을 찍었습니다.

7 그녀는 긴장되어 보입니다. 왜인지 추측할 수 있나요?

8 글쎄, 나는 그것이 그녀의 첫 번째 셀피였다고 생각해요.

9 그리고 그것은 아마도 세계 최초의 10대 소녀의 셀피였을 거예요.

10 여러분은 빅벤과 피사의 사탑과 같은 세계적으로 유명한 장소에서 셀카를 찍을 수 있습니다.

11 멋진 사진을 찍기 위해서, 단지 재미있는 포즈를 취하고 카메라 기술을 이용하세요.

12 여러분은 또한 재미있는 셀피를 찍기 위해 특별한 박물관을 방문할 수 있습니다.

13 예를 들어, 필리핀에는 유명한 셀프 박물관이 있습니다.

14 그곳은 셀피를 찍기 위한 특별한 장소들이 있습니다.

15 여러분은 그림들을 만질 수 있고 심지어 그림들 안으로 들어갈 수도 있어요.

16 다음 사진들을 보세요.

17 비록 그 소년들은 말을 타고 있는 것이 아니지만, 말을 타고 있는 것처럼 보입니다.

18 비록 그 남자는 단지 커다란 붓을 잡고 있지만, 모나리자를 그리고 있는 것처럼 보입니다.

19 한국에도 셀피 박물관이 있습니다. 나는 전에 춘천에 있는 한 박물관을 방문한 적이 있습니다.

20 여러분도 직접 그곳에 가는 게 어때요? 이 셀피들은 멋져 보이지만, 그것들은 좋은 생각이었나요?

21 난 그렇게 생각하지 않아요. 그것들은 안전해 보이지 않습니다.

22 여러분은 야생이나 이와 같이 높은 곳에서 셀피를 찍을 때 특별한 주의를 기울여야 합니다.

23 원숭이가 언제든지 당신을 물거나 또는 당신은 떨어질 수 있습니다.

24 여기 몇 가지 안전 수칙이 있습니다.

25 걸으면서 셀피를 찍지 마세요.

26 야생 동물들과 함께 또는 가까이에서 포즈를 취하지 마세요.

27 위험한 곳에서는 절대 셀피를 찍지 마세요.

28 나는 우리가 더 나은 학교생활을 만들기 위해 셀피를 이용할 수 있다고 생각해요.

29 우리는 학교에서 좋은 일을 할 수 있고 셀피를 찍을 수도 있습니다.

30 그리고 나서 우리는 학교 웹사이트에 사진을 올릴 수 있어요.

31 나는 한 달 동안 학교에서 식물과 꽃에 물을 주었습니다.

32 나는 또한 학교 도서관에서 선생님을 여러 번 도왔습니다.

33 그런 것들에 대한 내 셀피를 보세요.

34 저와 함께 더 나은 학교생활을 만들어 보는 건 어떨까요?

1 Have you ever heard of a "selfie"? When you take a photograph of yourself, it's a selfie.

2 The students from Minji's photo club have searched for information about selfies for one month.

3 Here are some of their presentations about selfies.

4 Did people in the past take selfies?

5 Though it wasn't easy at that time. the answer is yes.

6 Look at this photo of Princess Anastasia. She used a mirror to take a picture of herself.

7 She looks nervous. Can you guess why?

8 Well, I think it was her first selfie.

9 And it was probably the world's first teenage selfie ever.

10 You can take selfies at world-famous places like Big Ben and the Leaning Tower of Pisa.

11 To take great pictures, just do fun poses and use camera tricks.

12 You can also visit special museums to take fun selfies.

13 For example, there is a famous selfie museum in the Philippines.

14 It has special spots to take selfies.

15 You can touch the paintings and even step inside them.

16 Look at the following pictures.

17 Though the boys are not really riding horses, it looks like they are.

18 Though the man is just holding a big brush, it looks like he is painting the Mona Lisa.

19 Selfie museums exist in Korea, too. I have visited one in Chuncheon before.

20 Why don't you go there yourself? These selfies look great, but were they a good idea?

21 I don't think so. They don't look safe.

22 You should take special care when you take selfies in the wild or at high places like these.

23 A monkey could bite you at any time, or you could fall.

24 Here are some safety tips:

25 Don't take selfies while you're walking.

26 Do not pose with or near wild animals.

27 Never take selfies in dangerous places.

28 I think we can use selfies to make a better school life.

29 We can do good things at school and take selfies.

30 Then we can post the photos on our school website.

31 I've watered the plants and flowers at school for one month.

32 I've also helped the teacher at the school library many times.

33 Look at my selfies of those things.

34 How about joining me to create a better school life?

구석구석지문 TEST Step 1   p.57

Express Yourself-C

1. Have, heard

2. have, seen been to, in front of

3. took, museum

Project-Step 2

1. Safety Rules

2. Have, heard of

3. Though, be safe

4. shouldn't take

5. follow, directions

Link to the World

1. Riding

2. Riding, is, exciting

3. lots of skills

4. turn, freely, even jump

5. Though, easy, exciting

6. can start with

7. When, standing, balancing

8. be careful, should wear

9. shouldn't go, when, riding

구석구석지문 TEST Step 2   p.58

Express Yourself-C

1. Have you heard of the pyramids in Egypt?

2. Though I have never seen been to Egypt before, I'm standing in front of a pyramid in this picture.

3. I took it at the selfie museum.

Project-Step 2

1. Fire Safety Rules

2. Have you heard of fire safety rules?

3. Though there's a fire, you can be safe.

4. You shouldn't take the elevator.

5. You should follow the teacher's directions.

Link to the World

1. BMX Bike Riding

2. Riding a BMX bike is very exciting.

3. You can try lots of skills.

4. You can turn the bike freely and even jump with the bike.

5. Though it's not easy, it's very exciting.

6. You can start with standing skills.

7. When you try standing skills, balancing is very important.

8. But be careful. You should wear a helmet and gloves.

9. Also, you shouldn't go too fast when you're riding.

MEMO

MEMO

적중 100

영어 기출 문제집

정답 및 해설

천재 | 정사열